THE
BLAIR BEQUEST

Chinese Snuff Bottles from the
Princeton University Art Museum

Michael C. Hughes

The International Chinese Snuff Bottle Society

Published by The International Chinese Snuff Bottle Society

2601 North Charles Street, Baltimore, Maryland 21218

Photographs by Robert Hall Photography, London, UK.

Designed by Rosanne Chan

Produced by C A Design (Communication Art Design & Printing Ltd.), Hong Kong

ISBN 962-7502-62-6

Author's dedication

To Lisa, Iain, & Livia

Society's dedication

To our recently deceased best critic and friend,

Victor E. Graham, Ph.D.

Contents

Foreword

It is with great pride and a high sense of jubilation that the officers and board of directors of the International Chinese Snuff Bottle Society publish one of the most important snuff bottle collections extant. The Princeton University Art Museum was the recipient of the Colonel James A. Blair, Jr. Collection in 1936. Our Society has focused on this important museum collection for over thirty years along with some of the earliest collectors, namely, Lilla Perry, Bob Stevens and Edward C. O'Dell, all visiting the museum in the 1950s.

The first convention of our society was held in New York City in September of 1969 and the climax for that program was a visit to the university to see the bottles in display cases on permanent exhibition. The excitement engendered by seeing these bottles as a group motivated the society to ask the director of the museum, Allen Rosenbaum, to display the entire collection on our next visit which happened on the final day of the October 1979 Philadelphia convention. The fame of the collection expanded to the point that when planning for the New York 25th anniversary convention in 1993, the committee felt it was again necessary to take the entire convention of approximately two hundred persons to the museum for yet another exhibition at which time the director placed all of the bottles on view for our members to enjoy. This was no easy task as five hundred and thirty bottles are in the collection requiring that a special room with display cases be set up solely for our viewing.

With the foregoing fascination for the quality and range of the Princeton snuff bottles, it was concluded that the society should undertake a publication of this great collection using the highest level of photographic technology and an equally high standard of curatorial analysis for each bottle selected. The board of directors of the society voted in fall of 1995 to proceed in a diligent and measured manner to prepare this publication. We received formal written approval from the above-mentioned director, Allen Rosenbaum, in September 1996.

A major reason for the delay in publishing was the fact that the society was in the process of publishing a collection of inside-painted snuff bottles of the great master Ma Shaoxuan, and its completion was extended beyond our schedule forcing the Princeton catalogue to be delayed until 1999 when the photography for three hundred and eighty bottles was completed during the spring. Some months prior, the distinguished art scholar selected to write this catalogue, Michael C. Hughes, and I chose the bottles to be photographed. It should be obvious that any collection of over five hundred bottles would have some duplicates and/or similarities in style making it unnecessary to publish all of the bottles. Grateful appreciation is extended to Robert Hall, the eminent London photographer who artistically met all the challenges one encounters when photographing many different mediums. It should also be noted that Dr. Cary Y. Liu, associate curator of

Asian art at the museum, was helpful in allowing us to photograph the collection under high security conditions.

We are pleased that Michael C. Hughes accepted our request to be the author of the catalogue. He met this exacting task with great enthusiasm and spent untold hours out of his professional life to research the life of Colonel James A. Blair, Jr., which is tellingly revealed in his introduction. It is unfortunate that the university had very little documentation on the life of their alumnus but with a sleuthing instinct, Michael wrote, phoned, visited relatives and persons known to Colonel Blair enabling him to create the fascinating story told in the following pages. The catalogue entries are a testament to his scholarship, which is always challenged when writing about a wide range of styles and subject matter as observed in this elegant book.

All publications require an editor as astute as the author and as punctilious as a school teacher. This person has given unstintingly of her time, energy and expertise to perform all of the tasks a good editor must perform but wishes to remain anonymous. Berthe Hanover Ford is another person who must be mentioned for collating and proofing the final drafts, before going to press. Yet another person has been important in this long process of publishing, namely, Rosanne Chan of Communication Art Design & Printing Ltd. who has graciously and without complaint gone through many drafts and proofs to accommodate my every request.

None of the foregoing would have been possible if it were not for the Educational Fund of the International Chinese Snuff Bottle Society founded by Robert Hall and Hugh Moss. Both of them have made it possible for this and two other publications of the society to be funded by their efforts in raising funds at auctions, which have relieved members of their money in an atmosphere of joy at every convention over the past sixteen years.

John Gilmore Ford
President
International Chinese Snuff Bottle Society
Baltimore, Maryland
October 2002

Preface and Acknowledgments

In 1998, I was chosen by the International Chinese Snuff Bottle Society to write a book on the Chinese snuff bottles at the Princeton University Art Museum. The task of cataloguing the collection itself was not one that I was unfamiliar with, having spent the majority of my adult life cataloguing Chinese works of art at Christie's, the international auction house. However, trying to unearth information on Colonel James A. Blair Jr., who left the collection to Princeton in 1934, proved to be a far more demanding task that required sleuthing techniques rivaling those of Scotland Yard. The complete absence of family papers led to many circuitous paths of discovery. It has been an enormously fulfilling journey nevertheless and one that I hope will shed light on this extremely interesting, if elusive, collector.

The first undertaking, with the help of John Ford, was to select the snuff bottles to include in this book out of more than five hundred in the Blair Bequest. Based on degrees of damage, duplication or poor quality, the number was reduced to three hundred and eighty bottles, including pairs and sets.

The Princeton accession numbers, which all begin with the number 1936, the year the bequest actually entered the museum, are listed after each catalogue entry, followed, where known, by the Blair collection number which begins with the designation CB. All measurements are without stoppers, unless otherwise stated. For the sake of aesthetics and consistency, a small number of bottles without stoppers were photographed with those from other bottles. Imperial marks on many of the bottles have not been illustrated, often because the marks are partially obscured by painted accession numbers; in other cases because it was felt unnecessary. On descriptions where a mark is mentioned but not followed by the phrase 'and of the period,' a later date of production is suggested. All marks, unless otherwise stated, are on the base of each bottle. All the bottles are of 'flattened' form unless otherwise indicated. Wherever possible the *pinyin* system of transliteration has been used except for the titles of publications using an alternative system.

The introduction, catalogue entries and footnotes are entirely my responsibility and do not necessarily express the views of Princeton University.

This endeavor would have been impossible without the support of Cary Y. Liu, Associate Curator of Asian Art, and other members of the museum staff, to whom I am exceedingly grateful for giving so much of their precious time. These include Calvin Brown, Gerrit Meaker, Jessica Davis, Eliza Frecon, and Maureen McCormick, registrar.

I am particularly grateful to the photographer Robert Hall and his able assistant Arif Choudhury for the high quality results of their work; Rosanne Chan at C A Design for the superb layout of this book and her patience; Tonia Hoffert, Director, Seneca County Museum, Ohio, for her invaluable help tracking local records, her generosity with her time, and her extreme affability; Regan W. Lynn, graduate student, New York University, for her assistance transcribing handwritten catalogue entries; Elsa Glickman, for her tireless enthusiasm, suggestions on research avenues, and invaluable early sale records; John Newton for fine tuning the introduction; the late Professor Victor Graham, University College, University of Toronto, for his unflagging support of the project which, sadly, he will not see realized; C. M. Ma, Christie's, Chinese Paintings, International Department Head, for his translations of the Chinese inscriptions despite numerous deadlines and a hectic travel schedule; Shane McCausland for his translations for some entries; Jacqueline Haun, Archivist, the Lawrenceville School, New Jersey, for thoroughly exhausting all avenues of research in her school records; Valerie Komar and Nicole Wells, New York Historical Society; Deborah Ramano, Sawanakha Yacht Club; Gloria Adelson, researcher; the Family History Center of the Church of the Latter Day Saints, New York; the Research Libraries of the New York Public Library; the National Archives and Records Administration, New York, (NARA); Paul Yon, Director, Center for Archival Collection, Bowling Green State University; Norma Myers and Mike Cannady, Archives of Appalachia, East Tennessee State University; Rosemary Switzer, Seeley G. Mudd Manuscript Library, Princeton University; Travers Evans, Holland Lodge No. 8, F & A.M.; Anne Wright-Parsons, Senior Scientific Assistant, the American Museum of Natural History; the Library Staff, the American Museum of Natural History; Catherine M. Ellard, the New York Genealogical & Biographical Society; Elizabeth Munemura, Education Department, the Metropolitan Museum of Art, New York; Walter Karppi, Oyster Bay Historical Society; Becky Longobucco, Christ Church, Oyster Bay; William Carrew, The Memorial Cemetery, St John's Church, Cold Spring Harbor; Harriet Hawkins and Paula Laseter, the New Jersey Historic Society; Bill Watson and Richard A. von Doenhoff, the New York Yacht Club; Rachel Bradshaw, the Society of the Cincinnati, Washington, D.C.; Steven Wheeler, Archivist, the New York Stock Exchange; Lynda Dunn, Society for the Preservation of Long Island Antiquities (SPLIA); Deborah Lloyd, Senior Copyright Research Specialist, Library of Congress, Washington, D.C.; W. Barry Thomson for help on Kingsport research; Sharon Culley, the National Archives and Records Administration, Maryland, for locating our only known photograph of Colonel Blair as an adult; Ray and Judy Spinzia, authors, for help with the Blair family history; the Harvard Club library; Athena Zonars, Michael Bass and Niki Tiliakos, Chinese Department, Christie's, New York, for use of their extensive library; Roddy Ropner, Christie's, Singapore; Robert and Lindsey Hall and Peter Tunstall-Behrens for their support; Susan Lewis, Japanese Department, Christie's, New York, for last-minute fact checking; Rodney Richardson for his help in Oyster Bay research; Robert Kleiner for his helpful advice and for transporting by hand from London, at very short notice, the large package of transparencies urgently required by the printers in Hong Kong; Hugh M. Moss for his input on some entries and his encyclopaedic textual output in the field in general; and finally, John Gilmore Ford and the Board of Directors of the International Chinese Snuff Bottle Society for their patience and support during the lengthy gestation period of this book. To this I must add my deepest thanks to my wife, Lisa, for her unflagging support and for caring for our two children, Iain and Livia, during many working weekends and evenings.

Michael C. Hughes
January 2002

Colonel James A. Blair Jr. (1880–1934)

To imagine the world inhabited by the characters of a novel by Henry James or Edith Wharton is to transport oneself back to the world of Colonel James A. Blair.

The turn of the century was a time of splendor in America. It was a time of ascent for the nation in an increasingly global world. New York, Blair's home, was the most cosmopolitan city in the Union. It positively vibrated with life. The youthful energies of the country were mirrored in the industrious optimistic nature of the city. Despite some urban poverty, highlighted by the numerous tenements, many of its inhabitants were bristling with confidence

and economic prosperity. The sounds and sights of the city must have been irresistible to the twenty-year-old Blair. Behind this headlong rush into the new century, however, was a yearning for order, respect for the past and a return to classical ideals.

So it was for Blair. His family wealth and his own business success allowed for a privileged life. Wealth like Blair's, among the elite few, fostered cultural activities of many kinds, not least the collecting of art. For Blair this meant Chinese art.

The society portraits of his day reveal a deep interest in things Oriental by the elite classes. Sumptuous *fin de siècle* interiors were furnished with Asian objects, screens and fans, porcelains, prints, jades and semi-precious stones. Cecilia Beaux's circa 1900 portrait of socialite Mrs. Larz Anderson encapsulates this curiosity about the East. The subject wears an elegant dress of the period and glides across an opulent interior with massive fireplace, painted rococo mirror and gilt bronze sconces. At her side, on an Empire *guéridon*, sits a Japanese rock crystal sphere supported on a gilt bronze dragon base, and alongside it a Chinese amethyst figure of Budai. On the floor at her feet stands a small gold-leaf six-panel screen painted with Buddhistic lions. All is perfectly natural (fig. 1).

Fig. 1   Mrs. Larz Anderson by Cecilia Beaux, circa 1900. Courtesy of the Society of the Cincinnati, Washington, D.C.

The Early Years

The Blair family's early years in America, however, were a far cry from the sophisticated trappings of New York life at the turn of the century.

James A. Blair Sr. (1851-1939) was born in Hope, New Jersey, [1] on April 23, 1851, the youngest of eight children born to James Blair and Sarah A. Lindberry Blair who were of Scottish ancestry. [2] Their forefathers emigrated to America in two waves, the first in 1729 and the second in 1749. The opportunities in America appealed more than the rugged life at home. They settled in New Jersey. According to a local history this was 'to aid in establishing civil and religious liberty.' [3] Blair's grandfather served as a soldier in the War of 1812, the first record of a Blair fighting for his 'new' country, and he was the first of many Blairs to do so.

The family migrated to Ohio after the death of Sarah on August 8, 1853. She actually had been James Blair's second wife. He had three daughters from a previous marriage and four sons and two daughters with Sarah. He must have been in his late fifties when he fathered James A. Blair Sr., who was just two when his mother passed away. It must have been traumatic for the young boy to lose his mother, quickly followed by the move to Ohio.

Blair's grandfather, with the strong will that would characterize many of his descendants, moved the entire family by train and wagon to the Midwest. The family settled about 35 miles south of Lake Erie, the most southern of the five Great Lakes, on what was known as Judge Welch Farm, near the small town of Nevada in Wyandot County about 12 miles south east of Tiffin, the future birthplace of the protagonist in this story, James Alonso Blair Jr. [4]

His grandfather died in September 1867. At seventeen his father was an orphan. With his siblings, and his eldest brother William at its head, this remarkably close family not only survived but prospered.

Blair Sr. probably first moved to nearby Tiffin to attend Heidelberg College. There he met his future bride, Jessie Isabelle Myers (1858–1929). [5] They married on August 6, 1879. Their local church, Old Trinity Episcopal, was undergoing re-construction, so the service took place at the home of the bride's mother. The Trinity Church parish register, however, does list the marriage. [6] Her father, Peter F. Myers, ran a boarding house in Tiffin called Shawhan House where the couple would later live. Jessie Myers had spent her childhood in Tiffin, attending the Ursuline Academy in the center of town.

By the time of their marriage, Blair Sr. at the young age of 28, was already a well-established figure in the local banking community. His first banking position, indeed his first job, was with the

---

1. Obituary of James A. Blair Sr., *New York Times*, November 29, 1939, p. 23:4.

2. A 'correction' to the previous obituary, which appeared in the *New York Times*, December 2, 1939, p. 17:6, gives the spelling of James A. Blair Sr.'s mother's maiden name as Lindberry. However in *The History of Wyandot County*, Chicago, 1884, p. 694, the spelling is given as Lineberry, and on p. 1003, as Linaberry. Although the letter A. in Sarah A. Lindberry is never identified, it may well be the first appearance of the name Alonso, that her son and grandson would carry.

3. *The History of Wyandot County*, Chicago, 1884, p. 694, I am particularly grateful to Tonia Hoffert, Director of the Seneca Conty Museum, Tiffin, Ohio, for her help in researching local sources and histories.

4. *Advertiser Tribune*, Tiffin, Ohio, August 16, 1934.

5. Obituary of Jessie Isabelle Myers, *New York Times*, January 24, 1929, p. 27.

6. *Trinity Church Parish Register*, Tiffin, Seneca County, Ohio, 1870-1902, pp. 13-55. The register notes that Jessie was one of three daughters to Mrs. P. P. Myers and Mr. P Myers, all of whom married. However the father is not listed as a participant at the wedding for reasons unknown.

Commercial National Bank of Tiffin (fig. 2). The bank was opened for business on June 28, 1876. It had four officers: a president, vice president, cashier and assistant cashier. James A Blair Sr. filled the last role. He was also a director. The bank advertised aggressively in the local press. They dealt in bonds and securities, gold and silver coin, and foreign exchange amongst other activities, and happily stated they had $100,000 in capital. [7]

Business was booming. In 1879, Blair Sr. was able to purchase a plot of land from the estate of John Vollmer, at the northeast corner of Lafayette and Adams Street, on which he would build a town house the following year. Eleven months after the wedding and almost certainly in this house (fig. 3), Jessie gave birth to their only child, James Alonso Blair Jr., the future snuff bottle collector. [8]

His life began tumultuously. On the day that he was born, Monday, July 19, 1880, Ohio residents were recovering from a huge storm that had passed through the

Fig. 3   8 Adams Street, Tiffin, Ohio. House of the Blair Family and almost certainly the birth place of James Alonso Blair Jr.
Courtesy of the Seneca County Museum, Tiffin, Ohio.

area. The town of Monroe, 60 miles northwest, just across the state line in Michigan, was the most severely hit. The *New York Times* reported:

A storm broke over this city and its vicinity Sunday afternoon which in severity and destructiveness has never been equaled in this part of the country.... Hail and rain fell in enormous quantities and with frightful velocity... The foliage of the magnificent trees and dense ornamental shrubbery, for which the city is noted, was stripped from the branches and sent flying through the air... oats standing in the fields were prostrated, and grain was beaten out...the stained glass ornamental windows of every church in the city were more or less injured... large forest trees were blown down or twisted off like like wisps of paper. [9]

Fig. 2   Tiffin, Ohio, circa 1890. The building with 2nd floor awnings is the Commercial National Bank of Tiffin.
Courtesy of the Seneca County Museum, Tiffin, Ohio.

7.   Commercial Bank advertisement, *The Tiffin Weekly Tribune*, June 29, 1876.

8.   Blair Sr. and Jr. carried the name Alonso (sometimes listed as Alonzo). However, in the Register of his baptism, *op. cit.*, footnote (6), pp. 54-55, the middle name listed for James Blair Jr. is oddly not Alonso but Prentis. This anomaly can only be resolved by assuming that the parents changed their minds and re-registered the name Alonso at a later date, or that the clergyman made an incorrect entry. The name Prentis was probably derived from the mother-in-law, Mrs. P. P. Myers.

9.   *New York Times*, July 19, 1880, p. 1:3.

This violent start to life was only to prove a portent of the traumas of the Great War, which Blair was to witness first-hand. At the time of his birth, however, the storm must have been simply unnerving for his parents.

The Blair family was to spend the good part of the next decade in Tiffin, and as a child Blair would have become familiar with the relatively flat landscape punctuated to the north by low rolling hills stretching down into the Erie basin. As a state, Ohio was only seventy-seven years old when Blair entered the world. Early in the century the Iroquois had systematically eliminated other tribes and settlers from the hunting grounds south of the Great Lakes. However, by 1855, with the construction of the Soo Locks at the formerly impassable falls between Lake Superior and Lake Huron, and the building of the railways, Ohio opened up to the industrialization and urbanization it had heretofore avoided. (10)

In 1830, the population of Tiffin was a mere 400. By 1880 it had swelled to 7,879. A small pioneer settlement had become a bustling town. At the time of Blair's birth, the streets were still unpaved. In the summer they were covered with a dry powdery dust and on rainy days they were awash with mud. (11)

Fifty-two saloons catered to a thirsty population made up in part of German and British immigrants. There was even a German-language newspaper.

In 1883, for reasons unknown, but presumably to raise capital, Blair's father sold the relatively new house at 8 Adams Street and moved to Shawhan House, the boarding house run by Jessie's father.

In 1886 or 1887 it appears that the family, or at least Blair's father, was on the move again. This time, according to the local directories, their (or his) destination was Kansas City, Missouri. Blair Sr. is no longer listed as a cashier at the bank, but lists his business as 'hats, caps, boots and shoes, 120 Washington Street,' while listing his residence as Kansas City, Missouri. (12)

Most likely, Blair Sr. moved to Kansas, leaving his wife behind to run this small business enterprise and look after their son. The directory of 1892-93 lists the same business but his residence as New York.

A history of the bank published in a local paper of 1932 notes: 'James A. Blair, a native of Seneca County, who resigned his position with the bank while still a youth… went to Medicine Lodge, Kansas, and from there to New York City. Through his ability, Mr. Blair became one of the foremost financiers of New York.' (13)

It would appear that his eldest brother, William L. Blair, arranged the move. Nineteen years his senior, he had become the designated head of the family after their father's death and was himself a very successful banker. He was a founder of the Nevada Deposit Bank, Ohio, when it opened for business on May 5, 1873 and was later named its president. He was also president of the Farmers' Bank of Winfield, Kansas, and one of its principal shareholders.

Winfield is about 80 miles west of Medicine Lodge. In all likelihood James A.

10. Suzanne Winckler, *The Smithsonian Guides to Historic America – The Great Lake States*, New York, 1998, pp. 12-20 (introduction by Roger G. Kennedy, pp. 10-17).

11. Myron B. Barnes, *Between the Eighties, Tiffin, Ohio, 1880-1980*, Tiffin, 1982, pp. 9 and 19-20.

12. *Wiggins Tiffin Directory*, 1887-1888, p. 33.

13. *Daily Advertiser*, Tiffin, Ohio, August 4, 1932 (Centennial Edition), p. 13.

Blair Sr. took a position in his brother's bank in 1886 or 1887. At some point in the following three years, he would be named president of the Fidelity Trust Company of Kansas City.

With the complete absence of family documents to help us, it is difficult to ascertain when Blair Sr.'s family joined him in New York.

We know that he was living in the city by 1892 from the Tiffin directories. We also know that his son was enrolled in a private school on the Upper West Side in 1891. (14) Unfortunately we cannot check the New York Census records of 1890, as these were lost in a disastrous fire in January, 1921. It is probably safe, however, to assume that the family moved to New York City sometime between 1889 and 1891. (15)

The Family Business

The brokerage firm and banking house of Blair & Co. began business on May 2, 1890 at 10 Wall Street, in the former offices of the Manhattan Trust Company. By 1893 they had moved to larger premises at 33 Wall Street and in 1903 had built a magnificent new building at 24 Broad Street.

The senior partner was the patriarch of the family, John I. Blair (fig.4).

Fig. 4   John I. Blair, 1897. Family patriarch.
After King's View of the New York Stock Exchange by Moses King, New York, 1897, p.12.

As a young man he sold the skins of muskrats and rabbits he trapped. This subsequently developed, during and after the Civil War, into the bigger business of supplying the Union forces with clothing. Armed with great entrepreneurial talents and an uncanny ability for picking a winner, he was also able to exploit the frenzied growth in the country's transportation needs. He built and developed many great railroad systems, making a staggering fortune along the way. He was also one of the most generous benefactors of Princeton University, as the beautiful Blair Hall eloquently testifies. (16)

His massive fortune laid the foundations of the Blair empire. Many branches of the family enjoyed the fruits of his labors and continued his successes well into the twentieth century.

In 1890, the *New York Times* noted that: 'James A. Blair (Sr.) has been associated with John I. Blair in many business enterprises and is a man of broad experience in financial matters. He came from Kansas City to live and at his former home he was President of the Fidelity Trust Company and was connected with other financial institutions.' (17) By 1903, James A. Blair Jr. had also joined the family firm.

At the turn of the century, his father, James A. Blair Sr., had successfully continued the family legacy. He led many important underwritings for the firm and, like John I.

---

14. I am grateful to Jacqueline Haun, Archivist at the Lawrenceville School, New Jersey, for access to this information through Lawrenceville school records.

15. Obituary of James A. Blair Jr., *New York Times*, August 16, 1934, p. 17:4, where it is noted that, 'Though the Blair home was originally at Tiffin, Ohio... the family has been prominent in New York business and society for forty-five years.'

16. *New York Times*, August 24, 1899, p. 6:4 in an article about John I. Blair's birthday celebrations at Blairstown, New Jersey.

17. *New York Times*, May 3, 1890, p. 1:6.

Blair, profited handsomely from the railroads. In 1896, Blair Sr. headed a committee that drew up a plan, in effect a friendly takeover bid, for the reorganization of the Houston, East and West Texas Railway Company. It aimed to make the company solvent after three years of earnings insufficient to pay the interest on its bonded indebtedness, which amounted to almost $4 million. [18] The multi-facetted nature of their business is further illustrated in an 'Equipment Trust Agreement' dated December 1, 1901, between Blair & Co. and the St. Louis and San Francisco Railroad Company. [19] The railroad agreed to pay the sum of $1,695,818.33 for a variety of equipment, including rolling stock, supplied by Blair & Co. It all had to carry the company name on a metal plate. This was a huge deal by any standards of the day. [20]

Away from business, Blair Sr. and his wife were prominent in the social life of New York and Oyster Bay. He was a member of the Metropolitan Club; she belonged to the Colony Club. They also kept a summer home in Newport, Rhode Island, on Lower Bellevue Avenue, where the frenetic pace of social engagements continued.

The New York Years

By 1891, James Alonso Blair Jr. was

Fig. 5 Woodhall House, Class of 1895,
The Lawrenceville School, New Jersey.
Courtesy of The Lawrenceville School,
New Jersey.

attending Irving School, a small independent establishment on the Upper West Side of Manhattan at 54 West 84th Street. He would study there for three years before applying to the Lawrenceville School in New Jersey in July, 1894.

His application lists his home address as 160 West 59th Street and included three letters from his parents and one from Louis Dwight Ray, the headmaster of Irving.

Though Blair repeated his first year, his schooling at Lawrenceville passed by fairly uneventfully, save for one minor incident, when his father was required to send a telegram and letter to the headmaster, James Cameron Mackenzie, after he returned to school late from a weekend furlough. [14] Blair would spend two years at the school, living on campus at Woodhall House (fig. 5). He entered Princeton in the fall of 1899. Records indicate that he left Princeton in 1902, the year before he was scheduled to graduate. [21] However, another internal university newspaper reported that he left after his freshman year in 1900. [22]

By 1903 he was working for Blair & Co. at their newly built premises at 24 Broad

18. *Plan and Agreement for the Re-organization of the Houston, East and West Texas Railway Company*, New York, 1896.

19. *Blair & Co. and St. Louis and San Francisco Railroad Company – Equipment Trust Agreement*, New York, December, 1901.

20. The signatory for Blair & Co. on this document was John B. Dennis (see p. 20).

21. *Nassau Herald*, New Jersey, 1903 (month and day not specified), Mudd Library Records, Princeton University, Princeton, New Jersey.

22. *Princeton Alumni Weekly*, October 12, 1934, Mudd Library Records, Princeton University, Princeton, New Jersey.

Fig. 6   Ontare, northern front, 1910.
Architects: Carrère and Hastings.
Courtesy of the General Research Division,
The New York Public Library, Astor, Lenox and
Tilden Foundations. After *Town and Country*,
November 5, 1910, p. 34.

Street and residing with his father at 9 West 50th Street. This remained the same for at least the next seven years and possibly for as long as ten years as the very useful New York directories of the time attest. [23]

Unfortunately, Blair is not listed between 1911 and 1913. When he reappears in the 1913-14 directory, his occupation is listed as broker rather than banker and his home address is given as the Plaza Hotel. He was independent of the firm but still under the watchful eye of his father.

Oddly, the family is not listed in the 1900 or 1910 censuses for either Manhattan or New Jersey. Nor are they listed in Oyster Bay Cove (Nassau County)

records, where in 1909-10, James A. Blair Jr. built a massive Neo-French manorial home with large formal gardens called Ontare. [24] The architects, Carrère & Hastings, had also built the Blair & Co. premises at 24 Broad Street.

The grandeur of Ontare (figs. 6-8) epitomized the heights to which the family had risen, as did its location in that exceedingly wealthy enclave on Long Island's north shore, on the crest of a hill overlooking Oyster Bay.

The architects' uncharacteristically irregular plan provided numerous wall surfaces to show off their elaborate tapestry brickwork. An extensive terrace and spacious veranda with a fireplace promoted the enjoyment of the out-of-doors. The veranda overlooked a large formal garden and stable, a composition that *Town and Country* called: 'a triumph of landscape gardening… where art assists nature.' [25]

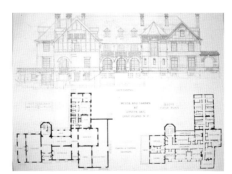

Fig. 8   Ontare, south elevation and floor plans, 1910.
Architects: Carrère and Hastings.
Courtesy of the Art and Architecture Collection,
Miriam and Ira D. Wallach Division of Arts,
Prints and photography, The New York Public
Library, Astor, Lenox and Tilden Foundations.
After *Architectural Forum* (The Brickbuilder),
Vol. XIX, No. 9, September 1910.

Fig. 7   Ontare, veranda and formal gardens, 1910.
Architects: Carrère and Hastings.
Courtesy of the General Research Division,
The New York Public Library, Astor, Lenox and
Tilden Foundations. After *Town and Country*,
November 5, 1910, p. 35.

23. *The New York Directories*, 1900-1934, National Archives and Records, New York.

24. Mackay Baker Traynor, *Long Island Country Houses and their Architects, 1860-1940*, New York, C. 1997, p. 106.

25. *Town and Country*, Vol. 65, Number 34, November 5, 1910, pp. 30-35.

Fig. 9   Colonel James A. Blair Jr. and officers of the Army Signal Corp, Production and Maintenance Department at the Air Service Production Center, No. 2, Romorantin, France, 16 November 1918. Thanks to the National Archives and Records Administration, Maryland.

The house included eleven guest bedrooms. It was built on Blair Road but sadly was later demolished. Various architectural journals and periodicals of the day illustrated the house lavishly.

The September, 1910 issue of *Brick Builder* noted that it was:

The first house to be constructed of brick similar in size and texture to many of those in Ancient Rome.... This house marks an epoch, in many respects, in the development of artistic brickwork in this country. The bricks are most unusual in size, being 18 inches long, 2 inches thick and 6 inches wide. They vary in color from a rich red to a deep blue with many intermediate shades of light and dark brown, purple and olive. Many of the individual bricks bear several colors each and all have a rough, rugged surface. [26]

Perhaps the beautiful brick buildings at Princeton influenced Blair's instructions to his architects.

Between 1913 and 1917 he continued life as a broker but took new apartments at the Plaza Hotel, off Fifth Avenue.

Just as his grandfather, James Blair, had fought the British in 1812, and his uncle, Theodore F. Blair (born 1844), had served with Company H, One Hundred and Forty-fourth Regiment Ohio Volunteer Infantry between May and August, 1864, James A. Blair Jr. expressed his patriotism through active military service. [27]

Some time prior to 1917, Blair Jr. enlisted in the New York National Guard and served as a 2nd lieutenant, captain and major. In 1917 he was commissioned as a major in the Army, and then assigned to Headquarters Eastern Department. On March 10, 1918, he was promoted to lieutenant colonel on duty with the Emergency Fleet Corporation and later commissioned colonel for General Staff Overseas. [15 & 28]

Fig. 10   Detail of fig. 9. Colonel James A. Blair Jr. stands at the end of the second last row.

26. *Architectural Forum* (The Brick Builder), Vol. XIX, No. 9, September, 1910, p. 215.

27. *The History of Wyandot County*, Chicago, 1884, pp. 1003-4. Theodore F. Blair had been a volunteer with the Ohio National Guard before his call-up.

28. *Who's Who in America*, 1897-1942, Chicago, Vol. I, p. 103.

The only known photograph of our elusive subject, as an adult, was taken on November 16, 1918, in Romorantin, France, five days after the German capitulation and the signing of the armistice (figs. 9 & 10). It depicts officers of the Army Signal Corp, Production and Maintenance Department at the Air Service Production Center, number 2, about a hundred miles from the Western Front. Blair is listed as a lieutenant. He stands at the end of the second-to-last row. The hard brim of his cap shades his eyes. He stands upright and wears a dignified dark moustache. At 38, he is visibly older than the men around him.

In April 1919 he was appointed Army Member of the American Aviation Mission to study the future aviation policies of England, France and Italy. He was honorably discharged on December 20, 1919. For his service in the Great War, he was to be decorated by Belgium, France, Italy and Serbia.

Back in civilian life he acted for a number of years as the treasurer of the American Committee of the Lafayette Memorial which cared for French war orphans at the Château Lafayette at Chavannis, France. He was also the treasurer of the National Allied Relief Committee, established after the Great War to assist survivors. [23]

The family firm in its original form ceased to exist after April 22, 1920, when it merged with the firm of William Salomon & Co. in an enlarged partnership, also known as Blair and Co. It later merged into the Bancamerica-Blair Corporation, control of which passed to the Transamerica Corporation. [29 & 30]

Corporate Life

Over the length of his professional career, which spanned the period from 1902 to 1934 with a break during the War, he served as a director for at least eight companies. Many of these were connected to the town of Kingsport in Tennessee, which sits in the state's northeastern corner near the Virginia border in the Appalachian range.

Kingsport was crucial in Blair's business life, as was John Bartlett Dennis (1866-1947), his father's colleague at Blair & Co. from its early days and a close family friend. He would play a role of paramount importance in Blair Jr's. career and would later inherit his residuary estate. He became one of Kingsport's most famous civic leaders and a local luminary. A highway named in his honor is still the main artery to the town.

Dennis was a visionary, determined to build an industrial city at Kingsport. He enlisted the services of a local merchant named J. Fred Johnson (fig. 11). With others,

Fig. 11 John B. Dennis (left) and J. Fred Johnson, circa 1910-20's.
Kyle Huddle Photograph Collection, Courtesy of the Archives of Appalachia, East Tennessee State University.

29. *New York Times*, February 10, 1937, p. 33:6.

30. *New York Times*, February 27, 1939, p. 26:2.

they bought large tracts of land and, in 1917, not only set out to build a city, but succeeded. In 1922 they formed the Kingsport Improvement Company, a real estate concern, which Blair Jr. joined a few years later. [31] The various industries that they developed in Kingsport were closely linked for industrial efficiency. Blair & Co. helped to finance the growth.

Dennis acted as Blair's guardian angel, placing him on various boards connected to this huge undertaking. Blair was named chairman of the executive committee of the Kingsport Press Inc. of Kingsport, Tennessee (fig 12), and president of its sales agency in New York. He was a director of three other companies closely connected to Kingsport: the Clinchfield Securities Company, and, as mentioned earlier, the Kingsport Improvement Company, both based in Kingsport, and also the Holliston Mills of Massachusetts, an important paper supplier.

In 1922 he was named vice president and treasurer of the International Coal Products Corporation, presumably connected to the Clinchfield Coal Corporation, in Kingsport, Tennessee. [32]

Two years later he was named vice president and treasurer at the publishing house of J. H. Sears & Co. Inc. where he oversaw its reorganization. Joseph Sears was for many years president of D. Appleton Century Company and, with Dennis, helped to establish the Kingsport

Fig. 12 Kingsport Press Inc. of Kingsport, Tennessee. Kyle Huddle Photograph Collection, Courtesy of the Archives of Appalachia, East Tennessee State University.

Press in Tennessee. [33] Blair would become its chairman.

The businesses of bookbinding and printing were well suited to the area. There was a plentiful supply of trees, and mills dotted the Holston River. The building of the railways and in particular the local Clinchfield depot at the intersection of Main and Broad Streets speeded distribution.

One of the company's early contracts with the Woolworth Stores, to supply books for sale at ten cents, proved especially lucrative. [33] The business boomed well beyond the lives of Blair and Dennis. It was one of the largest bookmaking concerns in the United States and survived almost the entire century. [34]

A pamphlet compiled in 1948 for those who visited the plant was entitled 'Bookmakers to America'. This was no shallow claim.

Blair must have traveled regularly between Kingsport and New York in his various business capacities. It would certainly explain his numerous moves from apartment to apartment over the city. Blair & Co. also had the luxury of their own private railroad car named 'The Clinchfield.' Blair Sr. used it on his return visits to Ohio

31. Eleny A. Lay, *An Industrial and Commercial History of the Tri-Cities in Tennessee-Virginia*, Kingsport, TN, 1982, p. 81 (quoting from *The Nation*, January 21, 1939).

32. *New York Directories*, 1922-25, National Archives and Records, New York.

33. Eleny A. Lay, *op. cit.*, p. 101.

34. Obituary of John B. Dennis, *New York Times*, February 13, 1947, p. 23:4.

and Blair Jr. presumably used it for his frequent trips down the East Coast, and perhaps on his one recorded return visit to his birthplace of Tiffin, sometime between 1917 and 1934. [4]

Blair Jr. also held directorships at the Macon, Dublin and Savannah Railroad, the Securities Investment Fund, and the Continental Trust Company of Baltimore.

Club Life

During his leisure time away from work, Blair led a comfortable club life. The list of clubs where Blair held memberships is remarkable. Membership in any one would be noteworthy. Membership in so many high-profile clubs was indeed impressive. They were limited to only the well-heeled, those cushioned by financial resources and aided by prominent social ties. Among the most notable were the New York Yacht

Club and the Metropolitan Club, in Manhattan, and the Seawanhaka Corinthian and Piping Rock, in Long Island.

The first was formed in 1844, and found its present home at 37 West 44th Street in 1901, thanks to the generous gift of a plot of land by J. P. Morgan. At the turn of the century it was one of the most exclusive associations in the city, with a sophisticated and very private membership; its 'commodores' included men of the Morgan, Vanderbilt and Astor families, as well as one of the Blair clan. James A. Blair Jr. joined on March 28, 1907. Other family members at that time included John Insley Blair and his son C. Ledyard Blair (fig. 13) who would be elected commodore for the years 1911-12. [35]

Blair Jr. owned a single-masted sloop, Neola, which was built by Gardner & Cox in 1902. It was constructed of bronze on a steel frame and was 91 feet in length and weighed 39 tons. It was moored in New York harbor. [36 & 37]

Prior to his election to the New York Yacht Club, Blair was already a member of another very exclusive yacht club, the Seawanhaka Corinthian in Oyster Bay. Its members were just as privileged as those of the New York Yacht Club. Blair remained a member until 1925.

Not far from Oyster Bay, and still set in Nassau County, is the magnificent Piping Rock Golf Club. In the wealthy town of Locust Valley, it was then, and still is, one of the most elite golf clubs on the Eastern Seaboard. Blair and John B. Dennis, who

Fig. 13 C. Ledyard Blair and three of his four daughters, circa 1910.
Courtesy of the General Research Division, The New York Public Library, Astor, Lenox and Tilden Foundations. After *Town and Country*, December 1910, p. 19.

35. C. Ledyard Blair was a director of the Clinchfield Ohio Railroad Co., the Clinchfield Coal Corporation, and many other corporations.

36. *Lloyd's List of Yachts of the United States and Canada*, 1910, p. 187.

37. New York Yacht Club, *Yearbook*, 1910, p. 38.

was also a member, must have enjoyed relaxing hours, hitting golf balls on the stunning course and escaping the pressures of corporate life.

The Metropolitan Club was founded in 1891 and moved in 1894 to new premises designed by Stanford White at the corner of Fifth Avenue and 60th Street. The cost, an extraordinary $2 million, was covered by the pledges of the original 700 members who included Whitneys, Browns, Roosevelts, Hamiltons, Cromwells, Morgans and Vanderbilts. [38]

Blair joined on October 17, 1905, four years and five months after his father's admission on May 21, 1901. John B. Dennis had been a member since 1894, the year the club moved to its Fifth Avenue address. The entrance fee at that time was $300 and the annual dues for a resident member were $125, a not insubstantial sum. [39]

Somewhat later in his relatively short life, at the age of 46, Blair became a member of the Holland Lodge No. 8, F. & A. M. He was the youngest of five members inducted that year. This Masonic lodge had innumerable worthy past members who included the likes of George Washington inducted in 1789; DeWitt Clinton, mayor of New York for twelve years and an unsuccessful candidate for president of the United States (he was defeated by James Madison), was inducted in 1790; John Jacob Astor joined in the same year. Franklin D. Roosevelt, one of the few Democratic members, was inducted in 1910. (Blair was a Republican.)

Fig. 14 Interior of the Holland Lodge No. 8, F. & A. M., New York City, New York, 1935.
Courtesy of the Holland Lodge No. 8, F. & A. M., New York City, New York.

When Blair joined, the lodge had moved premises to its present location at 71 West 23rd Street, near Sixth Avenue. Its interiors have not changed to this day (fig. 14). The Masonic principles of friendship, morality and brotherly love were central to Blair's character.

Other clubs in which he held privileges included the Racquet and Tennis Club in Midtown; the respected Army and Navy for military men (he held memberships in the New York and Washington branches); the Princeton Club, where he was a member from 1903 until his death in 1934; the Turf and Field; and the Lido Country. [15]

Blair was quite a sportsman in what spare time he had away from his busy corporate life. He was a yachtsman, aviation enthusiast, golfer, and tennis player. His exquisite snuff bottles displayed another side of his character, that of the cultured man.

The Final Years

On January 22, 1929, at the age of seventy-one, his mother died at the Plaza Hotel, of

38. Kenneth T. Jackson (Ed.), *The Encyclopedia Of New York City*, New York, 1995, pp. 755, 850 and 939.

39. *Annual*, The Metropolitan Club, New York, 1909.

heart disease after an illness of two months.

James Alonso Blair Jr. suffered a fatal heart attack on August 15, 1934, at the relatively young age of fifty-four, at his apartment on the top floor of the Buckingham Hotel at 101 West 57th Street, which he had shared with his father since 1926. (40 & 41)

James A. Blair Sr. would outlive his son by five years. He died at his home in Oyster Bay Cove on the morning of November 28, 1939, as another war engulfed the world.

And so, within a space of ten years, the life of this branch of the Blair family came to a close. All three would be laid to rest in the same plot at the magnificent Memorial Cemetery of St. John's Church at Cold Spring Harbor, near their beloved Oyster Bay (figs. 15 & 16). The cemetery, designed by the Olmsted brothers, is amongst the finest in the country. It is a botanic splendor with trees of every imaginable kind. The plot itself is set on the side of a stepped hill

Fig. 16 Colonel James A. Blair's tombstone at the Memorial Cemetery, St John's Church, Cold Spring Harbor, Long Island. Courtesy of the Memorial Cemetery, St John's Church, Cold Spring Harbor, Long Island. Photo credit: M. C. Hughes.

under a canopy of oak, yew, sycamore, pine and rhododendron. A clearing with a thick moss floor beckons the visitor. Three simple horizontal Italian marble slabs serve as the Blairs' tombstones. Jessie, Blair's mother, lies at the center flanked by her husband and only son. Inscribed on her stone is the following:

> Sleep sweetly tender heart in peace
> Sleep Holy Spirit blessed soul
> While the stars burn the moons increase
> And the great ages onward roll

The more simple tombstones of her husband and son are carved identically with an ivy border, with an encircled Greek cross above and an oak-and-acorn cluster below. Perhaps the cluster was a reference to the son's military service, perhaps no more than an aesthetic choice. Whatever the original intention, today a beautiful symmetry exists as a magnificent towering oak, which stands nearby, softly sheds its leaves on the graves below.

Fig. 15 The Blair Family plot at the Memorial Cemetery, St John's Church, Cold Spring Harbor, Long Island. Courtesy of the Memorial Cemetery, St John's Church, Cold Spring Harbor, Long Island. Photo credit: M. C. Hughes.

Two lengthy articles appeared in the *New York Times* after the death of Col. James A. Blair Jr. regarding his last will and testament.

The first, six days after his death, was entitled 'Blair Art To Museum: Colonel's Will Provides $10,000 to Care for Chinese Objects.' It noted that he had left his collection to the Metropolitan Museum of Art:

> Among the articles in the group is Colonel Blair's Collection of Chinese Snuff Bottles, considered to be the finest collection of its kind in the world. The will provided that the collection be kept in a separate room and that the $10,000 be used for its installation and maintenance, and provided that the bequest be accepted within a reasonable time. If the collection is not accepted by the Art Museum, the will provides for its transfer to Princeton University. [41]

The second article, on January 30, 1936, was entitled 'Col. Blair Left $955,030: Bulk of Art Collector's Estate Willed to a Friend.' It continued:

> The estate of Colonel James A. Blair Jr., corporation official and art collector, who died on August 14 [sic], 1934, was appraised yesterday at $1,063,657 gross and $955,030 net. He had securities worth $953,380, notes valued at $18,805, cash amounting to $44,582 and personal effects, including art objects, worth $16,463. Colonel Blair, who was unmarried, left his residuary estate to a friend, John B. Dennis of Oyster Bay. He gave a collection of Chinese snuff bottles, appraised as of 'nominal' value to Princeton University with $10,000 in cash to care for the collection. [42]

Therefore, at some time between 1934 and 1936, the Metropolitan Museum of Art declined the gift, and the bequest, as provided in the will, went to Princeton University.

The Metropolitan Museum of Art had substantial holdings of Chinese snuff bottles at this time, and had shifted its focus to other areas of Asian art. In hindsight, however, they allowed a superb collection, with great rarities, to slip through their hands, one that today has a value in the many millions of dollars.

Princeton University Art Museum can now proudly boast of its Chinese snuff bottle holdings.

Colonel Blair's Collecting

It was unlikely that Blair saw great art first hand prior to his move from Tiffin, Ohio. His father probably had a reasonably sophisticated library, as did most well-to-do families in the circles in which the Blairs doubtlessly moved. It is safe to assume that it was the move to New York at the age of about nine that first opened Blair's eyes to the world of art.

We may never know exactly what attracted Blair to Chinese art, in the absence of his personal papers, which were left in his will to friends, and to date have not been located. However, we can make some educated guesses at the variety of forces that influenced his taste.

40. *New York Directories*, 1933-34, National Archives and Records, New York.

41. *New York Times*, August 21, 1934, p. 12:2.

42. *New York Times*, January 30, 1936, p. 20:1.

Historically, Asia had played a pivotal role in American growth. After the American Revolution, commerce with China became an important part of U. S. trade. Tea was the principal import until 1820, with Chinese export wares (primarily porcelain) making up the bulk of the ballast on board the ships that made the arduous sea voyage from America to Guangzhou (Canton) and back again.

In the nineteenth century there were a number of important exhibitions which helped educate and develop American taste. One of the most important was in 1838 of the Philadelphia merchant, Nathan Dunn. His museum exhibited porcelains, lacquers, silks and screens and was hugely successful. In 1860, the year before the Civil War began, P. T. Barnum, rather more famous for his later circus company, held a popular traveling show of Oriental wares. [43]

In the 1870's, the first major museums in the country opened. The Corcoran in Washington (1870), the Metropolitan in New York (1870), and the Museum of Fine Arts, Boston (1876).

At the same time, premier Chinese collections were being built on the East Coast by the likes of Samuel P. Avery, Mr. and Mrs. Henry O. Havemeyer, Benjamin Altman, Heber Bishop, and J. P. Morgan in New York; Charles Lang Freer in New York and Washington; and W. T. Walters in Baltimore. Edward S. Morse, Sturges Bigelow, Denman Ross, and Ernest Fenollosa were doing the same for Japanese art in Boston. Interest in collecting Asian art was well established by the time Blair arrived on the East Coast.

Colonel Blair was a member of, and presumably a regular visitor to, the Metropolitan Museum of Art and the American Museum of Natural History.

The Metropolitan Museum's first investment in Oriental art was the purchase of the Samuel P. Avery Collection in 1879. It included six snuff bottles. In 1891, another ten snuff bottles were added from the Edward Moore bequest. In 1914, the first large group of bottles, one hundred and seventy, entered the collection as part of the Benjamin Altman bequest. In the 1920s, when Blair was most actively acquiring snuff bottles, the museum added many more to its holdings. A windfall of three hundred and fifty bottles from Edmond Converse in 1921, thirty from Mary Clark Thompson in 1924 and thirty-five from William Rhinelander Thompson in 1929, helped to swell the collection. [44] By 1921, therefore, Blair had access to well over five hundred bottles, albeit of mixed quality, at this museum alone.

On the other side of Central Park stands the American Museum of Natural History, which had, prior to 1931, a small but varied selection of snuff bottles. The first group of twenty-five bottles, from the Kunz Collection, entered the museum in 1891. This was followed in 1903 and 1904 with fifteen bottles from the Laufer Collection. Twenty-eight more bottles from the Tilson bequest entered the collection in 1920. By far the largest bequest came from the Drummond Collection in 1931 when over four hundred bottles entered the museum.[45] In terms of breadth of material, the Drummond Collection was similar to

43. Warren I. Cohen, *East Asian Art and American Culture*, New York, 1992, pp. 10-12, and 13.

44. I am grateful to Elizabeth Munemura, Education Department of the Metropolitan Museum, New York, for this information.

45. I am grateful to Anne Wright-Parsons, senior scientific assistant at the American Museum of Natural History, for this information.

Blair's. Glass, porcelains, agates, lacquers, jades and enamels can be found in profusion. In terms of quality and rarity of craftsmanship, however, it seldom came close to Blair's. Hardly surprising, when one considers that Drummond was a collector of minerals before art. Still, there were some exceptional examples of crystal, *laque burgauté*, jade and amber for Blair to feast his eyes on in the last few years of his life.

So where else might Blair have found information on snuff bottles?

There was relatively little published information available to him. Books and journals on snuff bottles were few and often limited in scope. If we leave aside the dealer and auction catalogues, he might have had access to perhaps fifteen publications in 1929, a far cry from the plethora available to us today. [46] A few magazine articles also appeared between 1896 and 1907. [47]

Where else might Blair have sought an educated opinion?

Without doubt, the dealers, collectors, stores and the auctioneers of his day,

Fig. 17 Interior of Colonel James A. Blair's New York apartment, circa 1928.
After Arts & Decoration, Winter, 1928.

particularly the former, were on his visiting card.

Some clues to this can be found in an article by Edward Wenham in the Winter 1928 edition of *Arts & Decoration*. [48] The article on the Blair collection sheds some light on his collecting habits but is deeply frustrating in its lack of information about the man himself.

With one exception, it is a sorely missed opportunity to hear the voice of the collector. One suspects it was Blair's choice to remain mute, and not the fault of the author. However, we can glean some information from the illustrations, and more by reading between the lines.

The article mentions that the collection, 'is a magnum in parvo for the student of eastern craftsmanship… Within the small space of three cabinets is the history of the earlier artistic advancement of the Oriental people'.

The three cabinets are illustrated *in situ* in his home along with a selection of bottles removed from their cabinets (figs. 17-18).

From the illustrations, about forty bottles in the collection can be identified. [49] Interestingly, one exceptional bottle, third

46. These included: the privately printed small edition by William Bragge, *Bibliotheca Nicotiana. A Catalogue of Books about Tobacco Together with a Catalogue of Objects Connected with the Use of Tobacco in All Its Forms*, Birmingham, England, 1880; Marcus B. Huish, *Chinese Snuff Bottles*, London, 1895; another privately printed photographic card catalogue of the Sharp Collection, *Chinese Miniature Vase and Snuff Bottle Collection*, New York, ca. 1900; Stephen W. Bushell, *Chinese Art*, Victoria and Albert Museum, London, 1904; the privately printed volume by Bernard Laufer, *Catalogue of a Collection of Ancient Chinese Snuff Bottles in the Possession of Mrs. George T. Smith*, Chicago, 1913; Bernard Laufer, *Tobacco and Its Uses in Asia*, Field Museum of Natural History, Chicago, 1924; A. W. Bahr, *Old Chinese Porcelain and Works of Art in China*, London, 1927; The *Handbook of the Benjamin Altman Collection*, the Metropolitan Museum of Art, New York, 1928; and *China and Japan in Our Museums* by B. March, New York, 1929.

47. Marcus B. Huish, 'A Little Appreciated Side of Art - Chinese Snuff Bottles,' *The Studio*, No. 8, June 1896, pp. 11-16; and Walter Leo Hildburgh, 'Chinese Methods of Cutting Hardstones', *Journal Royal Anthropological Institute*, xxxvii, 1907.

48. Edward Wenham, in an article entitled 'Antiques and Decoration,' *Arts & Decoration*, Winter, 1928, New York, pp. 58-59, 96 and 100.

49. The literature has been noted for each of these bottles in the relevant catalogue entries.

Fig. 18   A selection of snuff bottles from the collection of Colonel James A. Blair, circa 1928.
Left to right: Princeton No.165, unknown, Princeton No. 354, J & J Collection, No. 184, Princeton No. 180 and Princeton No. 302 .
After *Arts & Decoration*, Winter, 1928.

from the right in figure 18, and not part of the Blair Bequest, is almost certainly the same bottle now in the James Li Collection. It was included by Hugh Moss, Victor Graham and Ka Bo Tsang in *The Art of the Chinese Snuff Bottle, The J & J Collection,* New York, 1993, pp. 308-311, No.184. The earliest provenance listed by Moss et al., is Tongying [sic] & Co. of New York, though no date is given. Presumably Blair sold it directly to Ton-Ying & Co. after 1928 when the article was published.

The article also mentions, and this is of singular importance to our understanding of Blair's collecting habits, that: 'Col. Blair will tell you that he was first infused with enthusiasm to collect Chinese snuff bottles when he saw the Converse collection. Since that time he has made a close study of the various characteristics of his several hundred specimens.'

It is not quite clear if this close study is of his personal bottles or those of the Edmond Converse collection. If we assume Wenham was referring to Blair's own bottles, and given that roughly 200 are illustrated in the article, we can estimate that between 1928 and 1934, the year Blair died, he added another three hundred bottles to his collection. This is a staggering number to acquire in six years. Either Blair went on a buying rampage or he owned more bottles than he revealed to his interviewer.

The author continues, 'Incidentally it is of interest to observe that we are fairly safe in saying that the two most representative collections (of snuff bottles) existing today, are in America, one being that of Col. Blair and the other assembled by the late E. C. Converse, which is now in the Metropolitan Museum of Art.'

Later Wenham notes:

That the pursuit and acquisition of these beautiful examples of art is a never-ending pleasure is natural from the fact that the collector is continually hearing of a new discovery. Then he wonders if he has one of the same type. Thus there is always the lure of the unfinished chase. His quarry may be a duplicate of one he already has; it may be a finer example of one in his cabinets; it may represent some phase of the art previously unknown to him; or it may possibly be a unique specimen, the like of which no other collector has. Thus the enthusiast having procured the nucleus of his collection applies the process of addition and elimination. But there is one point that the far-seeing collector observes. He knows the pitfalls into which his lack of technical experience may lead him so he stifles his independence and wisely relies upon the advice of a connoisseur-dealer.

Finally, the author notes a conversation with the New York art dealer, Mr. Roland Moore, regarding Chinese snuff bottles.

Perhaps Moore was the 'connoisseur-dealer' alluded to in the article? Interestingly, he had a store at 42 East 57th Street which, despite Blair's many city addresses, was rarely ever more than a few blocks away from his home. Ton-Ying & Co. may also have been the dealer alluded to. It seems likely that they had dealings with Blair, as discussed above, regarding the magnificent enameled glass bottle now in the James Li Collection. We may never know for sure.

These were two of the many dealers to whom Blair had access for advice. Others he may easily have taken counsel from included S. S. Carvalho, Yamanaka, Fujita and Co., C. T. Loo, the Duveen Brothers, and Suval and Voron, Inc., all of whom had New York galleries. (50) It is quite likely, with his social connections, that he also spoke with the other collectors of his day like Mary Clark Thompson and Edmund C. Converse. Joseph Sears of J. H. Sears & Co. Inc. was also a snuff bottle collector and may well have influenced Blair.

Besides the dealers, we know that Blair bought at auction. The American Art Association, Inc., the American Art Galleries and the Anderson Galleries Inc. of New York City, handled many of the most important collections to come on the market at this time.

Fourteen bottles which sold at auction between 1914 and 1926 can be positively identified by catalogue illustration as bottles in the collection today. Another five can almost certainly be identified by catalogue illustration. One unillustrated bottle which sold on February 3, 1921, lot 1, is annotated alongside the catalogue entry with the buyer's name 'J A Blair'. It can not be identified with certainty as any bottle in the collection today, but it is evidence that Blair attended the auction or left a commission bid. (fig. 19)

A large group of bottles offered in these early sales were never illustrated, and might easily be bottles in the collection today. Unfortunately, woefully scant descriptive entries, with some notable exceptions for single collections, a lack of measurements, and insufficient buyer records make definitive identification impossible.

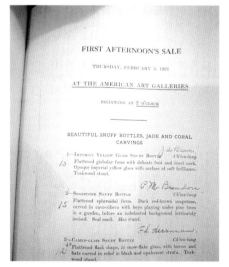

Fig. 19 American Art Galleries, sale catalogue, February 3, 1921. First page of the afternoon session. J A Blair purchaser of lot 1.
Thanks to Elsa Glickman for the use of her library for figs.19-33.

50. I am grateful to Elsa Glickman for the use of her extensive library of early auction catalogues and information on dealers in New York in the early years of the twentieth century.

At a time when art catalogues in general were sparsely illustrated and snuff bottles in particular were rarely depicted, it is astonishing that so many bottles in the collection have been positively identified. The actual purchaser of these positively identified bottles is unknown. While almost certainly Blair, it may have been an agent, a dealer or even another collector, who later sold on to Blair. The provenance, however, is iron cast.

Let us look at the bottles we can positively identify, in the order in which they appeared at auction.

On March 7, 1914, the American Art Galleries were entrusted with the sale of the private collection of the then well-known connoisseur-dealer, Mr. Edward Runge. Of twenty-one snuff bottles offered, lot 27, a massive jasper bottle (Princeton No. 72), eventually entered the collection. The buyer on this occasion was almost certainly Samuel S. Laird of Philadelphia. Ten years later, after his death, the bottle re-appeared at the same auction house in the sale of his noted collection of Eastern and Far Eastern art which included jades, snuff bottles, Japanese lacquer and netsuke, and Persian carpets, as well as European porcelain and glass, which took place January 7-12, 1924. Over one hundred and ninety-five snuff bottles were auctioned; one was the Edward Runge Jasper, lot 222 (fig. 20).

In both the 1914 and 1924 catalogues, the piece was generously illustrated, highlighting the importance placed on this bottle at that time. It is a magnificent specimen of its type, but its unusually large size would probably be considered a drawback by collectors today.

The next three bottles to appear at auction were the large ivory bottle, (Princeton No.100); and two delightful Imperial enamels (Princeton Nos. 356 and 361).

They belonged to the noted dealer, connoisseur, and authority on ancient Chinese art, Mr. A. W. Bahr, who had lived in Shanghai for over thirty years before finally settling in Connecticut.

The sale took place at the American Art Galleries, January 17-19, 1916. The ivory bottle, offered as lot 85, was called

Fig. 20 American Art Galleries, sale catalogue, Edward Runge Collection, March 7, 1914, lot 27 (Princeton No. 72).

Fig. 21 American Art Galleries, sale catalogue, A. W. Bahr Collection, January 17-19, 1916, lot 85 (Princeton No. 100).

Fig. 22 American Art Galleries, sale catalogue, A. W. Bahr Collection , January 17-19, 1916, lot 57 (Princeton No. 356).

Fig. 23 American Art Galleries, sale catalogue, A. W. Bahr Collection, January 17-19, 1916, lot 80 (Princeton No. 361).

Imperial and the catalogue entry noted that it was obtained from a 'Palace in Peking' (Beijing), which, sadly for us, is not named (fig. 21). The first of the two enamels, offered as lot 57, was listed as 'distinctly superior to ordinary enameled bottles' (fig. 22). The second of the enamels, lot 80, which sold at $250, is something of a riddle (fig. 23). The lot illustrated appears to be absolutely identical to the enamel in the Blair Bequest (Princeton No. 361), even down to the slightly uneven firing of the enamel where it joins the metal foot. Though not visible in the catalogue, the entry notes 'two small medallions of landscapes at the sides.' The Blair bottle does not have small landscape medallions. The catalogue also notes, without specifying the exact type of four-character mark, that 'the four seal-characters are for articles of Imperial use only, or for presents given by the Emperor as a special mark of favor.' This would suggest a *Yuzhi* mark. The Blair bottle has a *nianzhi* mark.

This author is unable to unravel this particular conundrum. It is possible that a 'sale room notice,' now missing, cleared up this confusion.

The first time that we can, with almost total certainty, identify Col. James A. Blair as a buyer of a snuff bottle at auction was in the Yamanaka sale held at the American Art Galleries on February 3, 1921. Fortunately, someone had written each buyer's name in ink above the lots in the catalogue I located. The annotation above lot 1, an un-illustrated yellow glass bottle (fig. 19), describes the buyer as 'J A Blair.' It seems highly improbable that this could refer to any other Blair. The globular bottle listed might well be one in the collection

Fig. 24 American Art Galleries, sale catalogue, Trowbridge Hall Collection, April 22, 1921, lot 58 (Princeton No. 105).

Fig. 25 American Art Galleries, sale catalogue, Elizabeth Andrews Collection, February 8-9, 1922, lot 35 (Princeton No. 159).

today (Princeton No. 118).

Later in the same year, on April 22, 1921, one hundred and seventy-three snuff bottles from the New York collector, Mr. Trowbridge Hall, were offered for sale by the American Art Galleries as part of a larger group of Asian objects. Amongst the primarily Chinese bottles were a number of Japanese examples which included lot 58, a fine *laque burgauté* bottle (Princeton No. 105), delicately inlaid with birds in flight above a naturalistically rendered lotus pond (fig. 24).

On February 8 and 9, 1922, at least two, and possibly four, bottles in the collection were auctioned at the same galleries during the sale of the extraordinary snuff bottle collection of Mrs. Elizabeth Andrews. Four hundred and forty-seven bottles were offered, and the sale definitely included the magnificent red overlay (Princeton No. 159) and the beautiful coral (Princeton No. 108). The first, lot 35, was dated Kangxi (fig. 25), and the second, lot 251, was dated Qianlong (fig. 26).

Fig. 26 American Art Galleries, sale catalogue, Elizabeth Andrews Collection, February 8-9, 1922, lot 251 (Princeton No. 108).

Fig. 27 American Art Galleries, sale catalogue, H. A. E. Jaehne Collection, April 10-12, 1923, lot 73 (Princeton No. 313).

Two other bottles, almost certainly the same bottles as those in the collection today, the bat-decorated porcelain (Princeton No. 211) and the undecorated amber (Princeton No. 88) were probably offered as lots 354 and 254 respectively.

Interestingly, the catalogue had an unusual introductory note prior to the first lot, which reads like a caveat:

> In the main, the periods to which the snuff bottles are ascribed are those given by the Chinese and Japanese collectors and dealers from whom the bottles were purchased in the Orient during the formation of Mrs. Andrews' collection, or given under subsequent revision by Mrs. Andrews upon consultation with Japanese experts.

This information not only adds to our knowledge of the provenance of these particular bottles, it also tells us something about the uncertainty of actual dating on the part of the auction house.

The next three bottles to appear at auction were the blue and white dragon-

decorated porcelain (Princeton No. 313), the porcelain figure of Liu Hai (Princeton No. 303), and the double crystal (Princeton No. 30). On April 10-12, 1923, The American Art Galleries offered the collection of the connoisseur Mr. H. A. E. Jaehne, which had been formed over the seventeen years he lived in Asia.

The foreword noted, 'for the collector of snuff bottles, there are examples in many different materials that have been cunningly wrought into a bewildering variety of forms and conceits.'

Once again we are fortunate enough to have a priced copy of the catalogue. The blue and white porcelain, offered as lot 73, was dated Yongzheng and sold at $17.50 (fig. 27); the delightful figural bottle of Liu Hai, lot 120, was dated Qianlong and sold at the remarkably high figure of $52.50 (fig. 28); and the unusual double crystal offered as lot 121, sold at the staggering price of $75 (fig. 29).

Fig. 28 American Art Galleries, sale catalogue, H. A. E. Jaehne Collection, April 10-12, 1923, lot 120 (Princeton No. 303).

Fig. 29 American Art Galleries, sale catalogue, H. A. E. Jaehne Collection, April 10-12, 1923, lot 121 (Princeton No. 30).

Fig. 30 American Art Galleries, sale catalogue, Ton-Ying Collection, February 5, 1925, lot 21 (Princeton No. 62).

Fig. 31 American Art Galleries, sale catalogue, Ton-Ying Collection, February 5, 1925, lot 70 (Princeton No. 348).

On January 7-10, 1924, the Edward Runge Jasper bottle, previously mentioned and illustrated (fig. 20), entered the collection via the Samuel S. Laird sale.

The remaining bottles that can be positively identified came from two sales, one of the well-known New York dealers, Ton-Ying & Co., the other, the dissolution sale of Suval and Voron, Inc., also of New York.

The sale on February 5, 1925, from the Ton-Ying Collection, included the shadow agate (Princeton No. 62) and the Yongzheng-marked enamel (Princeton No. 348). The first, lot 21, was dated Qianlong and charmingly listed as 'a vivid representation of La Fontaine's fable of the fox and the crow' (fig. 30), and the second, lot 70, was called Yongzheng and the ground color quaintly listed as 'rose du Barry' (fig. 31). The use of French terms at this time was obviously de rigueur.

The foreword to that sale noted, 'Mr. C. F. Yau, the president of Ton-Ying & Company, who has given his personal attention and judgment to gathering and assembling this collection, is intimately known to the great collectors of this country.... To the late Charles L. Freer, Mr. Yau brought examples of Chinese art... the best that had come under his intelligent scrutiny.'

A further portion of the collection was offered on January 29-30, 1926, and included amongst the one hundred and forty-one snuff bottles was another figural bottle of Liu Hai, lot 15, which may well be one of the two in the collection today (Princeton No. 302).

From 1926 until 1929, there appears to be a break in Blair's purchases at auction in the U.S. Perhaps this was the period when, according to his New York Times obituary, he was traveling and collecting.

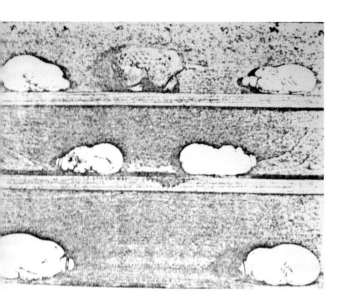

Fig. 32 Anderson Galleries Inc., sale catalogue, Suval & Voron Inc., April 2-4, 1929, lot 21 – center shelf right (Princeton No. 285), lot 31 – center shelf left (Princeton No. 287).

'Colonel Blair's collection of art objects, in part gathered during his travels in the Far East, includes what is said to be one of the most comprehensive groups of Chinese snuff bottles in the world.' (15)

Certainly this was a time when many Americans, particularly those working for academic institutions, were visiting China with purchasing as their main goal.

So it was on April 2-4, 1929, after a break of three years, that the first of the remaining bottles identified with the collection appeared at auction. The event was the dissolution sale of Suval & Voron, Inc., which was offered at the Anderson Galleries in New York. Amongst twenty-four snuff bottles auctioned were the white-glazed Buddhistic lion porcelain (Princeton No. 285) and the ochre-glazed squirrel porcelain (Princeton No. 287). The first was offered as lot 21. Though illustrated from the reverse, it is obviously the same bottle, as is clearly indicated by the identical profiles and, more importantly, the use of

an unusual mother-of-pearl stopper, which is identical both in shape and in the angle of insertion (fig. 32). The second was offered as lot 31 and catalogued as 'in the shape of a reddish-brown rabbit and decorated with fruits and flowers in colors.' It was dated Qianlong (fig. 32).

Another molded squirrel bottle (Princeton No. 286) might possibly be one of three such bottles offered in the sale as lots 412, 416 and 417.

The last sale where we can possibly identify a bottle in the collection today was held on January 24-25, 1930, at the American Art Association together with the Anderson Galleries Inc. Once again items from the Ton-Ying Collection were under the hammer. The sale was subtitled 'Important Porcelains (including pieces from the Imperial Collection).' Forty-five snuff bottles were offered. The *famille rose* molded double-gourd porcelain bottle (Princeton No. 246) was almost certainly offered as lot 220. Though the reverse is

Fig. 33 American Art Association & the Anderson Galleries Inc., sale
catalogue, Ton-Ying Collection, January 24-25, 1930, lot 220
(Princeton No. 246).

illustrated, the neck damage appears to match the damage on Blair's exactly. However, it is catalogued as Qianlong and notes that there is 'under foot a character seal mark in iron-red.' This bottle, however, bears a Jiaqing mark. Either the mark was misread in the original catalogue, or coincidentally, it is an identical model with identical damage.

We know then that Blair was collecting in New York from the auction houses. It is beyond doubt that he was also buying from dealers in the city. He may also have bought from the dealers and auctioneers in London during at least two trips in 1918 and 1919. These purchases, it seems, were supplemented with others on his travels in the East.

Perhaps, some day soon, the personal papers of James A. Blair Jr. will be discovered and the gaps in our knowledge of his collecting can finally be filled.

The year after his death, a groundbreaking exhibition took place in London that would change the way many in the West, particularly in Europe, viewed Chinese art. The International Exhibition of Chinese Art at Burlington House, the Royal Academy of Arts (November 28, 1935 – March 7, 1936) was breathtaking in its size and quality. No exhibition so comprehensive in Chinese art had ever taken place. Most importantly, the Chinese government was persuaded to loan previously unseen treasures from its national museums. Had he been alive, Blair would have taken immense pleasure in the inclusion of fifty-three snuff bottles. Some came from the great British collectors, Sir Percival David, Oscar Raphael, Capt. E. G. Spencer-Churchill, Capt. A. T. Ware, and Mr. and Mrs. Alfred Clark, and others were lent by the Chinese Government. Three magnificent Imperial glass bottles illustrated in the catalogue were probably loaned by the Chinese government and they firmly legitimized Blair's own collecting of Imperially-marked bottles. [51]

51. International Exhibition of Chinese Art, 1935-6, *Catalogue*, Royal Academy of Arts, London, p. 201, pl. 2175.

What we can say unequivocally is that Blair had great taste and an eye for bottles of Imperial quality. His choice of bottles was probably as astute, if not more so, than that of any other collector of his generation. He was able to amass a collection of great depth at a time when knowledge in the field was sorely lacking. He was able to do this while overseeing numerous business concerns, with a hectic travel schedule and limited time. Fortunately for us, he lacked neither conviction nor money. Once he had decided on his path, Blair followed his instincts passionately. What he left behind is a testament to his taste and vision.

Jade Bottles

1 | **Nephrite**

1750-1795
2 ⁷/₈ in. (6.3 cm.) high

Of oval shape and delicately carved as an aubergine or gourd with tendrils and leaves on the sides and a bat on the lower edge, the stone with some mottled gray inclusions

1936-650 (CB. 20 or 23)

The treatment of the collar suggests that this bottle is meant to depict an aubergine, rather than a gourd, despite the unusual flattened form. However, the inclusion of a bat, more commonly found in combination with gourds, confuses the picture. For other nephrite bottles of fruit form, see Hugh Moss, Victor Graham and Ka Bo Tsang, *The Art of the Chinese Snuff Bottle, The J & J Collection*, No. 9. See also the same authors, *A Treasury of Chinese Snuff Bottles, The Mary and George Bloch Collection*, Vol. I, Jade, No. 64, the 'Belfort Pomegranate'. All fall into a quite large group of fruit-shaped bottles, with relief carving of tendrils, smaller fruits and insects. This example, however, is distinct from the others in this group because of its un-naturalistic flattened form.

The quality is superb. Indeed, this bottle is so finely polished and sensitively treated, that an Imperial workshop provenance might easily be suggested.

2 | **Nephrite**

1750-1795

2 ⁷/₈ in. (7.3 cm.) long

Of natural pebble shape, delicately and finely carved overall with an unusual dense ground of small uniform stylized flower heads, with four large petals dividing four small petals, two thin lines dividing the flower heads down the narrow sides with further leafy foliage edging, similarly treated around the mouth

1936-565

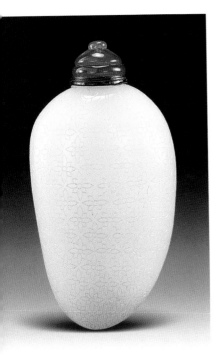

Retaining its pebble form, this bottle has been given masterpiece status by the extraordinary care taken by the lapidary in finely cutting the entire bottle with a perfectly ordered design of flower heads. They are evenly sized and spaced throughout, but never with the appearance of being squeezed in to fit the form. The edges are cleverly treated with foliage to mask any possible overlap of flower heads. The surface is softly polished.

The most comparable example is the 'Trojan Purse' bottle, illustrated by Hugh Moss, Victor Graham and Ka Bo Tsang, *A Treasury of Chinese Snuff Bottles, The Mary and George Bloch Collection*, Vol. I, Jade, No. 35; and also illustrated by Robert Hall in *Chinese Snuff Bottles V*, No. 31.

For another jade bottle of bitter melon shape, also finely incised with star-shaped flower heads within hexagonal cells over the entire surface, see *Masterpieces of Snuff Bottles in the Palace Museum*, No. 127.

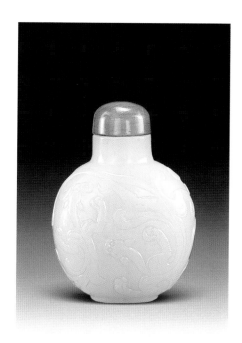

3 | Nephrite

1760-1800
2 in. (5.1 cm.) high

Of rounded shape, carved in low relief with three *chilong* in a continuous scene around the body, each biting the tail or trailing parts of another, on a simple oval foot

1936-626 (CB. 24)

For a bottle of similar type, see Hugh M. Moss, *Snuff Bottles of China*, No. 26.

4 | Nephrite

1780-1820
2 ³/₈ in. (6 cm.) high

Of aubergine shape, the fruit carved from a white jade pebble, the collar separately carved from spinach jade to form the leafy stem, the tip beautifully polished to a soft point

1936-814 (CB. 280)

This belongs to a well-documented group of white nephrite bottles with a separately cut calyx made from spinach-green nephrite, which were clearly made in some quantity. However, the collar on this example is superbly cut to fit snugly, in fact almost air-tight, against the white jade mouth. This feature, combined with the delicate naturalistic shaping of the fruit itself, renders this a masterpiece of lapidary art.

For nearly identical examples, see *Snuff Bottles in the Collection of the National Palace Museum*, No. 115, a boxed set of ten; and No. 112, catalogued as glass. See also Nos. 160-161, for single examples. For other examples, see No. 67 illustrated by Humphrey K. F. Hui and Christopher C.H. Sin in *An Imperial Qing Tradition*; Sotheby's, New York, The Bernice Straus Hasterlik Collection, 17 September 1996, lot 77; Sotheby's, New York, The Dr. Paula Hallett Collection, 2 December 1985, lot 114; Humphrey K. F. Hui and Peter Y. K. Lam in *The Imperial Connection, Court Related Chinese Snuff Bottles*, No. 81; and Hugh Moss, Victor Graham and Ka Bo Tsang, *A Treasury of Chinese Snuff Bottles, The Mary and George Bloch Collection*, Vol. I, Jade, No. 70.

For a white jade example with a jasper calyx, see *Masterpieces of Snuff Bottles in the Palace Museum*, No. 125; and another illustrated by Hugh M. Moss, in *Snuff Bottles of China*, 1970, No. 32. For a dark spinach nephrite bottle with an integral calyx, see Hugh Moss, Victor Graham and Ka Bo Tsang, *op. cit.*, No. 72.

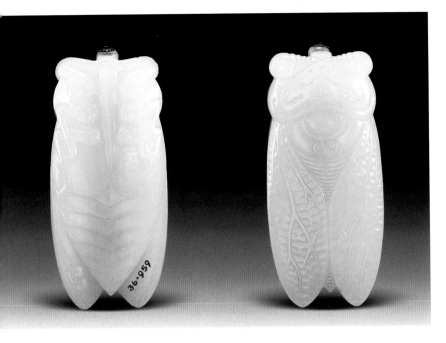

1750-1800
3 in. (7.6 cm.) high

Of naturalistic shape, the cicada superbly carved and incised in low relief with wings folded, fine details to all parts of the anatomy and with soft undulating dimples to the surface of the wings, the entire bottle with a soft attractive polish

1936-959 (CB. 22)

Literature: Edward Wenham, 'Antiques As Decoration,' *Arts & Decoration*, New York, Winter, 1928, illustrated p. 59.

The five bottles most comparable to Blair's are illustrated by Clare Lawrence, *Miniature Masterpieces from the Middle Kingdom, The Monimar Collection of Chinese Snuff Bottles*, No. 73; Parke-Bernet Galleries, New York, Mrs. Elmer A. Claar Collection, 2 December 1969, lot 147; Sotheby's, New York, The Bernice Straus Hasterlik Collection, 17 September 1996, lot 82; Christie's, London, 10 May 1976, lot 174; and another illustrated by Larissa Kouzmenko in an article entitled 'Snuff Bottles in the Museum of Oriental Art in Moscow,' *JICSBS*, Winter 1998, p. 16, fig. 5.

See also Hugh Moss, Victor Graham and Ka Bo Tsang, *A Treasury of Chinese Snuff Bottles, The Mary and George Bloch Collection*, Vol. I, Jade, No. 58, where the authors discuss the relative merits of Imperial provenance for this group of cicada carvings. They suggest that the existence of a similar cicada bottle in the Beijing Imperial collection, (see *Biyanhu shihua* [History of Snuff Bottles], p. 150, and also illustrated in *Masterpieces of Snuff Bottles in the Palace Museum*, No. 128), is an indication of possible provenance, though some bottles in the collection are later additions.

The depth of the interior carving bears similarities with other Palace jades but, most importantly, the authors note one other feature which suggests Court influence:

> On a creature almost entirely realistic and lacking even the usual formalization of the insect, there is one archaistic c-scroll motif between the wings behind the head (also found on Blair's example). This is derived from ancient jade carvings and was a feature of Palace decoration under the archaistically-

committed Qianlong Emperor. To have added so small an archaistic detail suggests that archaizing references were so second-nature to whoever designed this bottle, that its addition was automatic, regardless of the style of the rest of the carving. It is perhaps less likely that a private workshop not governed by a prevailing taste for archaisim would have thought to add such a minor detail to an otherwise entirely realistic carving.

For other slightly different examples, see Hugh Moss, Victor Graham and Ka Bo Tsang, *op. cit.*, p. 44, No. 7, Humphry K. F. Hui and Christopher C. H. Sin, *An Imperial Qing Tradition*, No. 77; Sotheby's, New York, The Alice B. McReynolds Collection, 16 April 1985, lot 16; and Sotheby's, Hong Kong, 5 May 1994, lot 1479.

For examples in other media, see Sotheby's, New York, The Dr. Paula Hallett Collection, 2 December 1985, lot 8, in porcelain and dated Jiaqing; Sotheby's, New York, The Janos Szekeres Collection, 27 October 1986, lot 20, also porcelain and dated Jiaqing; Bob C. Stevens, *The Collector's Book of Snuff Bottles*, No. 1027, in *laque burgauté*; and in *Chinese Snuff Bottles from the Collection of Mary and George Bloch*, by Robert W. L. Kleiner, No. 138, in brown rock crystal.

It is possible that this carving started life as a fondling piece and was later converted to a bottle as the carving of the mouth entrance does not display the same care and attention to detail as the rest of the bottle. However, this might simply be attributed to a later owner's opening up the mouth for ease of use.

6 | **Nephrite**

1780-1850
2 9/16 in. (6.6 cm.) high

Of rounded rectangular shape, the flawless stone almost pure white, neatly carved from the shoulder to the foot with bamboo basket-weave

1936-589 (CB. 26)

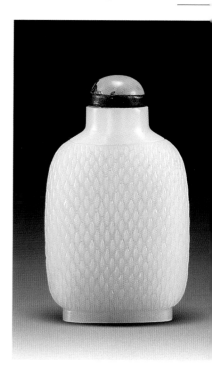

For similar examples, see Hugh Moss, Victor Graham and Ka Bo Tsang, *The Art of the Chinese Snuff Bottle, The J & J Collection,* No. 50; the same authors, *A Treasury of Chinese Snuff Bottles, The Mary and George Bloch Collection,* Vol. 1, Jade, No. 149, bearing the mark *Yangzheng shuwu* ('Studio for the Cultivation of a Righteous Mind'), a hallmark of the Jiaqing Emperor; and *Treasures from the Sanctum of Enlightened Respect: Chinese Snuff Bottles from the Denis Low Collection,* No. 37, for another bearing the hallmark *Xingyouheng Tang* ('Hall of Constancy'), a hallmark of the fifth Prince Ding, Zaichuan, who died in 1854. We may therefore be sure that this type of jade bottle was being produced at least between 1820, the end of the Jiaqing reign, and 1854, with a strong likelihood of a date late in the eighteenth century.

Robert Kleiner notes, *ibid.,* that 'baskets and basketweave symbolize the male child, a wish dear to the heart of Chinese culture.'

7 | **Nephrite**

1800-1900
2 3/8 in. (6 cm.) high

Of ovoid shape, neatly carved in low relief and incised with a cloth wrap with a star motif and tied by a knotted ribbon on one side

1936-720

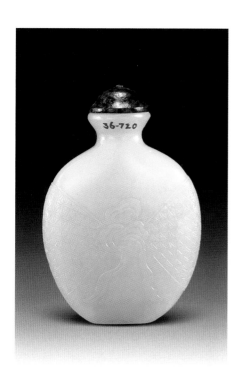

See bottle No. 344 in this collection, regarding the brocade design. The subject was a popular one during the reigns of the Yongzheng and Qianlong Emperors and was indicative of a gift. The sash, *shoudai,* can also signify longevity.

For two other jade bottles with identical petals incised on the tied cloth design, see Hugh Moss, Victor Graham and Ka Bo Tsang, *A Treasury of Chinese Snuff Bottles, The Mary and George Bloch Collection,* Vol. 1, Jade, Nos. 26 and 27, where the authors note that 'the word for this kind of cloth, commonly used in ancient China for wrapping, carrying and protecting a variety of objects, is *fu.* Like the bat (*fu*), it stands for happiness or good fortune.'

The six-petal flower heads are too stylized to hazard identification.

See also, *ibid.,* No. 28, for an example more closely linked in shape to the Blair bottle. The group as a whole is characterized by a preference for this spade shape with flaring neck. For another carved with *shou* characters, rather than petals, on the brocade, see Sotheby's, Hong Kong, The Eric Young Collection, Part IV, 28 October 1993, lot 1188.

See also a rounded rectangular bottle illustrated by Humphrey K. F. Hui and Peter Y. K. Lam in *The Imperial Connection, Court Related Chinese Snuff Bottles,* No. 61.

8 | Nephrite

1800-1830

1 ³/₄ in. (4.6 cm.) high

Of rounded shape, carved in low relief and incised on the two main sides with the obverse and reverse of a Mexican eight-reales coin bearing the head of Charles III of Spain on one side and the Spanish coat of arms on the other

1936-941 (CB. 35)

For a similar example in rock crystal, see Bob C. Stevens, *The Collector's Book of Snuff Bottles*, No. 459, where the author states it is based on a coin minted during the reign of Charles III of Spain (1755-1788) for the Mexican territories.

During the nineteenth century, Spanish dollars were common currency in China, especially in the sea ports, and snuff bottles imitating these coins were made in some quantity. Those most usually copied depict either Charles III (1760–1788) or Charles IV (1788-1808) of Spain.

For another example in white jade, see Sotheby's, Hong Kong, 3 November 1994, lot 998; and Christie's, New York, The Reif Collection, 18 October 1993, lot 118, for an example in honey-brown chalcedony where the catalogue states, 'The craftsmen who copied the colonial eight-reales often did a poor job of transcription and the spelling is incorrect or unreadable in some areas.' As on that example, the date on Blair's is illegible.

For two other examples in different materials in this collection, see Nos. 26 and 49.

Also see Robert W. L. Kleiner in *Chinese Snuff Bottles from the Collection of Mary and George Bloch*, No. 135; Parke-Bernet Galleries, New York, The Mrs. Elmer A. Claar Collection, 12 May 1970, lot 612.

A rock crystal bottle example illustrated by Alexander Brody, *Old Wine into Old Bottles, A Collector's Commonplace Book*, pp. 26-27 and 148, No. 26, bears the head of Charles III who died in 1788, but with a date of 1789. According to Victor E. Graham, *JICSBS*, Spring 1988, 'Coin Snuff Bottles', pp. 4-10, a Spanish royal decree empowered mint officials to continue using the effigy of the old king until new molds could be made showing the new king.

For a further discussion of this group, see Hugh Moss, *Chinese Snuff Bottles of the Silica and Quartz Group*, pp. 75-78.

9 | **Nephrite**

1750-1795
2 ¹/₈ in. (5.4 cm) high

Of irregular pear shape, the russet skin visible on each of the main sides and the base, the narrow sides plain

1936-802 (CB. 21)

The brown skin of this pebble almost appears to be folded around the lower half of the bottle and is cut to fit snugly in the hand.

For a discussion on the main source of jade pebbles, the Kunlin Mountains on the boundary of Chinese Turkestan and Tibet, and the two rivers Yurungkash and Karakash, which pass the town of Khotan, see Hugh Moss, Victor Graham and Ka Bo Tsang, A *Treasury of Chinese Snuff Bottles, The Mary and George Bloch Collection,* Vol. 1, Jade, No. 1. The authors illustrate a

yellow jade example with dark brown skin and note that 'The predominance of pebble material and even pebble-shaped bottles demonstrates the continuing passion of the Chinese for river-bed nephrite.'

This particular type of nephrite, white or celadon-white with a russet skin, was the most commonly used for pebble bottles. The shape of the bottle, of course, was entirely dictated by the shape of the pebble.

10 | Nephrite

1760-1820
2 7/16 in. (6.2 cm.) high

Of spade shape, very finely incised and gilt on one side with a swallow diving above lotus, and on the other with a sixteen-character inscription, the stone with a soft, attractive polish

1936-937 (CB. 30)

The inscription on this bottle is incomplete and therefore the meaning is uncertain, though it appears to be part of an Imperial poem. It is congratulatory, but to whom or what, is not included.

See Hugh Moss, Victor Graham and Ka Bo Tsang, *A Treasury of Chinese Snuff Bottles, The Mary and George Bloch Collection*, Vol. 1, Jade, Nos. 107-108, where jade bottles of this shape and decoration are called Imperial and said to be made largely, if not exclusively, under the auspices of the Qianlong Emperor. These bottles are unquestionably related to a group of porcelain bottles made in the Imperial kilns at Jingdezhen dating to the late Qianlong and early Jiaqing periods (see a more unusual quatrefoil

example in this collection, No. 203.) Ample evidence suggests that the jade examples pre-date the ceramic copies (see Hugh Moss, Victor Graham and Ka Bo Tsang, *The Art of the Chinese Snuff Bottle, The J & J Collection*, No. 235).

The same authors note in *A Treasury of Chinese Snuff Bottles, The Mary and George Bloch Collection*, Vol. 1, Jade, p. 261, that 'after 1760 there were as many as eight Imperial workshops for the production of jade' so the fact that a jade was Imperial during the later Qianlong period does not necessarily imply that it was made at the Palace workshops.'

Traces of worn gilding suggest that this bottle may have been originally gilt to highlight the design and calligraphy.

11 | Nephrite

1780-1850
2 3/8 in. (6.1 cm.) high

Of rounded rectangular shape, carved in high relief through the brown skin on one side with a boy on a pine-tree raft holding a book or an object, as his craft maneuvers choppy waters whilst passing a tall rock, all on a pale yellow jade ground, the reverse plain

1936-833 (CB. 29)

Formerly known as being of 'Han-type' jade, this group has more recently been re-named the 'Master of the Rocks' school on account of the similarities to jade bottles produced in the Suzhou area which so often depict majestic serrated rockwork. The rounded rectangular shape and the use of a yellow jade with a brown skin carved to form a silhouetted subject are fairly consistent features of the group. For other examples of a similar type, see Hugh Moss, Victor Graham and Ka Bo Tsang, *A Treasury of Chinese Snuff Bottles, The Mary and George Bloch Collection*, Vol. 1, Jade, Nos. 138-141.

12 | **Nephrite**

1800-1900
2 13/16 in. (7.2 cm.) high

Of slightly tapering rectangular shape, and with slightly convex sides with attractive horizontal markings, one narrow side with a two-character studio name, the base with a five-character inscription

1936-594 (CB. 31)

Literature: Edward Wenham, 'Antiques As Decoration', *Arts & Decoration*, New York, Winter, 1928, illustrated p. 59.

The five-character inscription on the base *Jie xin ji chun song* can be read as 'His heart relates to the spring pine'.

The inscription to the side of the bottle reads *Yitang*.

See Hugh Moss, Victor Graham and Ka Bo Tsang, *A Treasury of Chinese Snuff Bottles, The Mary and George Bloch Collection*, Vol. 1, Jade, Nos. 146-148 for a discussion on the name Yitang. The authors note that seven other bottles bearing this name are known (though the radical of the character *yi* has two forms). Six are marked on the base, three in the Bloch Collection (listed above), one in the Collection of James Li (see the same authors, *The Art of the Chinese Snuff Bottle, The J & J Collection*, No. 53), one in the S. L. Tan Collection, and another in a private Dutch Collection. The seventh was marked to the side, *Yitang Zhenwan*, after a poem about jade, and was sold at Christie's, New York, 2 December 1993, lot 403, where it was noted that it should be read as 'the "Hall of Understanding", a Hall of Na Yancheng, Governor of Shanxi and Gansu provinces, 1764-1833.' The misreading of the name as a hallmark rather than as an alternative name was incorrect but not far wrong as later pointed out by Hugh Moss, Victor Graham and Ka Bo Tsang, *op. cit.*, p. 380, No.146, where they note, 'Yitang is an alternative name of Nayancheng who was a poet, calligrapher and statesman with a long and varied career (see Arthur W. Hummel, *Eminent Chinese of the Ch'ing Period*, pp. 584-587, where Yitang is listed

as a *hao*, or assumed artistic name, whereas in some sources it is listed as a *zi*, an alternative given name).' Later they note that in 1809 he was posted 'to Yarkand, which together with its fellow oasis, Khotan, was at the heart of the nephrite trade.'

It is most probable, considering the fact that all bottles marked with his name are in jade, that Nayancheng must have had contact with the nephrite trade.

Blair's bottle bears the same radical in the *yi* character as the 'Yitang Pebble Jade' (No. 146 in the Bloch Collection) but in type of stone is much closer to another bearing the alternative *hao* (No. 147 in the Bloch Collection).

This bottle is by far the plainest in terms of the simplicity of shape and surface treatment. It is unusual that such a prized stone should be cut in such a manner. However, the material itself does evoke a powerful natural scene of a flat landscape pierced by a river running diagonally through it under a dark foreboding cloud, and perhaps the craftsmen, or possibly the patron, felt that it 'spoke' enough, and needed no further embellishment.

For another rounded rectangular bottle carved from a similar stone with raised characters of auspicious wishes on two sides, but without a *Yitang* mark, see Hugh Moss, Victor Graham and Ka Bo Tsang, *A Treasury of Chinese Snuff Bottles, The Mary and George Bloch Collection*, Vol. 1, Jade, No. 38.

13 | Nephrite

1770-1850
2 ¹/₁₆ in. (5.4cm.) high

Of ovoid form, carved unusually with the russet skin of the stone entirely covering one side and with the celadon core of the stone on the other side, well polished

1936-716 (CB. 18)

The stone has the appearance of jadeite but appears to be nephrite on close inspection. In shape it is almost identical to a nephrite example illustrated by Hugh Moss, Victor Graham and Ka Bo Tsang, *A Treasury of Chinese Snuff Bottles, The Mary and George Bloch Collection,* Vol. 1, Jade, No. 88, which is smaller and of paler color. For a pebble bottle with the brown skin completely covering one side while the reverse is wholly of core material, see *ibid.,* pp. 26-27, No. 6. For a larger jadeite example of rounded shape, the 'Lilla Perry Red Jadeite', see *ibid.,* No. 171.

14 | Jadeite

1850-1900
2 ¹/₄ in. (5.7 cm.) high

Of rounded spade shape, carved in low relief, cleverly utilizing a large apple-green inclusion, with a Buddhistic lion and cub on one side playing with beribboned balls near a *lingzhi* spray and on the other with two bats above water and below the moon and clouds

1936-844 (CB. 16)

The bottle most comparable to this one is illustrated by Bob C. Stevens, *The Collector's Book of Snuff Bottles,* No. 1016, and later sold at Sotheby's, Honolulu, 7 November 1981, lot 133. It is of globular shape and cleverly uses a caramel and calcified white stone to similarly wonderful effect, depicting *Budai* on one side and a Buddhistic lion chained to a post on the other.

For another bottle from the Eric Young Collection and sold by Sotheby's, London, 13 October 1987, lot 124, carved with dragons and waves, see Hugh Moss, Victor Graham and Ka Bo Tsang, *The Art of the Chinese Snuff Bottle, The J & J Collection,* No. 70.

15 | **Jadeite**

1850-1900
2 5/32 in. (5.5 cm.) high

Of rounded rectangular shape, carved in low relief on one side with a small building under winter trees and cliffs, and on the other side with a lone fisherman amidst further winter trees and cliffs, clearly incorporating a russet flaw

1936-799 (CB. 11)

Literature: Edward Wenham, 'Antiques As Decoration', *Arts & Decoration*, New York, Winter, 1928, illustrated p. 96.

For another rounded rectangular jadeite bottle carved with flowering prunus on each side, see Hugh M. Moss, *Snuff Bottles of China*, No. 8.

A jadeite bottle of identical shape and splashed on both sides, to a lesser degree, with emerald-green inclusions, see Sotheby's, New York, 1 July 1985, lot 133, from the Kardos Collection. See also Hugh Moss, Victor Graham and Ka Bo Tsang, *A Treasury of Chinese Snuff Bottles, The Mary and George Bloch Collection*, Vol. I, Jade, No. 178, where the authors discuss the distinctive group of jadeite bottles, usually of rounded rectangular shape in a wide range of colors, to which this example belongs. Like many of the group, Blair's has an uneven color confined to one side of the body. For another example, see Bob C. Stevens, *The Collector's Book of Snuff Bottles*, No. 453, carved with a sage and attendant in a landscape.

The style of carved decoration can be compared to a quartz bottle in the Princeton Collection, No. 35, and also to a jadeite bottle sold at the Parke-Bernet Galleries, New York, The Mrs. Elmer A. Claar Collection, 2 December 1969, lot 159, which also depict small huts amidst trees and rocks. Both the Claar bottle and the Blair example, despite being jade rather than crystal, could easily fall under the new designation 'The Rustic Crystal Master' (see No. 35).

16 | Jadeite

1820-1880
2 ³/₈ in. (5.6 cm.)

Of rounded shape and carved in low relief, using a diagonal brown flaw, with a phoenix and bamboo on one side and a crane near pine and *lingzhi* on the other, the base carved with rockwork

1936-834

17 | Jadeite

1850 –1900
2 ¹/₂ in. (6.3 cm.) high

Of natural finger citrus shape, supported on branches with foliage forming the foot and running up the sides, a bat carved on one side, the pale stone with apple-green and russet inclusions

1936-829 (CB. 15)

See an amber bottle depicting a finger citrus in this collection, No. 92.

This inedible citron is also known as Buddha's hand because of its likeness to fingers at one end. It is often placed in a bowl for decorative purposes and for scenting rooms, see C. A. S. Williams, *Outlines of Chinese Symbolism and Art Motives*, p. 51.

18 | **Jadeite**

1800-1900
2 ¹/₁₆ in. (5.3 cm.) high

Of compressed spade shape, the body with three horizontal green bands, carved in low relief on one side with orchids growing from rockwork below a cloud at the neck, and with a bat above a *lingzhi* spray rising from rockwork above a rushing stream on the other side, with a flat shallow oval foot

1936-782 (CB. 12)

It appears that no similar examples in jadeite are published, though there are certainly many nephrite bottles of this shape, mostly celadon in color, with similarly carved designs, see Robert Kleiner, *Chinese Snuff Bottles in the Collection of Mary and George Bloch*, No. 63. Generally the group of nephrite celadon bottles are dated to the eighteenth or early nineteenth century, which might suggest a fairly early production date for this example.

For examples of undecorated jadeite bottles with veins of apple- and emerald-green but more translucent, see Hugh Moss, Victor Graham and Ka Bo Tsang, *A Treasury of Chinese Snuff Bottles, The Mary and George Bloch Collection*, Vol. I, Jade, No. 172; Hugh Moss, Victor Graham and Ka Bo Tsang, *The Art of the Chinese Snuff Bottle, The J & J Collection*, No. 63; and Robert Kleiner, *op. cit.*, No. 104.

19 | **Jadeite**

1850-1900
2 ⁵/₁₆ in. (5.9 cm.) high

Of spade shape, carved in low relief on each side with sprays of chrysanthemums

1936-805 (CB. 10)

The neck is rather unusually cut on this bottle. One would normally expect a simple flaring or circular neck, but the craftsman has chosen a short faceted neck instead. The neck does not show any signs of having been reduced which might otherwise explain the strange shape.

For a hair crystal bottle of nearly identical profile and a similarly carved neck, see Hugh Moss, Victor Graham and Ka Bo Tsang, *A Treasury of Chinese Snuff Bottles, The Mary and George Bloch Collection*, Vol. 2, Quartz, No. 217. The unusual treatment of the necks on both these bottles might suggest that the workshops that produced them were in some way connected.

20 | **Jadeite**

1880-1930
2 ¹/₄ in. (5.6 cm.) high

Of ovoid shape, carved in low relief with a continuous scene of tree peony sprays rising from rockwork, the stone with paler gray inclusions on one side

1936-508 (CB. 7)

Of its type, this bottle is of the finest quality, with delicate carving of the rockwork and sensitive detailing to the knots on the branches. The mouth is unusually wide: the opening is more than twice the width of the lip. The interior is also very well hollowed.

This bottle can be compared in profile to an example sold at the Parke-Bernet Galleries, New York, 2 December 1969, lot 159.

21 | Jadeite

1820-1900
2 ³/₁₆ in. (5.6 cm.) high

Of ovoid shape, carved in low relief on both sides with a coiling *chilong*, the stone mottled with black veins and inclusions

1936-517 (CB. 5)

The stone is an extremely rich apple-green color throughout with some emerald flecks alongside the dark, almost black, veins which give the bottle an appearance of chloromelanite. The surface is glassy and the high quality carving of the dragon resembles the work on eighteenth century Palace-style glass bottles, see Hugh Moss, Victor Graham and Ka Bo Tsang, *The Art of the Chinese Snuff Bottle, The J & J Collection,* No. 369.

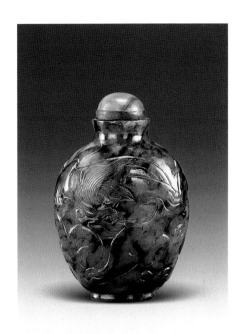

22 | Chloromelanite

1800-1900
1 ¹⁵/₁₆ in. (4.9 cm.) high

Of rounded shape, carved in dense low relief with the continuous scene of a four-clawed dragon writhing amidst clouds, the stone of deep tone with attractive black inclusions and a highly polished surface

1936-517

This bottle can be compared to a russet-brown jadeite bottle illustrated by Rachelle R. Holden, *Rivers and Mountains Far from the World,* No. 44, which has an overall carved decoration of bats amidst clouds. It is similar in profile but has a slightly spreading oval foot. It is dated by the author to 1730-1780. Both bottles convey the small gem-like quality of Imperial enamel bottles.

For another chloromelanite bottle and a discussion of the stone, see Hugh Moss, Victor Graham and Ka Bo Tsang, *A Treasury of Chinese Snuff Bottles, The Mary and George Bloch Collection,* Vol. 1, Jade, No. 184.

23 | **Jadeite**

1800-1900
2 in. (5.1 cm.) high

Of spade shape, the well-hollowed bottle of deep emerald-green tone with only minor pale inclusions, a simple flat oval foot

1936-717

The stone used in this bottle is of an exceedingly richly colored variety. It positively vibrates with color. The gem-like quality is enhanced by the superb high polish and small size. For a bottle more opaque but with a similar dark vibrant color, see Hugh Moss, Victor Graham and Ka Bo Tsang, *A Treasury of Chinese Snuff Bottles, The Mary and George Bloch Collection*, Vol. I, Jade, No. 179, the 'Ko Emerald Landscape' bottle. The authors also discuss the comparative merits of material and aesthetic qualities.

Chalcedony and
Other Hard Stone Bottles

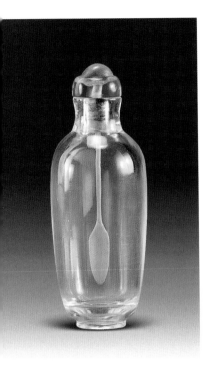

24 | Rock crystal

1770-1820
2 ¹¹/₁₆ in. (6.8 cm.) high

Of tapering baluster shape, the stone flawless and well hollowed

1936-810 (CB. 87)

For an aquamarine bottle of almost identical shape, see Bob C. Stevens, *The Collector's Book of Snuff Bottles*, No. 653, from the Paul Braga Collection.

A group of Imperial yellow jade bottles of this shape are also known. For examples, see Christie's, New York, The Reif Collection, 18 October 1993, lot 69; and *Snuff Bottles in the Collection of the National Palace Museum*, No. 126. As with the Imperial jade examples, the Blair bottle is extremely well hollowed, with

a nice weight when held in the hand. It seems quite plausible that this particular rock crystal bottle was the product of a lapidary working in the Imperial workshops.

For a faceted rock crystal bottle of slightly more *meiping* shape, see Helen White, *Snuff Bottles from China, The Victoria and Albert Museum Collection*, pp. 106-107, No. 4, which formed part of the Salting Bequest to the Museum in 1910.

25 | Rock crystal

1760-1860
2 ⁵/₁₆ in. (6 cm.) high

Of rounded shape, the stone of extreme clarity and well hollowed

1936-808 (CB.88)

Literature: Edward Wenham, 'Antiques As Decoration', *Arts & Decoration*, New York, Winter, 1928, illustrated p. 59.

For another bottle of flawless crystal, see Hugh Moss, Victor Graham and Ka Bo Tsang, *A Treasury of Chinese Snuff Bottles, The Mary and George Bloch Collection*, Vol. 2, Quartz, No.189. It is identical in height, though more fully rounded in shape because of a smaller foot. The authors discuss the use of crystal at the Court and note that one of the earliest recorded Imperial gifts of a snuff bottle was of crystal, given to an envoy of the Pope by the Kangxi Emperor late in his reign.

Crystal bottles appear to have been quite popular from the 1720's until the end of the nineteenth century. There is no question that a clear bottle was advantageous in viewing the grade and color of snuff and alerting the owner to replenishment requirements.

The dating of crystal bottles is often made difficult by the lack of decoration and the similarity in shape of many eighteenth and nineteenth century bottles.

26 | **Rock crystal**

1800-1830
1 ³¹/₃₂ in. (4.9 cm.) high

Of rounded shape, carved in low relief and incised on the two main sides with the obverse and reverse of a Mexican eight-reales coin bearing the head of Charles III of Spain and the Spanish coat of arms on the other, the narrow sides lobed horizontally

1936-976 (CB. 97 or 17)

For a very similar example, see Bob C. Stevens, *The Collector's Book of Snuff Bottles*, No. 459, where the author states it is based on a coin minted during the reign of Charles III of Spain (1755-1788) for the Mexican territories.

See also another very similar bottle illustrated by Hugh Moss, Victor Graham and Ka Bo Tsang, *A Treasury of Chinese Snuff Bottles, the Mary and George Bloch Collection*, Vol. 2, Quartz, No. 238, formerly in the Gerd Lester Collection, where the authors discuss at length this type of bottle.

The inscription on Blair's bottle is extremely difficult to read, partly because it is carved in exceedingly low relief but also because the craftsman seems to have dealt with the inscription in a very cursory manner. Unfortunately, we cannot read the date, although the remaining inscription does appear to read Charles III, and the reverse appears to include an 'S' for the mint in Santiago.

For examples of eight-reales coins minted in South America, including Bolivia and Chile, see F. Calicó, X. Calicó and J. Trigo *Monedas Españolas desde Juana y Carlos a Isabel II 1504 a 1868*, pp. 373-374.

See bottle No. 8 in this collection for further discussion of this group.

27 | **Rock crystal**

1820-1880
3 5/8 in. (9.1 cm.) long

Carved as an open-mouthed carp with fan tail tucked over to one side and simply delineated scales, the interior softly etched to give a frosty appearence

1936-595 (CB. 195 or 101)

Literature: Edward Wenham, 'Antiques As Decoration', *Arts & Decoration*, New York, Winter, 1928, illustrated p. 59.

It is rare to find a goldfish or carp carved out of rock crystal. Jade and agate are the preferred materials. The carving here is extremely well executed, though the somewhat large size makes handling a little cumbersome. Nevertheless, the corpulent nature of this particular fish is very much in keeping with the pun *jinyu* for 'goldfish', which is homophonous with the term meaning 'gold and jade', whilst *yu* alone can also signify 'plenty' or 'surplus'.

For an example in celadon jade, see Hugh Moss, Victor Graham and Ka Bo Tsang, *A Treasury of Chinese Snuff Bottles, the Mary and George Bloch Collection,* Vol. I, Jade, No. 52 and No. 54, in artificially stained nephrite, formerly in the Arthur Gadsby Collection.

28 | **Rock crystal**

1850-1900
3 5/8 in. (9.2 cm.) high

Carved as two conjoined fish leaping from a wave base, their scales neatly carved, the interiors softly etched to give a frosty appeareance

1936-586 (CB. 66 or 99)

Literature: Edward Wenham, 'Antiques As Decoration', *Arts & Decoration*, New York, Winter, 1928, illustrated p. 59.

For another rock crystal example, see Sotheby's, London, The Baronesses Sapuppo and d'Essen Collection, 14 November 2000, lot 68. Their collection was formed in Europe prior to the 1930s, and was therefore contemporary with that assembled by Col. James A. Blair in America. Although separated by an ocean, these collectors obviously shared parallel tastes, as the large number of similar bottles attests.

For a more flattened double fish bottle in white jade, see Sotheby's, London, The Eric Young Collection, Part 1, 3 March 1987, lot 130.

For a double fish in carnelian, with the two carp intertwined rather than perpendicular to each other, and only one mouth cut for a stopper, see Robert W. L. Kleiner in *Chinese Snuff Bottles from the Collection of Mary and George Bloch,* No. 171.

The double fish motif was a popular one, as it expressed wishes for abundance, rank, conjugal felicity, as well as Buddhist sentiments.

29 | **Rock crystal**

1780-1850
2 ¹/₂ in. (6.4 cm.)

Of ovoid shape, one side embellished with an amethyst figure of a bearded scholar and youthful assistant holding a *qin,* standing near bamboo sprays and looking up at a bat carved in low relief, the reverse with a pine tree and a second swooping bat

1936-848 (CB. 12)

This bottle began life as a plain crystal bottle. It was then carved with a bat, pine and bamboo, either before or after the application of a small amethyst carving of a scholar and assistant. Whatever the order, the design is a very cohesive one. The embellishment is highly successful, and the additional color certainly adds drama to the depiction.

For another crystal bottle with added amethyst embellishment of a sage seated to one side, see Hugh M. Moss, *Chinese Snuff Bottles: 5*, p. 25, No. 7.

30 | **Rock crystal**

1850-1900
2 ¹/₂ in. (6.3 cm.)

Comprising two bottles conjoined at their midsection, one taller of rectangular shape, the other of rounded shape, both carved in relief, the taller with two coiling *chilong* on the outside face and bat fixed-ring handles on the narrow sides, the smaller with one coiling *chilong*

1936-847

Provenance: American Art Galleries, New York
The H. A. E. Jaene Collection,
10-12 April 1923,
lot 121, sold at $75.00.
(See fig. 29 in the Introduction.)

For other examples of double bottles, see Hugh Moss, Victor Graham and Ka Bo Tsang, *A Treasury of Chinese Snuff Bottles, The Mary and George Bloch Collection*, Vol. 2, Quartz, Nos. 249-252.

See also Robert Hall, *Chinese Snuff Bottles II*, No. 39, from the Marian Mayer Collection. The smaller bottle in that example is cut from the central section of the larger bottle and, unlike this example, its foot does not touch the ground.

31 | **Rock crystal**

1780-1850
2 ³/₈ in. (6.2 cm.) high

Of rounded shape, with a cylindrical neck and a shallow oval foot

1936-581 (CB.103)

Also known to snuff bottle collectors as 'smoky crystal' or 'tea crystal', brown rock crystal ranges in color from extremely pale, with just the slightest tinge of beige, to a very deep tone, almost black.

In shape, this bottle can be compared to a clear rock crystal bottle illustrated by Hugh Moss, Victor Graham and Ka Bo Tsang, *A Treasury of Chinese Snuff Bottles, The Mary and George Bloch Collection*, Vol. 2, Quartz, No. 189, where it is described as 'a faultless sculptural statement. It resounds with confidence. It is a form to be reckoned with. Like so much else in art that is truly memorable it is also pared of unnecessary frills. The conception is as pure as the material.'

32 | **Rock crystal**

1770-1850
2 ³/₈ in. (6.2 cm) high

Of rounded rectangular shape, the stone with a relatively dense grouping of primarily vertical tourmaline needles throughout, the oval foot shallowly carved, the bottle well hollowed

1937-797

For a full explanation of the needle-like inclusions in a variety of crystal bottles, see Hugh Moss, Victor Graham and Ka Bo Tsang, *A Treasury of Chinese Snuff Bottles, The Mary and George Bloch Collection*, Vol. 2, Quartz, No. 193. For many years the term 'rutile' has been used to describe the entire range of different colored 'needles' found in the matrix of such bottles. However this misleading nomenclature can now be dispensed with. The authors note:

> Tourmaline, rutile and actinolite are the three minerals which make up the range of hair crystals. Tourmaline provides the hair-like crystals for the black range of material, the most common among early snuff bottles. Rutile, a rarer material in early snuff bottles but still reasonably well known, crystallizes a coppery-red or golden color; while actinolite, the rarest of the three in snuff bottles, forms green needle-crystals.

33 | **Rock crystal**

1850-1900
3 7/32 in. (8.1 cm.) high

Of tapering cylindrical shape, carved in high relief with an ascending four-clawed dragon coiling around the body

1936-989

The subject is reminiscent of those on *cloisonné* and jade incense vessels, also of cylindrical shape, themselves possibly influenced by the design on pillar carpets, see Hu Weibiao, *The Imperial Palace, Chinese Landscape Storehouse*, (pages un-numbered), for a view of the major room of the Yangxian Hall in which a jade pillar incense burner with gilt-metal pagoda roof is illustrated.

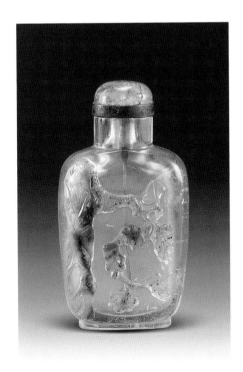

34 | **Rock crystal**

1800-1900
2 1/2 in. (6.3 cm.) high

Of rounded rectangular shape, carved in high relief on one side using moss-green inclusions to depict a leafy fruiting branch, possibly mulberry, hanging from a rock face or a stylized tree trunk, the other side plain but for a small butterfly to the top right in low relief

1936-975 (CB. 93 or 43)

The green inclusions in this bottle, probably chlorite, have been simply edited to silhouette the subject against the clear ground. It is rare to find chlorite inclusions in crystal bottles. For another, much finer example, see Hugh Moss, Victor Graham and Ka Bo Tsang, *A Treasury of Chinese Snuff Bottles, The Mary and George Bloch Collection*, Vol. 2, Quartz, No. 365.

35 | **Rock crystal**

1830-1900
2 ⁵/₁₆ in. (5.9 cm.) high

Of rounded rectangular shape, carved in low relief on one side with two figures in a boat in a fast-running current near a cliff with pine and a pavilion, the reverse with further pine and two small boats, the stone with a soft yellow tone

1936-965 (CB. 94)

This bottle belongs to a group recently attributed to 'The Rustic Crystal Master', and dated between 1730 and 1880. This designation, introduced by Hugh Moss, Victor Graham and Ka Bo Tsang, *A Treasury of Chinese Snuff Bottles, The Mary and George Bloch Collection*, Vol. 2, Quartz, Nos. 254-257, was made to try and distinguish a school, rather than one specific craftsman responsible for a distinctive, consistent individual style (possibly based on the artistic personality of a single artist – thus the designation), that is identified by rustic scenes, often winter landscapes, in the tradition of literati painting. That is, a series of fairly standard, well-established shorthand forms to depict various landscape elements. Precise depictions were less important than the esoteric language of form, line, color and texture.

Compare also with the decoration on a jadeite bottle in this collection, No. 15. Not only is the subject matter the same but the style of carving is remarkably similar. It is possible that both bottles were made at the same center, if not the same workshop.

For another example, see Robert Kleiner, *Precious Playthings: Important Chinese Snuff Bottles from the Mack Collection*, No. 49.

36 | **Rock crystal**

1770-1830
3 ⁵/₁₆ in. (8.4 cm.) high

Of rounded rectangular shape, carved in high relief through a white skin on one side with three goats below rockwork and the sun, the darker body incised with plantain, sprigs of bamboo and rockwork

1936-592 (CB. 110)

This rather large bottle uses the thick white skin of this somewhat cumbersome stone to great effect. It cleverly integrates a flaw in the stone to form the rockwork, and the details of curly wool on the rams are a sensitive touch. The subject, a popular one on snuff bottles, is more often found on inside-painted or agate bottles. Three goats and the rising sun form the rebus *San yang kaitai*, which can be read as 'looking forward to spring's arrival' or the rebirth of nature in spring and the coming of renewed prosperity.

It can be best compared to a similar smoky rock crystal example illustrated by Rachelle R. Holden, *Rivers and Mountains Far from the World*, No. 60. and another illustrated in *Zhongguo Biyanhu Zhenshang* (Gems of Chinese Snuff Bottles), No. 287.

For examples in chalcedony, see Hugh M. Moss, *Chinese Snuff Bottles of the Silica and Quartz Group*, No. 113; and *Chinese Snuff Bottles, A Miniature Art from the Collection of Mary and George Bloch*, No. 236.

37 | **Rock crystal**

1820-1900
2 ¹/₂ in. (6.2 cm.) high

Of rounded rectangular shape, carved in high relief through a white and green skin on one side with lotus rising from water, one pad carved from the green area of skin, waves cut from the clear stone, the reverse plain

1936-685

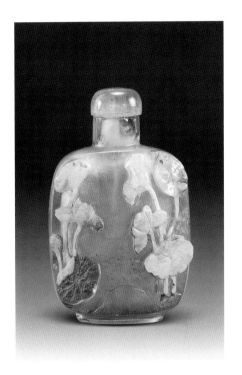

For a dendritic chalcedony bottle with the same subject, with a green skin and honey-brown ground, see Hugh Moss, Victor Graham and Ka Bo Tsang, *A Treasury of Chinese Snuff Bottles, The Mary and George Bloch Collection,* Vol. 2, Quartz, No. 311. It too has formalized waves carved around the foot to define the pond. It is classified as 'Official School', a new and fairly wide ranging designation (that can also be assigned to others in this collection including Nos. 52, 54, 55, 58-63) and which the authors note in Vol. 2, Quartz, pp. 206-207:

> We have chosen the name 'Official School' over 'Imperial School' for two reasons: to distinguish it from other groups of specifically Imperial chalcedony bottles already well established and recognized as Imperial; and because much of the subject matter for the decorated examples of this school is ideally suited to the official class, those scholars appointed by the Emperor to administer his Empire. Although we believe that the impetus for the group as a whole was Imperial, produced in large quantities as gifts to aspiring officials, it cannot have failed to elicit a response from other workshops and it is unlikely that everything that appears to be from the group will prove to be Imperial, or even official. It is also likely that they were produced in several different workshops.

38 | **Rock crystal**

1800-1880
2 ³/₁₆ in. (5.6 cm.)

Of rounded rectangular shape, carved in high relief through a white skin on one side with two boys at play, one holding a *ruyi* scepter suspending a musical stone, the other side carved in medium relief from the darker area with a bat and peach tree rising from rockwork

1936-754

For another example of the use of a contrasting skin with a black background to depict a figural scene, see Sotheby's, New York, The Neal W. and Frances R. Hunter Collection, 15 September 1998, lot 243.

39 | Rock crystal

1820-1880
2 ¹/₂ in. (6.4 cm.) high

Of tapering rounded rectangular shape, carved in high relief through a white skin on one side with a cat seated under magnolia and peony, and in low relief on the other with cranes and lotus

1936-642 (CB. 107)

The cat is usually depicted chasing or watching a butterfly, thus forming a rebus for longevity. For an example in jasper, see Hugh Moss, Victor Graham and Ka Bo Tsang, *The Art of the Chinese Snuff Bottle, The J & J Collection*, No. 145.

40 | Rock crystal

1850-1900
2 ⁵/₈ in. (6.1 cm.)

Of slender hexagonal shape, carved in low relief on each side, using the white skin to depict panels of individual tree or flower sprays, alternately in vases and including prunus, pine, bamboo, magnolia, hibiscus and begonia

1936-640 (CB. 106)

For a smoky crystal bottle of identical shape but inscribed with a poem on all sides, see Hugh Moss, Victor Graham and Ka Bo Tsang, *A Treasury of Chinese Snuff Bottles, The Mary and George Bloch Collection*, Vol. 2, Quartz, No. 361. It and another of the same hexagonal shape, which sold at Sotheby's, New York, 22 September 1995, lot 202, bear the same hallmark *Xingyouheng Tang*, of the fifth Prince Ding. It is entirely possible that this bottle came from the same workshop.

41 | **Amethyst**

1780-1820
2 ⁷/₁₆ in. (6.3 cm.) high

Two slender tapering baluster bottles conjoined at the main face, one face amethyst in color, the other transparent, the narrow sides carved in low relief with two bats forming handles, the transparent side carved with hanging prunus

1936-723 (CB. 118)

It is interesting to note the numerous double bottles in rock crystal published, which include one in this collection, No. 30; and another illustrated by Bob. C. Stevens, *The Collector's Book of Snuff Bottles*, No. 469, to name but two.

Amethyst double bottles, however, are extremely rare. For one other example, see Hugh M. Moss, *Snuff Bottles of China*, No. 90.

For a discussion of the use of amethyst in snuff bottles, see Hugh Moss, Victor Graham and Ka Bo Tsang, *A Treasury of Chinese Snuff Bottles, The Mary and George Bloch Collection,* Vol. 2, Quartz, No. 192, where it is noted that a reasonable body of finely made amethyst bottles were produced from at least the mid-Qing period onwards.

42 | **Amethyst**

1780-1850
2 ¹/₂ in. (6.4 cm.) high

Of baluster shape, finely carved in low relief with bamboo and clouds on one side and chrysanthemums and clouds on the other, the stone with attractive vertical purple inclusions, and some clear areas

1936-603 (CB. 117)

The carving is of very good quality. Two areas, however, with cloud design just below the neck are very deeply carved, in contrast to the remaining decoration, because of difficulties in cutting around some flaws in the stone.

43 | **Tourmaline**

1800-1900
2 ¹/₃₂ in. (5.2 cm.) high

Of rounded rectangular shape, the stone plain with an attractive pink tone to the lower half and a pale yellow-green tone to the upper half

1936-971 (CB. 123)

Until recently, it was believed that three hundred bottles made from tourmaline were confiscated from notorious Prime Minister Heshen in 1799 as recorded in *Snuff Bottles in the Collection of the National Palace Museum*, p. 40. However, recent research by Peter Y. K. Lam has proven that the document from which this information was drawn to be false, see Humphrey K. F. Hui and Peter Y. K. Lam, *The Imperial Connection, Court Related Chinese Snuff Bottles*, p. 36.

Despite this fact, and although it is known that many tourmaline bottles are of late manufacture, it was a material that was popular at Court in the mid-Qing dynasty and used primarily in jewelry. Many portraits of the period depict lavish necklaces of colored stone which, though difficult to identify in the paintings, include tourmaline. Necklaces and pendants made from tourmaline are recorded, see Spink & Son Ltd., *Chinese Jewellery, Accessories and Glass*, Nos. 34, 37 and 38 (pendants) and No. 19 (composite necklace).

See also bottle No. 45 in this collection for further discussion of tourmaline bottles.

44 | Rose quartz

1840-1900
2 in. (5. cm.) high

Of melon shape, carved in high relief on one side with a grasshopper on a beet growing from rockwork, the reverse plain, the stone of strong color

1936-1030 (CB. 122)

For a discussion of rose quartz in snuff bottle production, see Hugh Moss, Victor Graham and Ka Bo Tsang, *A Treasury of Chinese Snuff Bottles, The Mary and George Bloch Collection*, Vol. 2, Quartz, No. 195.

45 | Tourmaline or beryl

1750-1800
2 ¼ in. (5.7 cm) high

Of rounded rectangular shape, carved in the Imperial glass style with archaistic dragons suspending tassels all on a finely incised *leiwen* ground

1936-727 (CB. 125)

The stone appears to be tourmaline, though beryl cannot be ruled out. See No. 43 in this collection for a discussion on the use of tourmaline in bottles.

For a discussion on the relationship of tourmaline and beryl bottles and the link with Imperial glass bottles, see Hugh Moss, Victor Graham and Ka Bo Tsang, *A Treasury of Chinese Snuff Bottles, The Mary and George Bloch Collection*, Vol. 3, Stones other than Jade or Quartz, No. 413.

For a tourmaline bottle attributed to the Palace workshops, 1765-1800, see Clare Lawrence, *Miniature Masterpieces from the Middle Kingdom, The Monimar Collection of Chinese Snuff Bottles*, No. 38. The author notes (without naming the source, but presumably *Tributes from Guangdong to the Qing Court*,) that 'In the thirty-sixth year of Qianlong (1772), Li Shiyao, the Viceroy of Guangdong and Guangxi, presented the Qianlong Emperor with the following item which was listed in the presentation list sent up

to the Imperial Household Workshops in Yangxin Hall at the Palace: tourmaline necklace with pearl.'

It is clear therefore that the stone was available for snuff bottle production, and there seems to be no particular reason to doubt that at least some were made at this time.

The archaistic design can be closely linked to bottles made in nephrite, glass and quartz, attributed to the eighteenth century Imperial Palace workshops. See Clare Lawrence, *ibid.*, No. 75, for a white nephrite example. The dragons are more fluid than those on this example, which are more stylized and in keeping with the archaic bronze prototypes. See also Robert W. L. Kleiner, *Chinese Snuff Bottles from the Collection of Mary and George Bloch*, No. 66, for a yellow glass example of rounded shape but with a similar surface treatment and design elements; and *Chinese Snuff Bottles*, No. 227, for an example in quartz.

46 | **Chalcedony**

1820-1880
2 ⁵/₈ in. (6.6 cm.) high

Comprising two carp joined at the midsection, the scales simply delineated, the eyes inset with glass

1936-675 (CB. 46)

Although many other double-fish bottles exist, this appears to be one of only a few examples in chalcedony following a rather stiff perpendicular form, more usually seen in porcelain vases of the Qing period.

For a single fish agate bottle of similar form but lacking defined scales, see Sotheby's, Hong Kong, The Edward T. Chow Collection, 9 June 1981, lot 184; and another in creamy brown quartz, also lacking scales, illustrated by Hugh M. Moss, *Chinese Snuff Bottles in the Silica or Quartz Group,* No. 216.

For a clear rock crystal example in this collection, see No. 28.

47 | **Chalcedony**

1750-1800
2 ¹/₁₆ in. (5.3 cm.) high

Of baluster shape, carved in Imperial style in low relief with a central band of coiling *chilong* between lotus lappets at the foot and a *ruyi* band at the shoulder divided by lion-mask fixed-ring handles below plantain at the neck

1936-736 (CB. 243)

Though unmarked, this bottle appears to form part of a small, well-documented group of Imperial workshop chalcedony bottles.

See No. 251 in *Chinese Snuff Bottles in the Collection of Mary and George Bloch* by Robert Kleiner. It bears a *Qianlong yuzhi* mark ('Made by Imperial command of the Qianlong Emperor'). The lower portion is not as rounded as this example, and the neck is more waisted; however, the design of coiling dragons at the central section is similar, and the use of lotus lappets at the foot, *ruyi* at the shoulder, and stiff plantain-like leaves at the neck is nearly identical.

Kleiner notes that the incised pendant leaf motif at the neck is often found on glass snuff bottles from the Imperial workshops.

Archaistic decoration of this type can also be seen on a Qianlong-marked chalcedony vase in the Palace Museum, Beijing, illustrated in *Zhongguo yuqi quanji,* Nos. 207-208.

For an unusual Yongzheng-marked chalcedony double bottle, see *A Congregation of Snuff Bottle Connoisseurs,* No. 184.

See also Hugh M. Moss, *Chinese Snuff Bottles of the Silica and Quartz Group,* Nos. 194-195 for bottles related to this group but bearing vertical calligraphic panels on the sides, rather than the more unusual coiling dragons of this example.

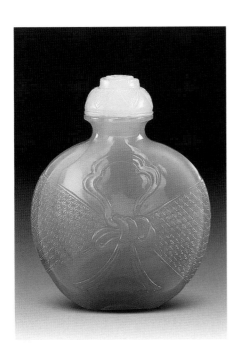

48 | **Chalcedony**

1770-1850
2 ⁵/₁₆ in. (5.9 cm.) high

Of rounded shape, carved in low relief and incised with a cloth-wrap with a dense pattern of six-pointed stars or flower heads tied by knotted ribbons

1936-605 (CB. 33)

For a discussion of the significance of the brocade-wrapped vessel, see bottle No. 344 in this collection.

For another chalcedony agate bottle very similarly carved, see Sotheby's, Hong Kong, 5 May 1994, lot 1392.

49 | **Chalcedony**

1800-1830
1 ¹⁵/₁₆ in. (4.9 cm.) high

Of rounded shape, well carved on the two main sides with the obverse and reverse of a Mexican eight-reales coin bearing the head of Charles III of Spain on one side and the Spanish coat of arms on the other

1936-1022

For a very similar example, see *Zhongguo Biyanhu Zhenshang* (Gems of Chinese Snuff Bottles), No. 36.

See bottles Nos. 8 and 26 in this collection for a discussion of this type of bottle.

This example appears to bear the date 1788, the year of the death of Charles III although the carving is a little indistinct.

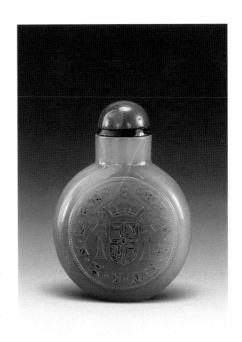

50 | **Chalcedony**

1770-1850
2 5/16 in. (5.9 cm.) high

Of rounded rectangular shape, very well hollowed leaving a thin translucent body with attractive snowy inclusions, one side with a five-character inscription

1936-745

The inscription *Bing xue jin cong ming* is an idiom that can be read as 'Clear and pure as ice and snow', a very appropriate inscription considering the nature of the stone itself.

The stone is obviously similar to 'macaroni agate' which is identical in color but where the inclusions resemble various kinds of pasta.

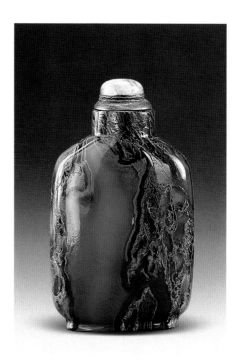

51 | **Agate**

1850-1900
2 9/16 in. (6.5 cm) high

'Moss agate,' of rounded rectangular shape, with attractive inclusions throughout, one side with primarily moss-green inclusions, the other with a translucent area edged in rusty orange, suggestive of Taihu rockwork, the interior not very well hollowed

1936-788

For a discussion of the term 'moss agate' and dendritic chalcedony, see Hugh Moss, Victor Graham and Ka Bo Tsang, *A Treasury of Chinese Snuff Bottles, The Mary and George Bloch Collection*, Vol. 2, Quartz, No. 199.

52 | **Agate**

1800-1880
2 ²³/₃₂ in. (6.9 cm.) high

Of rounded rectangular shape, a large abstract smoky inclusion on one side suggestive of a large peach, the reverse plain

196-563 (CB. 39)

This is a masterpiece of shadow agate artistry. The dark natural marking in this stone was so evocative of a peach that the artist has simply completed the illusion by carving a leafy spray. Even later damage, a short star crack, does not detract from its effectiveness.

53 | **Agate**

1850-1900
2 ³/₈ in. (6.1 cm.) high

Of rounded rectangular shape with attractive white and dark inclusions, the narrow sides carved with lion-mask fixed-ring handles

1936-526 (CB. 41)

Though the markings on this bottle are no more than abstract, a fanciful reading of the central trapezoidal inclusions on one side suggests a neolithic jade blade. The lower corner of the blade even has a 'hole' as one would expect to find on the originals. A close inspection of the 'hole' also suggests the correct method of drilling with a hole tapering conically. For similar neolithic blades, see *Chinese Archaic Jades and Bronzes* by James J. Lally, Nos. 25-55.

54 | Chalcedony

1780-1850
2 ¹/₂ in. (6.3 cm.) high

Of rounded rectangular shape, the plain main faces of honey tone with soft inclusions, the narrow sides carved through a darker skin with a stylized *lingzhi* handle on one and a descending *chilong* on the other

1936-584 (CB. 42)

This is a most unusual bottle in its use of the darker skin to form the handles on the narrow sides rather than a design for the main faces. However, the result is quite extraordinary, producing a quietly powerful masterpiece.

For another chalcedony bottle, of unusual cylindrical form, but similarly using an area of darker material to form a descending *chilong*, see Hugh Moss, Victor Graham and Ka Bo Tsang, *The Art of the Chinese Snuff Bottle, The J & J Collection*, No. 132. However, it has a rather rudimentary style of carving compared to this bottle.

The choice of asymmetric handles is another highly unusual feature, which suggests this particular carver had a singular vision.

For a discussion of the attribution of agate bottles bearing stylistic similarities to the 'Stevens Deer Master' school, see Hugh Moss, Victor Graham and Ka Bo Tsang, *A Treasury of Chinese Snuff Bottles, The Mary and George Bloch Collection*, Vol. 2, Quartz, Nos. 326-327. It is a sub-group of the recently named 'Official School' (see bottle No. 37 in this collection), a useful designation to help broaden our understanding of an otherwise complex group of agates. The main characteristic of the 'Stevens Deer Master' bottles is the use of an opaque beige material of pale color that sits on the surface of the more usual dark brown skin set against a pale translucent ground. The carving is imaginative, well rounded, and sculpturally very powerful.

55 | **Chalcedony**

1770-1830
2 1/16 in. (5.3 cm.) high

Of rounded rectangular shape, carved using orange-brown and black inclusions on one side, two monkeys with neatly incised fur, seated on rockwork, one holding a peach, a third monkey also holding a peach seated on rockwork on one of the narrow sides, the reverse lightly banded

1936-795

For another bottle carved with three monkeys in a rocky landscape, see Hugh Moss, Victor Graham and Ka Bo Tsang, *A Treasury of Chinese Snuff Bottles, The Mary and George Bloch Collection,* Vol. 2, Quartz, No. 317. It is classified as 'Official School – 1740-1840' (see bottle No. 37 in this collection for a discussion of this designation). The authors also note that the bottle incorporates distinctly 'Zhiting School of Suzhou' features, such as the superimposition of minor Suzhou detailing; a plain reverse, more often than not; and a scene that is conceived primarily in two dimensions rather than in the round.

For another chalcedony example depicting three monkeys, one holding a peach, see Sotheby's, New York, Bottles from the Montclair Art Museum, New Jersey, 22 September 1995, lot 159.

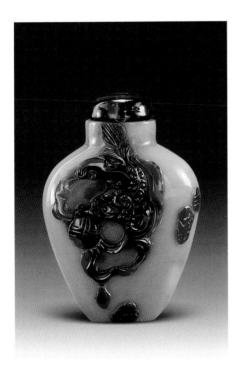

56 | **Chalcedony**

1850-1900
2 15/16 in. (6.0 cm.) high

Of baluster shape, carved through a dark brown and russet skin with a descending Buddhistic lion playing with a beribboned ball, three small inclusions carved as two cubs and a small ball, the reverse with light banding

1936-783

57 | **Agate**

1800-1900, the embellishment possibly later
2 ²/₈ in. (5.7 cm.) high

Of rounded shape, the stone embellished on one side with a darker agate or jasper caparisoned elephant with a vase on its back cut from a separate black and red stone, the other side with abstract misty inclusions

1936-796 (CB. 53)

An elephant with a vase on its back forms a rebus for 'A sign of peaceful times'. 'Vase' and 'peace' share the same pronunciation *ping* and *xiang* - elephant - is a pun for *xianxiang*, meaning 'phenomenon'. The combination is known as *taiping youxiang*, a most auspicious phrase.

58 | **Agate**

1780-1850
3 ¹/₄ in. (8.2 cm.) high

Of rounded shape, carved in low relief from a dark inclusion in the stone with an elderly sage holding open a scroll painting, a bat at his side, the reverse side carved with four bats using soft inclusions to great effect

1936-564 (CB. 62)

This is a very fine bottle with superbly executed subtle details which make the best use of the stone. It is well hollowed and unusually large. Following the recently published tome by Hugh Moss, Victor Graham and Ka Bo Tsang, *A Treasury of Chinese Snuff Bottles, The Mary and George Bloch Collection*, Vol. 2, Quartz, Nos. 319-325, this bottle can now be assigned to the 'Cameo Ink-play Master' and might even be Imperial. The authors attribute the bottles to a small sub-group of the 'Official School' (see another bottle in this collection, No. 55). They suggest that the work, or at least the concept, is 'the work of one artist, who may have had his own workshop, but who also appears to have worked for the Court and possibly at the Palace workshops or some other Imperial facility.' The sobriquet 'Cameo Ink-play Master' derives from the fact that, 'all his recognizable works are cameos to some extent, combining varied relief work using different colors in the material with some of the most imaginative and masterly ink-play works in the medium.'

Because the fifth Prince Ding (died 1854) had at least one bottle of this type in his collection, the authors consider it safe to consider him a mid-Qing master, working between the late Qianlong period and about 1860.

59 | Agate

1800-1900
3 in. (7.7 cm.) high

Of rounded rectangular shape, carved from the natural dark inclusions with a standing duck or goose, presumably feeding on one side, and paler inclusions on the reverse

1936-585 (CB. 3?)

The craftsman has successfully edited the markings in the stone and purposely left a few dot-like inclusions to remain under the bird's beak to suggest either droplets of water or food dribbling out. For other shadow agate bottles depicting a duck or ducks, see Hugh Moss, Victor Graham and Ka Bo Tsang, *The Art of the Chinese Snuff Bottle, The J & J Collection*, No. 276; and the same authors, *A Treasury of Chinese Snuff Bottles, The Mary and George Bloch Collection*, Vol. 2, Quartz, Nos. 272-274. The authors note that both collections are rich in extraordinary silhouette agates, thereby giving the false impression that masterpieces of this type are commonplace.

60 | Agate

1800-1900
2 1/4 in. (5.8 cm.) high

Of rounded rectangular shape, carved through a dark inclusion on one side with a phoenix, *fenghuang*, the reverse plain

1936-734 (CB. 34)

The carver has carefully drawn out of a dark inclusion the silhouette of a regal phoenix with strong swirling tail plumes, looking back over its shoulder.

The bottle can be compared to another illustrated in *Chinese Snuff Bottles, A Miniature Art from the Collection of Mary and George Bloch*, No. 226, where the bird is mistakenly called a rooster, presumably on account of the face of the bird, which is described by Hugh Moss, Victor Graham and Ka Bo Tsang, *A Treasury of Chinese Snuff Bottles, The Mary and George Bloch Collection*, Vol. 2, Quartz, No. 278, as resembling a 'startled chicken' whilst correctly describing the bird as a phoenix. The tail feathers are trifurcated, a feature common to depictions of this mythical bird.

61 | Agate

1800-1900
1 ¹³/₁₆ in. (4.6 cm.) high

Of spade shape, carved through dark inclusions on one side to reveal two figures wearing hats on a canopied boat; the other side with abstract markings vaguely suggestive of a fish and lotus

1936-743 (CB. 48)

The carver of this bottle had to work hard editing the darker skin and inclusions to produce this successful portrayal of two men on a canopied boat, hurtling, it would seem, downstream. The cutting away of the material to reveal the design is very evident around the central section when the bottle is turned to catch a slanting light.

See Hugh Moss, *Chinese Snuff Bottles of the Silica and Quartz Group*, No. 100, where he illustrates an example with two figures in a boat near a shoreline with other figures. See also Hugh Moss, Victor Graham and Ka Bo Tsang, *The Art of the Chinese Snuff Bottle, The J & J Collection*, Nos. 128-129. The first depicts five figures on a boat, the second numerous figures in a boat beneath a cliff with an armed archer. Both use a similar area of curved natural inclusion to form the hulls of the vessels.

Other examples which bear comparison are illustrated in *Chinese Snuff Bottles, A Miniature Art from the Collection of Mary and George Bloch*, No. 228, which shows a fisherman in a sanpan to one side and fish and lotus to the other; *The Au Hang Collection of Chinese Snuff Bottles*, No. 174, also with two men in a boat but with further abstract inclusions suggestive of rockwork; and Bob C. Stevens, *The Collector's Book of Snuff Bottles*, No. 538, with a single bearded fisherman in a boat landing a fish, from the Charles V. Swain Collection.

62 | Agate

1800-1880
2 ⁵/₁₆ in. (5.9 cm.) high

Of large rounded rectangular shape, carved on one side using the dark markings with a large and a small bird standing in the branches of a tree, looking at a bear or fox nearby, another inclusion resembling a bat or rockwork, with a shadowy inclusion on the reverse suggestive of a rising carp and fronds

1936-786 (CB. 49)

Provenance: American Art Association, Inc., New York
The Ton-Ying Collection, 5 February 1925, lot 21.
(See fig. 30 in the Introduction.)

For another shadow agate depicting a bear and eagle on one side, see Hugh Moss, Victor Graham and Ka Bo Tsang, *A Treasury of Chinese Snuff Bottles, The Mary and George Bloch Collection*, Vol. 2, Quartz, No. 278, where it is noted that the design of an eagle, *ying*, and bear, *xiong*, was a standard image used to evoke ideas of courage, loyalty and achievement, qualities perceived as inherent in a hero, *yingxiong*.

63 | **Agate**

1780-1850
2 ³/₁₆ in. (5.6 cm.) high

Of spade shape, carved through dark inclusions on one side with two monkeys amidst rocks with the upper torso and head of a man carved in the inclusion to the left of them with his arm raised holding a stick cut from a vertical inclusion, the reverse plain

1936-775 (CB. 57)

This bottle has rather unusual subject matter on one narrow side presumably dictated by the discovery of an unforeseen flaw in the material. The carving of two playful monkeys is itself a common one. It is, however, the addition of what appears to be a human head and shoulders brandishing a stick to the lower left side of the scene that raises eyebrows. A monkey brandishing a stick, usually poking at a beehive or bee, *fenghou*, or poking at a wrapped official seal, *fenghou guayin*, can both read as wishes of advancement. However, the large size of the head and the features of the figure on this bottle indicate it is not a monkey.

For other agate bottles depicting monkey scenes, see Robert Kleiner, *Chinese Snuff Bottles in the Collection of Mary and George Bloch*, Nos. 268-269, both incorporating bees in the design, and with one monkey brandishing a stick. See also Hugh Moss, Victor Graham and Ka Bo Tsang, *A Treasury of Chinese Snuff Bottles, The Mary and George Bloch Collection*, Vol. 2, Quartz, Nos. 281-285.

For jade bottles depicting playful monkeys, see Hugh Moss, *Chinese Snuff Bottles of the Silica and Quartz Group*, Nos. 187-188.

64 | **Carnelian**

1800-1880
2 ³/₄ in. (7 cm.) long

Carved as a goggle-eyed fan-tailed carp, the tail swept to one side, the belly of the fish incorporating a white inclusion carved as a lotus pad with flower head and bud from the otherwise rusty-orange stone

1936-853

Of all the published examples of carnelian fish, this exquisite bottle is amongst the finest. The vibrant rusty-orange-red of the upper portion of the stone contrasts beautifully with the lower white areas carved as a lotus on the underside. The lapidary has made wonderful use of the different colored layers of the stone.

See Hugh Moss, Victor Graham and Ka Bo Tsang, *A Treasury of Chinese Snuff Bottles, The Mary and George Bloch Collection*, Vol. 1, Jade, No. 56 for a black and white nephrite fish bottle which uses the different colors of stone to very similar effect.

For a celadon jade fish bottle with a sweeping fan-tail, see Robert Kleiner, *Chinese Snuff Bottles*

in the Collection of Mary and George Bloch, No. 90.

For another carnelian fish, described as 'red agate', see *Snuff Bottles in the Collection of the National Palace Museum*, No. 331.

For a carnelian bottle depicting entwined carp, see Robert W. L. Kleiner, *Chinese Snuff Bottles from the Collection of Mary and George Bloch*, No. 171.

A very lively fish in yellow chalcedony is illustrated in *Chinese Snuff Bottles, A Miniature Art from the Collection of Mary and George Bloch*, No. 238.

65 | **Carnelian**

1770-1850
2 ¹/₈ in. (5.4 cm.) high

Of tapering oblong shape, carved and incised using the natural inclusions with a cell-pattern around the body, neatly tied at one narrow side, itself carved in relief with hanging prunus using the natural wavy inclusions

1936-718 (CB. 83 or 93)

The motif of a tied cloth or brocade around a snuff bottle was a popular one. It was a decorative device indicative of a gift, as gifts were often presented at court wrapped in precious brocade.

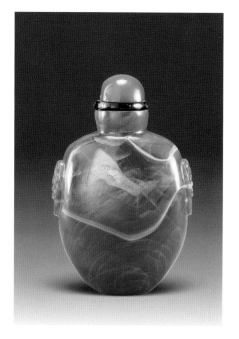

66 | **Carnelian**

1850-1900
2 ¹/₈ in. (5.5 cm.) high

Of spade shape, an attractive orange-toned stone with pale white bands, the narrow sides carved with lion-mask fixed-ring handles, the neck unusually carved with wide mouth and internally tapering neck ending in a small opening

1936-634

For a discussion of the use of carnelian in snuff bottle production, see Hugh Moss, Victor Graham and Ka Bo Tsang, *The Art of the Chinese Snuff Bottle, The J & J Collection*, No. 162.

67 | Carnelian

1820-1850, incised *Xingyouheng Tang* four-character mark, Daoguang
2 in. (5.1 cm.) high

Of rectangular shape, carved in low relief on one side with a carp and lotus within a shaped panel, and on the other side with a goose below lotus, the narrow sides carved with beribboned cash symbols in shaped panels

1936-748

Literature: Edward Wenham, 'Antiques As Decoration', *Arts & Decoration*, New York, Winter, 1928, illustrated p. 59.

This bottle bears the hallmark *Xingyouheng Tang* ('Hall of Constancy'), of the fifth Prince Ding, Zaiquan. He was also known by the name Yunlin zhuren. A certain amount is known about this interesting royal figure, though not his date of birth, see Hugh Moss, *A Treasury of Chinese Snuff Bottles in the Mary and George Bloch Collection*, Vol. I, Jade, pp. 390-393. The authors give a brief biography of the Prince based on those given by Zhaoying, in Arthur W. Hummel, *Eminent Chinese of the Ch'ing Period*, Washington, 1943, pp. 728-729.

A summation of their remarks is as follows:
1790's - Born. Great-great-grandson of the Qianlong Emperor
1808 - Attended Palace school for Princes under tuition of Tang Jinzhao
1816 - Appointed nobleman of tenth rank
1834-5 - President of the Board of Ceremonies
1835-6 - President of the Board of Works
1836 - Inherited rank of fifth Prince Ding
1848 - Published collection of his own verses entitled '*Xingyouheng Tang chuji*'
1854 - Died

From the number of bottles bearing his hallmark, it is safe to assume that the Prince collected snuff bottles. At least five inscribed bottles can be found in the Mary and George Bloch Collection, either in nephrite or agate. See Hugh Moss, Victor Graham and Ka Bo Tsang, *A Treasury of Chinese Snuff Bottles, the Mary and George Bloch Collection*, Vol. I, Jade, No. 150-154; and Robert Kleiner *Chinese Snuff Bottles in the Collection of Mary and George Bloch*, No. 252.

Other bottles bearing this mark are also published, see Paul Moss, *Documentary Chinese Works of Art in Scholars' Taste*, Nos. 110-111. The first is in crystal, the second in agate.

See also, Sotheby's, Hong Kong, The Eric Young Collection, Part IV, 28 October 1993, lot 1187, for an octagonal nephrite example.

The decoration on this bottle, a goose or mandarin duck below lotus on one side and a carp amidst lotus on the other, was a popular one in the Qing arts and expressed long life and happiness. This is further supported by the double cash handles on the narrow sides. It is an outstanding bottle enhanced by the unusual carving of the shaped border within the rectangular border itself and the neat calligraphic hallmark.

A variety of works of art other than snuff bottles bearing this four-character mark are known, including gourd vessels (generally considered questionable), an Yixing teapot, jade and soapstone brushwashers, *Duan* inkstones and a glass overlay waterpot, see Hugh Moss and Gerard Tsang, *Arts from the Scholar's Studio*, Nos. 108-111; and No. 145. See also, Paul Moss, *op. cit.*, No. 109.

68 | Agate

1770-1850, Suzhou
2 ¹/₄ in. (5.7 cm.) high

Of spade shape, carved in deep relief using the dark inclusions, with five Buddhistic lions at play amidst rockwork, three on one side and two on the other, one being handed a ball by a single human figure alongside a seven-character inscription in grass script on the face of a cliff

1936-1024 (CB. 85)

The inscription *Jin qiu shi xi cai yun shen* is a celebratory new year blessing but can literally be read as 'Lions play with a beautiful, splendid ball, under colorful deep clouds'.

In size and shape this bottle can be linked with a well-documented group of Suzhou agates, most with short inscriptions carved in low relief or incised, see Hugh Moss, Victor Graham and Ka Bo Tsang, *The Art of the Chinese Snuff Bottle*,

The J & J Collection, Nos. 138-141.

For another agate, not attributed to Suzhou, but dipicting a similar scene with a human figure and a Buddhistic lion, see *ibid.*, pp. 238-239, No. 147.

For a discussion of attribution to the 'School of Zhiting', a Suzhou sub-group, see another bottle in this collection, No. 70.

69 | **Agate**

The bottle, 1850-1930, the embellished plaques earlier, 1750-1850
2 ⁷/₁₆ in. (6.3 cm.) high

Square, with simple borders inset with earlier Suzhou agate rectangular panels depicting a scholar with a Buddhistic lion looking at a ball near a small building to one side, and an Immortal with a whisk standing amidst clouds, with a bat and a bird nearby, another figure near a bridge and rockwork below

1936-1021

For a discussion of attribution of Suzhou pendants and snuff bottles to the 'School of Zhiting', see another bottle in this collection, No. 70.

See also a bottle with similar subject matter illustrated by Hugh Moss, Victor Graham and Ka Bo Tsang, *A Treasury of Chinese Snuff Bottles, The Mary and George Bloch Collection*, Vol. 2, Quartz, No. 371.

70 | **Chalcedony**

1730-1820, Suzhou
2 ⁵/₁₆ in. (5.9 cm.) high

Of rounded shape, carved in relief using the black and brown inclusions to reveal a plump bird standing on a leafy fruiting branch rising from rockwork with *lingzhi* on one side, and with a wide expanse of classic serrated rockwork on the other with leaves on the lower right edge

1936-946

The carver has made exquisite use of two types of colored inclusions. Black markings have been used for the leafy foliage and the feathers of a chubby bird standing on its branches, whilst the reddish brown inclusions have been masterfully used for the numerous full berries of the fruiting branch. On the reverse, three misty patches of the same reddish brown have been carefully cut in an arched pattern with serrations to give an extraordinary three-dimensional quality to the rockwork. The richness of the whole design is enhanced by both the bulbous shape of the bottle and the rounded high relief given solely to the plump bird, which literally jumps out of the surface plane.

The most comparable example published appears to be that illustrated by Clare Lawrence, *Miniature Masterpieces from the Middle Kingdom, The Monimar Collection of Chinese Snuff Bottles*, No. 61. It also depicts a plump bird on one side and serrated rockwork on the other, though the bottle is smaller and the design not as richly decorated.

Lawrence adds an interesting footnote about the plethora of large Taihu rocks in the ornamental gardens of Suzhou, known as the 'City of Gardens'. Whilst not suggesting that this was the inspiration behind the extensive use of serrated rockwork by the 'Suzhou School' of snuff bottle carvers, she does state that this characteristic is therefore hardly surprising.

For another more elongated Suzhou bottle depicting a bird on a tree spray, see Bob C. Stevens, *The Collector's Book of Snuff Bottles*, No. 575; also illustrated by Sotheby's, New York,

The Bob C. Stevens Collection, Part II, 26 March 1982, lot 87.

For a discussion of the Suzhou School and, in particular, a new designation 'School of Zhiting' (to which this bottle can now be assigned) with dates ranging between 1730-1860, see Hugh Moss, Victor Graham and Ka Bo Tsang, *A Treasury of Chinese Snuff Bottles, The Mary and George Bloch Collection*, Vol. 2, Quartz, No. 366, where it is noted that 'There has been a casual assumption, ever since we first recognized a group of jade and chalcedony bottles as being linked by style and associated with the town of Suzhou, that these represented Suzhou style as a whole, with perhaps most of the workshops in the town producing similar wares. This belief is no longer sustainable.'

Their reasoning is soundly based. Jades other than snuff bottles and pendants, many in the Imperial collections in Beijing and Taipei, are known to have been ordered at Suzhou for the Court, but none bear the 'accepted' Suzhou characteristics of rockwork with serrated ridges with small indentations. They are, however, carved with the distinctly three-dimensional angular planes, as are the snuff bottles and pendants. The authors therefore suggest that a single workshop, which they have named the 'School of Zhiting', is probably responsible for the separate Suzhou snuff bottle and pendant style, working within the larger context of Suzhou production. The designation derives from the art name of one of the earlier artists who produced Suzhou-School bottles, see *ibid.*, Vol. 1, Jade, No. 122, where a bottle signed by him (one of six recorded) is illustrated.

71 | Agate or Jasper

1850-1920
2 7/16 in. (6.2 cm.) high

Of spade shape, the unusual orange-toned stone with soft mustard and pink striations throughout

1936-621

It is difficult to classify this particular stone. It is a most unusual orange-toned color rarely seen in snuff bottles. It might well be a type of jasper based on its opacity and color. Jasper is often mistaken for glass because of the swirling inclusions found in some varities.

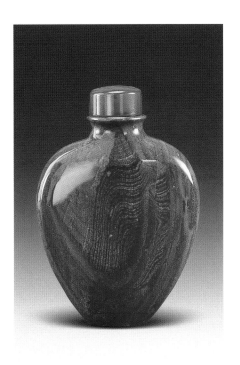

72 | Jasper

1800-1900
3 1/4 in. (8.2 cm.) high

Of rounded rectangular shape, carved in high relief from the mustard-brown skin with a lady under a sterculia tree near Taihu rockwork, a hoe over her shoulder, with a basket of peaches suspended on it, and a whisk in her other hand, the reverse plain

1936-1044 (CB. 80 or 263)

Provenance: American Art Galleries, New York
The Edward Runge Collection, 7 March 1914, lot 27.
American Art Galleries, New York
The Samuel S. Laird Collection, 7-12 January 1924, lot 222.
(See fig. 20 in the Introduction.)

Literature: Edward Wenham, 'Antiques As Decoration', *Arts & Decoration*, New York, Winter, 1928, illustrated p. 59.

Another bottle of this type was sold at Christie's, London, April 20, 1970, lot 109. It depicted a lady Immortal on a tree raft with a boy carrying a basket of peaches on his back.

73 | Jasper

1800-1900
2 ³/₈ in. (6.2 cm.) high

Of rounded rectangular shape, the main faces gently rounded, the narrow sides with lion-mask fixed-ring handles, the stone with attractive markings

1936-664

For another similar bottle of paler green tone, see Hugh Moss, Victor Graham and Ka Bo Tsang, *A Treasury of Chinese Snuff Bottles, The Mary and George Bloch Collection*, Vol. 2, Quartz, No. 206.

74 | Agate or Jasper

1820-1880
2 ³/₈ in. (5.7 cm.) high

Of rounded rectangular shape, one side carved from the red skin with a figure of Zhong Kui, the Demon Queller, holding his sword and looking at a swooping bat incised with a *Wang* character ('king'), the reverse with a demon holding a cup over a wine jar, with another bat nearby

1936-566 (CB. 60)

Zhong Kui was a popular mythological subject who was said to have appeared in a dream to the Tang Emperor Minghuang. Having exorcised the Emperor's demons, Zhong Kui was then immortalized in paintings distributed throughout the land. See Hugh Moss, Victor Graham and Ka Bo Tsang, *The Art of the Chinese Snuff Bottle, The J & J Collection*, No. 217.

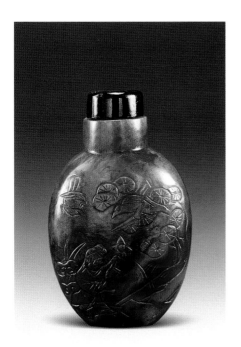

75 | Agate or Jasper

1840-1900
2 ¹/₂ in. (6.3 cm) high

Of ovoid shape, carved in low relief with a lady and two birds under a pine on one side and a boy with chick under a leafless tree on the other, the stone attractively mottled

1936-573

Though the material has the appearance of soapstone, it is in fact of extreme hardness with a high polish.

The subject is rather hard to discern, though the artist may have meant to portray a Daoist female Immortal punting her tree craft to one side. However, the cursory cutting of the stone makes it difficult to establish whether this is the case.

76 | Amygdaloidal basalt

1800-1900
2 ¹/₄ in. (5.7 cm.) high

Comprising two rectangular bottles with canted corners, the stone with attractive horizontal markings, each vessel carved with a rectangular panel on all four sides

1936-591 (CB. 138)

This may be the only published example of a double bottle of rectangular shape made from this material. Most bottles carved from this stone are of rounded shape.

For other examples in this seldom-used but attractive stone, see Hugh Moss, *Chinese Snuff Bottles: 6. Chinese Snuff Bottles from the Collection of the Rt. Hon. The Marquess of Exeter, K.C.M.G.*, No. S.16; and Hugh Moss, Victor Graham and Ka Bo Tsang, *The Art of the Chinese Snuff Bottle, The J & J Collection*, No. 75, where the authors discuss the origins of the stone and how, strangely, the material is not used outside snuff bottle production.

The inclusions in this particular bottle are suggestive of flying bats.

77 | **Fossiliferous limestone**

1800-1900
2 $^{11}/_{32}$ in. (6 cm.) high

Of tapering rectangular shape with canted corners and convex narrow sides, the black stone with attractive white markings

1936-811 (CB. 135)

For another similar bottle, see Robert W. L. Kleiner, *Chinese Snuff Bottles from the Burghley House Collection,* No. 91.

78 | **Limestone Conglomerate**

1800-1900
2 $^{1}/_{2}$ in. (6.3 cm.) high

Of rounded rectangular shape, the stone with attractive pebble-like inclusions on both sides interspersed with more slender rectangular and oval inclusions

1936-801 (CB. 134)

There are two types of puddingstone; one is a quartz conglomerate, the other is a limestone conglomerate. This bottle falls into the second category. For two other examples, see Hugh Moss, Victor Graham and Ka Bo Tsang, *A Treasury of Chinese Snuff Bottles, The Mary and George Bloch Collection,* Vol. 3, Stones other than Jade and Quartz, Nos. 398-399, where it is noted that it is this material and not the quartz puddingstone that was frequently copied in porcelain of the Qianlong period.

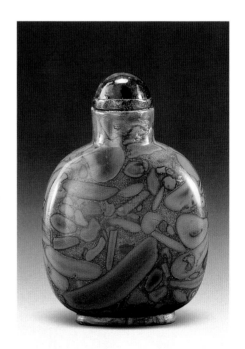

79 | **Fossiliferous limestone**

1800-1900
2 ¹/₂ in. (6.2 cm.) high

Of pebble shape, the black stone with pale cream, gray and green inclusions

1936-845 (CB. 136)

This bottle appears to be of fossiliferous limestone but might also be an amygdaloidal basalt. Unlike most bottles made from this material, it has been left as a pebble rather than carved with a foot and shaped.

80 | **Fossiliferous limestone**

1800-1900
2 ⁷/₃₂ in. (5.8 cm.)

Of ovoid shape, the reddish-brown matrix enclosing a mass of dotted round white cells

1936-822 (CB. 137)

For three other bottles made from this particular type of limestone, with a brown ground suffused with diverse white markings of various sizes, see Bob C. Stevens, *The Collector's Book of Snuff Bottles*, Nos. 673-674; and another illustrated by Helen White, *Snuff Bottles from China, The Victoria and Albert Museum Collection*, pl. 50, No. 1.

The carving of this particular stone, which broadens the inclusions as the stone narrows to the edge, gives it an alluring quality. The inclusions almost appear to be rushing off the rounded edge. For other bottles with the same mesmerizing effect, see Hugh Moss, *Chinese Snuff Bottles: 6. Chinese Snuff Bottles from the Collection of the Rt. Hon. The Marquess of Exeter, K.C.M.G.*, p.147, No. S.19; and another in this collection, No. 77.

81 | **Fossiliferous limestone**

1800-1900
2 1/4 in. (5.7 cm.) high

Of rounded shape, the stone gray on one side with a fine cell-network, and on the other side, cream with black cell-like inclusions, somewhat cursorily carved lion-mask fixed-ring handles on the narrow sides

1936-828 (CB. 133)

For two examples with similar star-burst inclusions, see Bob C. Stevens, *The Collector's Book of Snuff Bottles*, Nos. 680-681. For another with fewer but larger markings entitled 'The Fossilized Fireworks Display', see Hugh Moss, Victor Graham and Ka Bo Tsang, *A Treasury of Chinese Snuff Bottles, The Mary and George Bloch Collection*, Vol. 3, Stones other than Jade and Quartz, No. 400; and another with more evenly-spaced markings, the 'Fossilized Peacock's Tail', *ibid.*, No. 401.

82 | **Amygdaloidal basalt**

1800-1900
2 1/4 in. (5.7 cm.) high

Of spade shape, the black stone with pink, gray and green inclusions

1936-827 (CB. 139)

For an example of rectangular shape, see Hugh Moss, Victor Graham and Ka Bo Tsang, *The Art of the Chinese Snuff Bottle, The J & J Collection*, No. 75; and the same authors, *A Treasury of Chinese Snuff Bottles, The Mary and George Bloch Collection*, Vol. 3, Stones other than Jade or Quartz, No. 404 for a spherical example.

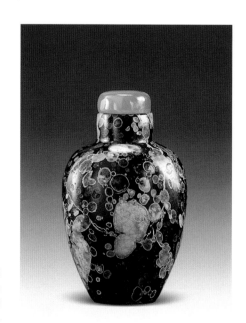

83 | **Turquoise**

1780-1850
2 ⁵/₈ in. (6.8 cm.) high

Of rounded rectangular shape, carved in deep relief with a scholar in a boat passing through a ravine with pine on one side, a boy in the mountains peering down from above and a scholar and attendant standing by a rock face on the other

1936-956 (CB. 131, 231 or 631)

It is rare to find such a large piece of turquoise used for a bottle, particularly one with so few inclusions in the stone. From the deep and fine carving, it seems apparent that the lapidary had immense joy with this stone. This is a delightfully chunky bottle, and the subject appears to be scenes from one story. A scholar, possibly Mi Fu, and assistant are carved on one side, preparing to write calligraphy on a rock, while the same scholar is carved seated in a boat in a ravine to the reverse, watched by his assistant from a rock above.

The closest comparisons can be drawn with smaller jade bottles of the 'Master of the Rocks'

type, see Hugh Moss, Victor Graham and Ka Bo Tsang, *A Treasury of Chinese Snuff Bottles, the Mary and George Bloch Collection*, Vol. 1, Jade, No. 136.

For other turquoise bottles, see Bob C. Stevens, *The Collector's Book of Snuff Bottles*, No. 651, which is carved in low relief with stylized archaistic dragon panels and is now in the Mary and George Bloch Collection; *Masterpieces of Snuff Bottles in the Palace Museum*, No. 151; and Humphrey K. F. Hui and Christopher C. H. Sin in *An Imperial Qing Tradition*, No. 117.

84 | **Turquoise**

1800-1880
2 ⁵/₁₆ in. (5.9 cm.) high

Of spade shape, with attractive green patches edged in yellow on the dark matrix

1936-819

For another example of similar shape but using less of the black matrix, see Bob C. Stevens, *The Collector's Book of Snuff Bottles*, No. 601.

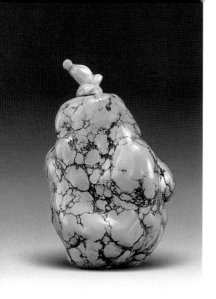

85 | Turquoise

1770-1850
2 in. (5.1 cm.) high

Of irregular lumpy pebble shape, the stone of attractive color with thin veins of matrix

1936-812 (CB. 130)

For other similar examples, see Hugh Moss, Victor Graham and Ka Bo Tsang, *A Treasury of Chinese Snuff Bottles, The Mary and George Bloch Collection*, Vol. 3, Stones other than Jade and Quartz, No. 418; Sotheby's, New York, Bottles from the Montclair Art Museum, New Jersey, 22 September 1995, lot 197; and Sotheby's, London, The Baronesses Sapuppo and d'Essen Collection, 14 November 2000, lot 93. See also three of small size carved as fruit, illustrated in *Snuff Bottles in the Collection of the National Palace Museum*, Nos. 402-404.

86 | Lapis lazuli

1820-1880
1 15/16 in. (5 cm.) high

Of melon shape, the lobed body carved in relief with two long-tailed birds amidst prunus on one side and a single bird with prunus on the other, the stone with attractive gold flecks amidst the white inclusions of the otherwise dark blue stone

1936-732 (CB. 128)

For a lengthy discussion on lapis lazuli and its possible sources inside and outside China, see Hugh Moss, Victor Graham and Ka Bo Tsang, *A Treasury of Chinese Snuff Bottles, The Mary and George Bloch Collection*, Vol. 3, Stones other than Jade or Quartz, No. 414.

87 | Lapis lazuli

1850-1920
3 in. (7.6 cm.) high

Of pear shape, the stone of brilliant dark blue tone with areas of pale inclusions mottled throughout

1936-614 (CB. 127)

It is very unusual to find a lapis lazuli snuff bottle of this extended pear shape. It may have started life as a miniature vase and been later converted to a snuff bottle by the simple addition of a stopper and spoon.

Organic Bottles

88 | **Amber**

1750-1800
2 in. (5.1 cm.) high

Of rounded shape, the clear amber with fine crizzling throughout

1936-813 (CB. 147)

Provenance: Almost certainly the American Art Galleries, New York
The Elizabeth Andrews Collection, 8-9 February 1922, lot 254.

For another, slightly less bulbous amber bottle, see *Snuff Bottles in the Collection of the National Palace Museum*, No. 383. See also, *The Au Hang Collection of Chinese Snuff Bottles*, No. 228, also displaying a fine network of 'crizzling', a term primarily used in describing early glass.

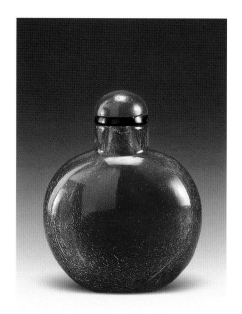

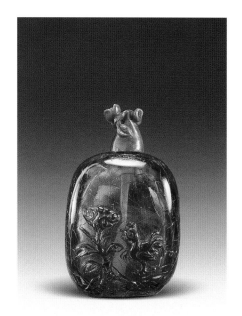

89 | **Amber**

1850-1900
1 5/8 in. (4.2 cm.) high

Of rounded rectangular shape, carved in low relief on one side with a cockerel and cockscomb, the other side plain, the bottle with crizzling throughout

1936-726 (CB. 148)

The cockeral and cockscomb can form the rebus *Gong (Guan) Shang Jia Guan*, which can be read as 'receiving official promotions in succession'.

90 | **Amber**

1750-1790
2 ⁵/₈ in. (6.7 cm.) high

Of ovoid shape, carved on each side with an oval cartouche enclosing a coiling archaistic phoenix and a *chilong*, possibly representing a stylized character

1936-830 (CB. 150)

For a similar amber bottle, see Robert Kleiner, *Chinese Snuff Bottles, The White Wings Collection*, No. 155.

Similar decoration of Imperially-inspired archaistic dragons can be found on glass, jade and *duan* inkstone bottles.

The most comparable glass bottle appears to be an amber-red example from the collection of Mrs. Elmer A. Claar, sold at the Parke-Bernet Galleries, New York, 12 May 1970, lot 430, though of slightly more compressed form.

The technique and style of carving are reminiscent of an amber glass bottle illustrated by Robert Kleiner, *Chinese Snuff Bottles in the Collection of Mary and George Bloch*, No. 142, which is carved with sprays of Indian lotus. The bottle is a classic example of the Mughal-style

carving that was popular at court after the Qianlong conquests of Xinjiang and Khotan in 1759. The Emperor, so beguiled by the beauty of Mughal craftsmanship, had a workshop set up within the Palace to imitate Mughal jade production. Also see, Teng Shu-p'ing, *Hindustan Jade in the National Palace Museum*.

For an inkstone example, see Hugh Moss, Victor Graham and Ka Bo Tsang, *A Treasury of Chinese Snuff Bottles, The Mary and George Bloch Collection*, Vol. 3, Stones other than Jade and Quartz, No. 393.

For a jade example carved with paired phoenix, see Hugh Moss, Victor Graham and Ka Bo Tsang, *A Treasury of Chinese Snuff Bottles, The Mary and George Bloch Collection*, Vol. 1, Jade, No. 90.

91 | Amber

1800-1900
2 ¹/₂ in. (6.4 cm.) high

Of rounded tapering rectangular shape, carved in high relief with an elegant female Immortal with a basket of *lingzhi* on a pole over one shoulder, and a peach in her left hand, a crane holding a *lingzhi* in its beak beside her, all near tree peony, the reverse with three boys at play, some black inclusions in the translucent amber

1936-524

For another amber bottle of rounded shape, but similarly carved in relief with figural scenes which are typically out of scale with the landscape, see Hugh Moss, Victor Graham and Ka Bo Tsang, *The Art of the Chinese Snuff Bottle, The J & J Collection*, No. 295. The authors discuss at length the source of amber for the Chinese carvers, dismissing the long-held notion that opaque yellow was only Baltic in origin and translucent red only Burmese.

92 | Amber

1780-1850
2 ¹/₂ in. (6.3 cm.) high

Of fruit shape, one side semi-translucent with the finger-citrus carved at an angle to follow the opaque inclusions below the surface of the material

1936-839 (CB. 146)

For a very similar amber bottle, though less opaque than this one, see *Snuff Bottles in the Collection of the National Palace Museum*, No. 389, and also illustrated on the front cover.

See also two more opaque amber types: Christie's, London, 9 October 1972, lot 175; and Parke-Bernet Galleries, New York, The Mrs. Elmer A. Claar Collection, 2 December, 1969, lot 68.

93 | **Amber**

The bottle 1800-1850, the embellishment of
Shibayama type, Japan, 1850-1930
2 ⁷/₁₆ in. (6.3 cm.) high

Of large rounded rectangular shape,
embellished in mother-of-pearl, lacquer, gilt,
coral and other materials, in a continuous
scene of a variety of flowers including peony,
narcissus, prunus, chrysanthemum and
bamboo rising from and around pierced
rockwork, peaches carved on the stopper

1936-671 (CB. 152)

Literature: *Newsletter of the Chinese Snuff Bottle
Society of America*, June, 1974, p. 10, No. 20.

This bottle is closely associated with one
illustrated by Bob C. Stevens, *The Collector's
Book of Snuff Bottles*, No. 1024, subsequently
sold at Sotheby's, New York, 26 March 1982, lot
211; again at Sotheby's, Hong Kong, The Eric
Young Collection, Part IV, 28 October 1993,
lot 1081. It was also illustrated in the *JICSBS*,
Winter 1993, p. 40, fig. 3. The metal collars on
the neck of both bottles are identical. This
example, however, retains an amber stopper
with the same metal fitting, suggesting that the
Stevens bottle was re-stoppered at some time
in its more recent history. Whilst the decorative
use of gold lacquer, colored *hiramakie*, *okibirame*
and *aogzi* is similar on both bottles, the Stevens
example depicts a pair of exotic long-tailed birds
and another crested bird perched amidst peony
while this bottle is decorated with a naturalistic
floral and rockwork setting.

In inlay technique and subject matter this bottle
actually relates more closely to two other
bottles. The first is illustrated by Robert W. L.
Kleiner, *Chinese Snuff Bottles from the Collection
of Mary and George Bloch*, No. 217; the second,
also originally in the Bob C. Stevens Collection,
is illustrated by Hugh Moss, Victor Graham and
Ka Bo Tsang, *The Art of the Chinese Snuff Bottle,
The J & J Collection*, No. 301. The authors refer
to the Princeton bottle and note that:

The distinctive type of embellishment
known as 'Shibayama' was developed
toward the end of the eighteenth
century by Onogi Senzo of Shibayama, a
small village in Chiba prefecture across
the bay from Tokyo. When Onogi moved
to Tokyo he changed his name to
Shibayama, which then developed into a
generic term for decoration combining
lacquer and the embellishment of a
number of other materials.

The authors then note various similarities to
two Japanese carved and inlaid amber bottles
signed by Tansan, and another unsigned bottle
attributed to Tansan.

The signed bottles, both in the J & J Collection
and illustrated in the same publication,
Nos. 299-300; and the unsigned example,
all have the same very neat shallow foot with a
flat rim, something seldom, if ever, seen on
Chinese amber pebble bottles. That the
decoration of the Princeton bottle is very similar
to the inlay on all these examples, suggests a
very strong link between them.

For a lengthy discussion of Japanese inlaid and
carved bottles, see an article by Robert Hall in
the *JICSBS*, Autumn 1996, 'The Japanese
Connection', pp. 4-15.

94 | Amber, mounted in embellished silver

1800-1900
2 ⁷/₈ in. (7.2 cm.) high

Of oval shape, the pale amber softly carved to appear almost molded, with a coiling *chilong* on each side within a key-pattern roundel, the silver mounts embellished with lapis lazuli, coral, malachite, turquoise and aventurine, the neck with a thin band of *leiwen* mirroring the roundel just below the stopper

1936-690 (CB. 159)

For two similarly mounted bottles with semi-precious stone inlays, see *Zhongguo Biyanhu Zhenshang* (Gems of Chinese Snuff Bottles), Nos. 396-397.

95 | Tortoiseshell, mounted in embellished silver

1850-1900
4 ¹/₂ in. (11.2 cm.) high

Of oval shape, the material of dark semi-translucent tone, the silver mounts inset with malachite, rose quartz, lapis lazuli, turquoise and aventurine, the collar of metal with lion-mask handles on the shoulders

1936-1068 (CB. 165)

The tortoise is considered to be one of the earliest spiritual symbols in China, and tortoiseshell was a prized material. See Hugh Moss, Victor Graham, and Ka Bo Tsang, *The Art of the Chinese Snuff Bottle, The J & J Collection*, p. 41, for further discussion on its powerful longevity symbolism.

96 | Coconut shell mounted in embellished silver

1850-1920
2 ⁵/₈ in. (6.6 cm.) high

Of rounded purse shape, the silver mounts inset with lapis lazuli, coral, aventurine, malachite and turquoise, the collar of metal with lion-mask handles on the shoulders

1936-653 (CB. 164)

Other coconut shell bottles are illustrated by Hugh Moss, Victor Graham and Ka Bo Tsang in *The Art of the Chinese Snuff Bottles, The J & J Collection*, Nos. 277-279.

97 | Ivory, mounted in embellished silver

1850-1900
6 in. (15.2 cm.) high

Of ovoid shape, the ivory of yellow tone, the silver mounts inset with coral, aventurine, malachite, turquoise and lapis lazuli, the collar of metal with lion-mask handles on the shoulders

1936-1068 (CB. 166)

98 | Ivory

1750-1850, Qianlong four-character incised seal mark

2 ¹¹/₁₆ in. (7 cm.) high

Of oval shape, carved in high rounded relief in a continuous scene with nine Buddhistic lions chasing five beribboned balls on a wave ground

1936-966 (CB. 154)

Opinions vary greatly as to which bottles of this type should be called Chinese and Imperial, and which should be called Japanese. This bottle is a strong candidate for placement in the first category when compared to others assigned there. The closest comparison can be drawn with a Qianlong-marked example of almost identical design illustrated by Hugh Moss, *Chinese Snuff Bottles: 6. Chinese Snuff Bottles from the Collection of the Rt. Hon. The Marquess Of Exeter, K.C.M.G.*, p. 5, No. O.4; and also illustrated by Robert W. L. Kleiner, *Chinese Snuff Bottles from the Burghley House Collection, Stamford, England*, No. 142, and attributed to the Beijing Palace workshops. Another, also called Chinese and dated to the Qianlong period, was sold at Sotheby's, New York, 1-2 June 1993, lot 223.

However, the model is probably best known through the fairly large number of Japanese copies, see Robert Kleiner, *Chinese Snuff Bottles in the Collection of Mary and George Bloch*, No. 320. The juxtaposition of the lions on the body and the treatment of the lappets and *leiwen* at the neck are almost identical to this one. The only glaring difference is to be found in the proportions of the bottle and the depth of the surface carving. The above example is slender, with quite low relief and has an elongated neck, whereas the Japanese copy, carved in very high relief, is more of a spade shape and more compressed altogether. Both bottles appear to have later stoppers. The Japanese examples usually have separately attached necks, whilst the Chinese bottles have an integral neck. The Chinese examples are generally suffused with a minute network of crackle and cracks, caused by age, largely absent in the Japanese versions.

For another Japanese ivory bottle, see the Parke-Bernet Galleries, New York, The Mrs. Elmer A. Claar Collection, 2 December, 1969, lot 57. For Japanese lacquer examples based on the Imperial ivory bottles, see Hugh Moss, Victor Graham and Ka Bo Tsang, *The Art of the Chinese Snuff Bottle, The J & J Collection*, Nos. 315-316. Another classified 'Japanese or Chinese' is illustrated by Hugh Moss, *op. cit.*, pp. 12-13, No. O.27.

99 | Ivory

1800-1880
3 in. (7.6 cm.) high

Of spade shape, carved in medium relief and painted with a dismounted gentleman under a willow tree with his consort nearby returning to her chariot, her maid holding a wine ewer, the other side carved with figures holding fans in a walled courtyard, the narrow sides with rockwork and plantain and *ruyi* lappets below *leiwen* at the neck

1936-964 (CB. 155)

The scene is probably taken from the *Dream of the West Chamber.*

For a similar bottle with a figural pavilion scene, see Robert W. L. Kleiner, *Chinese Snuff Bottles from the Burghley House Collection, Stamford, England*, No. 137.

100 | Ivory

1790-1880
3 ³/₁₆ in. (8.1 cm.) high

Of large spade shape, carved in high relief and painted in bright colors with numerous boys at various activities in or near pavilions in a continuous scene, a chrysanthemum head carved on the base and stopper

1936-963 (CB. 156)

Provenance: American Art Association, New York
The A. W. Bahr Collection, 17-19 January 1916, lot 85. (See fig. 21 in the Introduction.)

For a similar ivory example with figural pavilion scenes, see Robert W. L. Kleiner, *Chinese Snuff Bottles from the Burghley House Collection, Stamford, England*, No. 137.

The design of numerous boys at play, often called 'one hundred boys', was a popular one in ceramic production. For a pair of Qianlong-marked Imperial vases, similarly depicting boys at play on a terrace, see Sotheby's, Hong Kong, 2 November 1998, lot 409. As subject matter, it was often used on gifts given at the start of a New Year. The motif was a wish for abundant offspring and wealth.

This bottle can be compared to two cinnabar lacquer bottles in this collection, Nos. 102-103.

101 | Cinnabar lacquer

1770-1800
2 9/16 in. (6.5 cm.) high

Of spade shape, carved in the Ming style with four boys, one holding a baby on his back, playing under pine and sterculia, and five boys playing a board game on the other side, all on a diaper ground

1936-816

For a group of similar bottles, see *Masterpieces of Snuff Bottles in the Palace Museum*, Nos. 192-195.

This belongs to a well-known group of lacquer bottles that bear similar characteristics of spade shape, flared neck, carved figural decoration, stoppers with integral bronze finial, and often a flat bronze foot. Most of the figural landscapes depicted on this group are scenes from popular novels, myths, legends, dramas and opera. The method of carving mirrors that used on other types of lacquer vessels used from the fourteenth century onwards, employing formalized diaper grounds with a different pattern on each plane.

This bottle probably retains its original stopper

102 | Cinnabar lacquer

1750-1800
2 3/8 in. (5.6 cm.) high

Of compressed, tapering bulbous form with a flared neck, carved in high relief with two figures at a pavilion entrance on one side, and two female figures, one holding a fan, in a rocky wooded landscape on the other

1936-973

The bottle most comparable to this one is illustrated by Robert Kleiner in *Chinese Snuff Bottles from the Collection of Mary and George Bloch*, No. 196, which depicts scenes from *Liao Zhai zhi yi* (Strange Tales Recorded by the Studio of Idle Talk). There is a strong likelihood that this bottle depicts other scenes from the same tales. If the Blair bottle were a little more rounded in shape, they could almost be a pair.

For other examples, see Hugh Moss, Victor Graham and Ka Bo Tsang, *The Art of the Chinese Snuff Bottle, The J & J Collection*, Nos. 310-312. The authors discuss the possible Palace workshop origins of such bottles at length, by comparison with known Imperial molded porcelain bottles from the Qianlong and Jiaqing reigns with their ubiquitous formalized chrysanthemum stoppers; and similarities to examples in the Imperial Collection in Beijing. Following simple logic, they argue convincingly that:

Carved cinnabar lacquer was popular at the Qing court and was certainly produced there in quantity, and we know the Imperial passion for snuff bottles, yet if we exclude this group, there are no cinnabar lacquer bottles sensibly attributable to the Palace workshops – which must have made them.

This bottle, therefore, probably does represent Palace workshop production and, in common with the Imperial ivories, they were the pattern for much of the porcelain bottle production at Jingdezhen, including the stoppers.

For other examples in this group, see *Masterpieces of Snuff Bottles in the Palace Museum*, Nos. 192-193, the first depicting the Yuan painter Ni Zan, who was fastidious about cleanliness, and the second depicting the story of the calligrapher Wang Xizhi, who drew inspiration in calligraphy from geese; Hugh M. Moss in *Chinese Snuff Bottles*, No. 3; and Helen White, *Snuff Bottles from China, The Victoria and Albert Museum Collection*, Nos. 1-2.

103 | **Cinnabar lacquer**

1770-1840
2 ⁵/₁₆ in. (6 cm.) high

Of compressed, tapering bulbous form, carved in relief with a male and female figure being brought a ewer, presumably with wine, at a pavilion entrance on one side, and a figure carrying books and pulling a cart in a landscape on the other

1936-815 (CB. 523)

See a similar bottle illustrated by Robert W. L. Kleiner, *Chinese Snuff Bottles from the Burghley House Collection, Stamford, England*, No. 134.

104 | **Two-tone Lacquer**

1760-1820
2 ¹/₂ in. (6.3 cm.) high

Of spade shape, carved through black and red lacquer in a continuous scene with two unusual coiling one-clawed dragons amidst clouds on a cinnabar diaper ground, a later silver mount with partially visible stamped seal

1936-831

The bottle is unusually heavy for its size and is almost certainly lacquered over a metal body, now obscured by the later silver neck mount.

In shape and material, if not decoration, this bottle is quite similar to the three previous bottles, Nos. 101-103.

The base has a *shou* character carved on it, not dissimilar to one on a bottle illustrated by Hugh Moss, Victor Graham and Ka Bo Tsang, *The Art of the Chinese Snuff Bottle, The J & J Collection*, No. 310, attributed to the Palace workshops.

The unusual design of coiling one-clawed dragons appears to be unique amongst lacquer bottles. The design might be better compared with glass overlay bottles, upon which indeed it might be based. However, the quality of the carving leaves much to be desired and suggests a nineteenth century production date. It does not appear to be a Japanese copy of the type illustrated, *ibid.*, Nos. 316-317, which uses different colored layers of lacquer to highlight the subject.

105 | *Laque burgauté*

1800-1900, incised Qianlong four-character seal mark, Japanese
2 ³/₄ in. (7 cm.) high

Of large spade shape, decorated on a light lacquered wood ground with two cranes above lotus on one side and a figure gathering lotus in a boat on the other side

1936-809

Provenance: American Art Galleries, New York
The Trowbridge Hall Collection,
22 April 1921, lot 58.
(See fig. 24 in the Introduction).

For a ceramic bottle depicting lotus gatherers and a discussion of the subject, see bottle No. 249 in this collection.

106 | *Laque burgauté*

1800-1900
2 ³/₈ in. (6.1 cm.) high

Each of the two pear-shaped bottles decorated with a six-petalled flower-head diaper ground, one bottle with a chrysanthemum-centered roundel on each side, the other with a stylized butterfly-shaped panel on each side

1936-731-2

1936-731-1

For a similarly decorated bottle almost certainly from the same workshop, see *Zhongguo Biyanhu Zhenshang* (Gems of Chinese Snuff Bottles) No. 425. It is dated to the Guangxu period (1875-1908).

107 | Chinese or Japanese lacquer and *laque burgauté*

1780-1880

2 ⁵/₈ in. (6.6 cm) high

Shaped like an aubergine, with molded leaves at the neck decorated in *laque burgauté*, each petal inlaid with a different flower head or diaper pattern below a thin band and flower heads on a chevron ground

1936-1032 (CB. 512)

For a lengthy discussion on the likely production center for a small group of brown lacquer bottles on a light-weight textile base, see Hugh Moss, Victor Graham and Ka Bo Tsang, *The Art of the Chinese Snuff Bottle, The J & J Collection*, Nos. 306-309.

Fuzhou, Yangzhou, Guangzhou and Beijing were all lacquer-producing cities as, of course, were various centers in Japan and the Ryukyu Islands.

108 | Coral

1770-1820

2 ³/₈ in. (6 cm.) high

Of large rounded rectangular shape, carved in medium relief with a *qilin* in a landscape emitting a cloud of vapor from its mouth supporting a book on one side, and a horse below the sun and clouds on the other side, divided by *lingzhi* and rockwork on the narrow sides

1936-587 (CB. 142)

Provenance: American Art Galleries, New York
The Elizabeth Andrews Collection,
8-9 February 1922, lot 251.
(See fig. 26 in the Introduction.)

For another coral bottle carved with a nearly identical scene of a mythical *qilin* emitting a cloud of vapor supporting a book, see *Chinese Snuff Bottles*, No. 258, later offered at Christie's, New York, 1-2 December 1994, lot 548.

See also Sotheby's, London, 5 December 1983, lots 86 and 87, for two more coral bottles, the second depicting a horse emitting a vapor cloud supporting a *yin-yang* symbol.

For another bottle with a horse on one side, that is almost identical to Blair's, and must surely be from the same workshop, if not the same hand, see Christie's, New York, 2 December 1993, lot 440. The bottle has particularly fine handles on the narrow sides, depicting bats suspending beribboned cash, an unusual feature.

Coral bottles, until the recent publication by Hugh Moss, Victor Graham and Ka Bo Tsang, of *A Treasury of Chinese Snuff Bottles, The Mary and George Bloch Collection*, Vol. 3, Stones other than Jade and Quartz, Nos. 426-435, have been assigned to the organic section of publications on snuff bottles. There are obviously very good reasons for their transfer to the stone section, but too late for practical purposes to apply to this volume.

109 | **Coral**

1850-1900
2 ³/₁₆ in. (5.6 cm.) high

Of tapering rectangular shape, carved in low relief in a continuous scene with the sun setting below waves on one side and a bat and clouds above, the reverse with a carp leaping from the waves emitting a cloud of vapor supporting a temple and a flying stork with a necklace in its beak descending from the shoulder

1936-725 (CB. 143)

For another small coral bottle carved with bats above waves, see Robert W. L. Kleiner, *Chinese Snuff Bottles from the Collection of John Ault*, No. 100.

The subject of bats seems to have been a popular one on coral bottles. In fact, there is a disproportionately high number of examples depicting them, either as the main subject or as a subsidiary part, compared with other subjects.

For numerous other coral bottles with bat subjects, see Hugh Moss, Victor Graham and Ka Bo Tsang, *A Treasury of Chinese Snuff Bottles,*

The Mary and George Bloch Collection, Vol. 3, Stones other than Jade and Quartz, Nos. 427, 430-431, 433 and 435.

For another bottle of slightly earlier date (1820-1850), see Robert Kleiner, *Precious Playthings: Important Chinese Snuff Bottles from the Mack Collection*, No. 71, and a lengthy discussion of coral and its use at court.

The sound of the word for bat, *fu,* can also mean happiness. A bat, *fu,* and clouds, *yun,* can form the rebus *fuyun,* which can be read as 'a hope for good fortune.'

110 | Walrus ivory

1800-1900
2 ⁹/₁₆ in. (6.5 cm.) high

Of rounded rectangular shape, the surface plain but enhanced with a green dye, presumably to imitate jadeite

1936-509 (CB. 4)

For a bottle of similar shape but carved in low relief with animals and trees, see Robert W. L. Kleiner, *Chinese Snuff Bottles from the Collection of John Ault*, No. 108. The author suggests, as is most likely, that the ivory is stained to imitate jadeite. For another example closer to Blair's, see Hugh Moss, *Snuff Bottles of China*, No. 146.

111 | Mother-of-pearl

1850-1900
2 ⁵/₈ in. (6.7 cm.) high

Of melon shape, the lobed elongated body carved in low relief with leafy tendrils and a melon on one side, and a butterfly and leafy tendrils on the other

1936- 855 (CB. 141)

For another example also carved with butterflies and flowers, see *Zhongguo Biyanhu Zhenshang* (Gems of Chinese Snuff Bottles), No. 427. For a rounded bottle carved with Shoulao on one side plus a fish and a bat on the other, see *Snuff Bottles in the Collection of the National Palace Museum*, No. 408; and another very similar to this is illustrated by Robert W. L. Kleiner in *Precious Playthings: Important Chinese Snuff Bottles from the Mack Collection*, No. 72. The author suggests that the group as a whole came out of one workshop, probably in Guangdong, which had a tradition of carving mother-of pearl throughout the Qing dynasty.

Mother-of-pearl has, until the recent publication by Hugh Moss, Victor Graham and Ka Bo Tsang, *A Treasury of Chinese Snuff Bottles, The Mary and George Bloch Collection*, Vol. 3, Stones other than Jade and Quartz, pp. 192-193, been assigned to the organic section of publications on snuff bottles. The new designation under stones is a little surprising, but the authors do address the subject of mother-of-pearl and the ambiguous nature of the material.

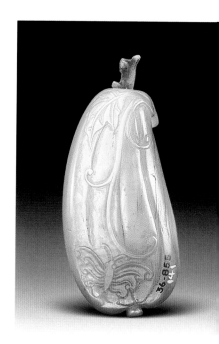

112 | **Pearl-encrusted glass**

1800-1900
1 $^7/_8$ in. (4.8 cm.) high

Of pear shape, the pearls of small and varying size, encrusted in a yellow paste on the clear glass bottle, visible only at the mouth.

1936-1046 (CB. 531)

Literature: Edward Wenham, 'Antiques As Decoration', *Arts & Decoration*, New York, Winter, 1928, illustrated p. 96.

See Helen White, *Snuff Bottles from China, The Victoria and Albert Museum Collection*, fig. 2 for an illustration from the 1850's of a similar bottle. See also another of fruit or pepper shape sold at Christie's, London, The Ko Family Collection, Part VI, 8 November 1976, lot 207. Unfortunately, the material on which the pearls are encrusted is not mentioned in the catalogue entry. Another is illustrated in *Chinese Snuff Bottles* by Suzie and François Lorin, Fall 1997, No. 137, where it is noted that the bottle itself is carved from a single piece of mother-of-pearl, then applied with split pearls on a bee's wax ground.

This bottle might easily have been placed in the embellished glass section of this volume but the immediate reading of it as mother-of-pearl is sufficient reason for placing it in the organic section. See the preceding bottle, No. 111, regarding the 'new' designation of mother-of-pearl under 'stone.' In this case, it would clearly have confused the issue entirely if placed in that section.

113 | **Jet**

1800-1900
2 $^3/_8$ in. (5.6 cm.) high

Of rounded rectangular shape, with plain sides and oval foot

1936-1020 (CB. 158)

For other similar examples, see Sotheby's, New York, Bottles from the Montclair Art Museum, New Jersey, 22 September 1995, lot 182; Christie's, New York, The Rachelle R. Holden Collection, 21 March 2000, lot 186; and Alexander Brody, *Old Wine into Old Bottles, A Collector's Commonplace Book*, p. 122. See also, Schuyler V. R. Cammann, *Substance and Symbol in Chinese Toggles*, p. 79, where the author notes:

> Like amber, this is also a fossilized organic material from ancient trees, rather than a true mineral, but unlike amber it came from the actual wood, being closely related to coal. The Chinese scholars of the medieval period said that pine resin after a thousand years turned into amber, and amber after a thousand years turned into jet, *xi*. Therefore, if amber was a symbol of longevity, this was doubly so.

Glass Bottles

114 | **Glass**

1750-1800
2 ¹/₄ in (5.7 cm.) high

Of faceted octagonal shape, the main sides quartered, the facets rising to the center, the glass with a fine network of crizzling

1936-643 (CB. 262)

This unmarked bottle forms part of a well-documented group of undecorated monochrome glass bottles of faceted shape, which can be dated from incised marks to the reigns of the Yongzheng, Qianlong, Jiaqing, Daoguang, Xianfeng and Tongzhi Emperors.

For another bottle of deep blue color, but with circular panels on the main faces, see Hugh Moss, Victor Graham and Ka Bo Tsang, *The Art of the Chinese Snuff Bottle, The J & J Collection*, No. 332. The authors note that with this particular type of bottle, 'we have a very strong clue to the evolution of the popular faceted Beijing Palace snuff bottles in glass and enamels on metal or glass of the Qianlong period.' A small waterpot and cover, with allover facets cut like a gemstone, are the only pieces of glass in the Beijing Palace Museum with a Kangxi mark (1662-1722), and the mark is *Kangxi yuzhi* ('Made by Imperial command of the Kangxi Emperor'). It is illustrated by Yang Boda in an article, 'An Account of Early Qing Dynasty Glass' in *Scientific Research in Early Chinese Glass*, pp. 131-150, No. 135. At that time the Palace workshops were under the direction of the Westerner, Kilian Stumpf, and European influence in design as well as manufacture is clearly evident in the workshops. Bohemian glass of the seventeenth and eighteenth centuries is well known for faceting, and similarities with early Palace workshop production suggest a clear connection. Faceting became a popular method of decoration from the Yongzheng period onwards. An octagonal fluted vase of similar transparency but blue, bearing a *Yongzheng nianzhi* mark, is also illustrated by Yang Boda, *ibid.*, p. 135, Nos. 3 and 4.

Only one snuff bottle of this type with a Yongzheng mark appears to be published, see Christie's, Hong Kong, The Louise and Christopher Randall Collection, 31 October 1995, lot 1853.

One of the finest and earliest examples of this octagonal monochrome type (though carved with inscriptions) was sold at Christie's, New York, 23 March 1995, lot 165A, and subsequently at Christie's, New York, The Rachelle R. Holden Collection, 21 March 2000, lot 118. The superb quality of the inscriptions, delicate carving, and proportions of the facets, combined with the Qianlong seal mark, indicates high Imperial provenance.

Most glass bottles of octagonal shape have quarter-faceted main faces, as does this one. The majority appear to be of opaque glass, and are usually yellow in color. Translucent bottles are much fewer in number and predominantly ruby-red in color. Some are blue; others, including amethyst, lime green (*Xi hu shui*), and sky-blue are very rare.

For two Jiaqing-marked examples, also translucent, see *Masterpieces of Snuff Bottles in the Palace Museum*, No. 48; another is illustrated by Robert W. L. Kleiner, *Chinese Snuff Bottles from the Collection of John Ault*, No. 12. They are both of slightly compressed form, unlike the more elongated profile of the later bottles. The bottles with Daoguang, Xianfeng and Tongzhi marks are often of opaque glass, though not exclusively. It should also be noted that two other bottles from the Palace Collection in Beijing, one with a Xianfeng mark, the other with a Tongzhi mark, are made from transparent clear glass. The paucity of translucent bottles compared to the surfeit of opaque examples might suggest that the former were preferred by the Imperial Family and inner Court circles while opaque bottles were made for more general Imperial Household usage.

For a later Xianfeng-marked example in amber glass, see *Masterpieces of Snuff Bottles in the Palace Museum*, No. 53.

115 | **Glass**

1770-1850
2 ¹/₂ in. (6.3cm.) high

Of spade shape, carved in relief on one side with Li Po, the drunken poet, resting on a stack of books, a boy assistant and wine container at his side, seven rectangular seals carved on the other side, with fixed-ring mask handles on the shoulders

1936-772 (CB. 261)

The seals carved on this bottle are imitation characters merely forming a decorative pattern.

This is a rare example of a glass bottle very closely imitating dark amethyst. Only one other similar bottle appears to be published, see

Sotheby's, London, The Eric Young Collection, Part III, 24 April 1989, lot 188. Like this bottle, it was made from a heavy dark purple glass and carved in relief on one side with a standing figure with a dog.

116 | **Glass**

1750-1795

2 ³/₈ in. (5.8 cm.) high

Of rounded shape, the mustard-yellow glass carved in low relief on both sides with a single butterfly above a peony, with Imperial-style symmetrical meandering foliage rising up the narrow sides

1936-670

The decoration here is unusual. The symmetric stylized floral decoration can be linked with that of a group of Imperial bottles carved in the Mughal style with European influence; see a jade example illustrated by Robert Hall in *Chinese Snuff Bottles III*, No.17 ; and a red glass example illustrated by Robert Kleiner in *Chinese Snuff Bottles, The White Wings Collection*, No. 50. The peony foliage at the bottom center of the main face can be compared to the decoration on the narrow sides of another Imperial yellow glass bottle with a Qianlong mark from the Dodge Collection, see Sotheby's, New York, 17 March 1997, lot 22. The combination of stylized Mughal decoration carved in such a fine manner, and the use of an Imperial yellow glass surely indicates a Palace workshop provenance.

See also Christie's, Hong Kong, 3 November 1996, lot 655 for a yellow glass bottle similarly carved in a layered effect with confronted dragons replacing the floral decoration of this example, though presumably from the same workshop.

117 | Glass

1750-1800
2 21/32 in. (6.7 cm.)

Of tapering baluster shape, carved with a diagonal diaper pattern on the body and neck between plantain lappets around the foot, mid-body and neck, and an opposing c-scroll band below the shoulders, with bovine masks on the narrow sides

1936-918 (CB. 216)

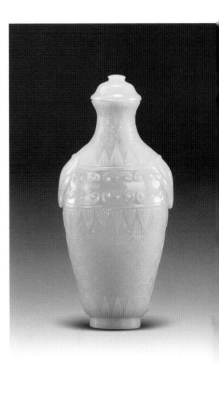

No identical bottle appears to be published; however, this bottle can be associated by color, form, carving and quality of glass to a group of Qianlong-marked bottles and others attributed to the Imperial Palace workshops.

The design of cross-hatching on the body and neck, the central band of c-scrolls and the bovine masks are all borrowed from the patterns to be found on archaic Chinese bronzes and jades, though redefined in a Qing dynasty idiom.

Although the neck has been slightly polished on this bottle, the stopper may well be the original, conforming in shape, as it does, to other Imperial examples, and identical in color and tone to the bottle itself.

An Imperial yellow bottle of baluster form, similarly following an archaic model but carved with phoenix, lappets and *lingzhi*, and attributed to the Palace workshops, is illustrated by Clare Lawrence in *Miniature Masterpieces from the Middle Kingdom, The Monimar Collection of Chinese Snuff Bottles*, No. 111. The author discusses at length the use of the color yellow in the Imperial Court in the eighteenth and nineteenth centuries.

A well-known and widely published Imperial yellow bottle from the Bloch Collection is illustrated in *Chinese Snuff Bottles, A Miniature Art from the Collection of Mary and George Bloch*, No. 63. It has a similar flattened baluster form, but is undecorated save for lion-mask handles on the shoulders. The base is incised with the four-character seal mark *Qianlong nianzhi* ('made in the Qianlong period').

Another baluster-shaped Imperial yellow bottle, plain except for carved mask and ring handles on the shoulders, is illustrated by Robert Hall in *Chinese Snuff Bottles IV*, No. 87.

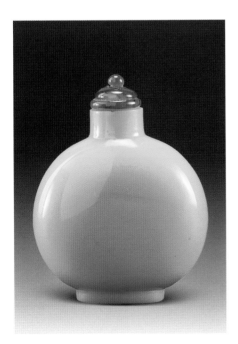

118 | Glass

1790-1880
2 1/4 in. (5.7 cm.) high

Of rounded shape, with oval foot and cylindrical neck, the glass of deep opaque yellow with some minor swirling

1936-914 (CB. 218)

Provenance: Possibly the American Art Galleries, New York
The Yamanaka Sale, 3 February 1921, lot 1.

119 | **Glass**

1750-1800
2 ⁵/₁₆ in (6.1 cm.) high

Of rounded rectangular shape, well carved in very low relief with two sinuous *chilong* amidst dense clouds in a continuous scene

1936-769 (CB. 224)

For another translucent glass bottle carved with squirrels and vine, see Robert Kleiner, *Chinese Snuff Bottles from the Collection of John Ault*, No. 19.

120 | **Glass**

1770-1850
2 ¹/₃₂ in. (5.2 cm.) high

Of rounded shape, delicately carved in low relief with orchids growing from rockwork on one side and *lingzhi* on the other, fixed-ring lion-mask handles on the narrow sides

1936-777 (CB. 225)

For another green glass bottle carved in low relief with insects and flowers, see Sotheby's, New York, The Gerry P. Mack Collection, 25 October 1997, lot 11.

121 | **Glass**

1780-1850
2 ¹³/₃₂ in. (6.1 cm.)

Of translucent lime-green glass, the pear shape carved with a *chilong* climbing up each narrow side, their tails intertwining to form the foot

1936-751 (CB. 226)

For a very similar example, see *Zhongguo Biyanhu Zhenshang* (Gems of Chinese Snuff Bottles), No. 48. For another in blue glass, see Sotheby's, New York, The Gerry P. Mack Collection, 25 October 1997, lot 45. See also *The Au Hang Collection of Chinese Snuff Bottles*, No. 26, where the author explains that these bottles were carved from a solid piece of glass, and not blown as was usually the case.

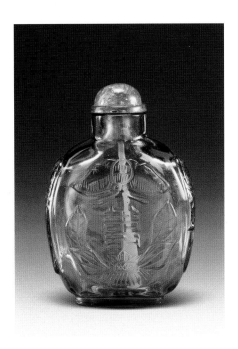

122 | **Glass**

1800-1880
2 ³/₁₆ in. (5.6 cm.) high

Of translucent olive-green glass, the rounded rectangular bottle carved in low relief with a double *shou* character enclosed by a butterfly above and stylized lotus below, the narrow sides with elongated mask and ring handles

1936-737 (CB. 102)

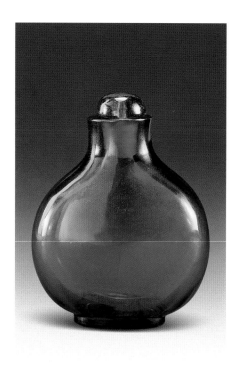

123 | Glass

1908-1911, Xuantong engraved four-character mark on the base and of the period
2 ⁷/₁₆ in. (6.2 cm.) high

Of rounded shape and even tone, the oval foot neatly though shallowly cut

1936-912 (CB. 227)

Bearing a Xuantong mark, this bottle cannot have entered the collection prior to 1908 and probably did so in the late 1920's. However, it does show that Blair was not averse to buying nearly contemporary bottles to strengthen the diversity of his collection.

For a bottle of similar color, though more elongated in shape, bearing a Daoguang four-character mark, see Hugh Moss, Victor Graham and Ka Bo Tsang, *The Art of the Chinese Snuff Bottle, The J & J Collection*, No. 342, where the authors discuss the decline in standards of glass production from the mid-nineteenth century onward.

124 | Glass

1750-1850
2 ¹/₂ in. (6.3 cm.) high

Of rounded shape, the neck cylindrical and very slightly waisted, the foot of flat oval shape, the glass of vibrant dark blue, with some bubbles visible

1936-596 (CB. 20 or 203)

It is unusual to find a glass bottle of so rounded a form. The foot is very simply cut to allow the line of the bottle to remain almost unbroken, in a manner more usually seen on rock crystal bottles.

For deep blue glass bottles of different shapes and bearing Qianlong reign marks, see *Snuff Bottles in the Collection of the National Palace Museum*, Nos. 252-254.

125 | **Glass**

1770-1830
2 ³/₈ in. (6.1 cm) high

Of rounded shape, the glass unusually carved in the Imperial style with archaistic dragon roundels on each side and *chilong* handles on the narrow sides

1936-933 (CB. 204)

The style of carving of the dragon roundels on this bottle is similar to the treatment of a dragon panel on a red glass bottle illustrated by Robert Hall, *Chinese Snuff Bottles II*, No. 79 and might, therefore, be related by workshop to another bottle in this collection, No. 129.

126 | **Glass**

1770-1870
2 ⁵/₈ in. (6.7 cm.) high

Of baluster shape, with flared neck, rounded shoulders and compressed body

1936-206 (CB. 779)

For two semi-translucent monochrome glass bottles of similar shape, see Clare Lawrence, *The Alexander Brody Collection of Chinese Snuff Bottles*, Nos. 124-125. For a bottle of slightly slimmer shape and with handles on the narrow sides, see Sotheby's, New York, 30 May-1 June 1994, lot 635. It is dated to the eighteenth century.

127 | **Glass**

1750-1800
2 ⁵/₈ in. (6.6 cm.) high

Of multi-faceted double gourd shape of strong rich burgundy color, the cylindrical neck flaring slightly

1936-915

For another rare example of a multi-faceted double gourd shaped bottle of amber-colored glass, see Clare Lawrence, *Miniature Masterpieces from the Middle Kingdom, The Monimar Collection of Chinese Snuff Bottles,* No. 104, which she attributes to Beijing production between 1720-1800.

This bottle is possibly a product of the Imperial workshops.

128 | **Glass**

1770-1850
2 ³/₁₆ in. (5.6 cm.) high

Of slightly flattened circular shape with a circular snuff dish carved at the center of each main face, the lateral sides flattened

1936-604 (CB. 184)

For a nearly identical example, see Sotheby's, Hong Kong, 3 November 1994, lot 825.

For another translucent red glass bottle carved with a relief circle on each main face rather than a concave circle to form a snuff dish, see Sotheby's, New York, 17 March 1997, lot 69.

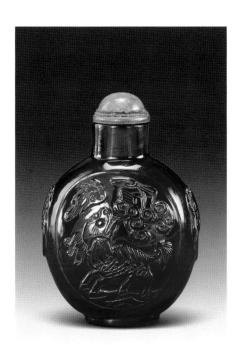

129 | **Glass**

1780-1850
2 ³/₈ in. (6.1 cm.) high

Of rounded shape, carved in low relief with a circular panel on each side, one enclosing horse wading in water, emitting a cloud of vapor from its mouth supporting two fish, all near pine, the other side with a stork flying above a *qilin* with a swirl of vapor from its mouth supporting a book, fixed-ring mask handles at the shoulders

1936-763 (CB. 185)

See another transparent red glass bottle illustrated by Robert Hall, *Chinese Snuff Bottles II*, No. 79 and formerly in the Marian Mayer Collection; and another in amber glass sold at Sotheby's, New York, The Gerry P. Mack Collection, 25 October 1997, lot 5.

The unique and idiosyncratic carving of the clouds of vapor emerging from the mouths of these animals is mirrored in the treatment of the tails of the *chilong* carved on the Hall bottle and the phoenix carved on the Mack bottle. Undoubtedly they must be from the same workshop, if not from the same hand.

130 | **Glass**

1800-1880
2 ⁵/₃₂ in. (5.5 cm.) high

Of rounded rectangular shape, unusually carved with pierced *chilong* handles from the shoulder to the foot, the main sides plain

1936-742

For another glass bottle similarly carved with *chilong* on the narrow sides, see Christie's, South Kensington, The Gerry P. Mack Collection, 4 October 1999, lot 175.

131 | Glass

1770-1850
2 ³/₁₆ in. (5.6 cm.) high

Opaque white glass of baluster shape, carved in relief as a wine container enclosed in a rope-twist basket with ring handles at the shoulder

1936-767 (CB. 241)

Literature: Edward Wenham, 'Antiques As Decoration'. *Arts & Decoration*, New York, Winter, 1928, illustrated p. 96.

Though the model for this bottle is well known in porcelain from Jingdezhen, this appears to be the only known example in glass.

A porcelain bottle molded in the form of a wine jar, with weaving to imitate bamboo, was sold by Sotheby's, Hong Kong, 3 November 1994, lot 1032. It bore the inscription *Zhuang Yuan Hong*, the name of a popular rice wine, which is also a rebus for achieving top honors in the Imperial Examinations at the Hanlin Academy. For other porcelain examples, see Sotheby's, New York, The Janos Szekeres Collection, 27 October 1986, lot 2; and *Hidden Treasures of the Dragon* by Humphrey K. F. Hui, Margaret Polak, and Christopher C. H. Sin, No. 292.

A blue and white porcelain bottle of slightly different form was sold at Christie's, New York, The Reif Collection, 18 October 1993, lot 42, bearing various calligraphic cartouches, including the name of a wine shop, *Fuxing laodian,* and the characters *chen jiu* ('old wine') below further characters *Zhe Shao* (Shaoxing County – Zhejiang), a province famous for wine production.

For a much larger vase of similar design with calligraphic panels referring to Zhaoxing wine, see Gunhild Avitabile, *Vom Schatz der Drachen: Chinesisches Porzellan des 19, und 20, Jahrhunderts aus der Sammlung Weishaupt* (From the Dragon's Treasure: Chinese Porcelain from the 19ᵗʰ and 20ᵗʰ Centuries in the Weishaupt Collection), p. 41, fig. 35.

132 | Glass

1800-1880
2 ⁵/₁₆ in. (5.9 cm.) high

Blush-pink glass, of circular shape, carved in relief with a central flower head surrounded by swirling petals, probably depicting peony, the narrow edges deeply grooved with fine c-scrolls

1936-636 (CB. 259)

The naturalistic color of this glass definitely suggests that the flower depicted is indeed a peony. For a similar bottle in clear glass but with the addition of stiff leaves carved around the neck, see Robert W. L. Kleiner, *Chinese Snuff Bottles, The White Wings Collection*, No. 52.

For another bottle carved with the same flower head on the center of each side listed as depicting a mallow, see Hugh Moss, Victor Graham and Ka Bo Tsang, *The Art of the Chinese Snuff Bottle, The J & J Collection*, No. 357. The authors add the caveat that 'the identification with the mallow seems, although well established, tenuous, since mallows have five petals rather than six.'

For an uncarved rounded bottle of similar color, see *ibid.*, p. 552, No. 327, where it is noted that the distinctive pink coloring is achieved by sandwiching a brightly mottled layer of pink glass between two milky white layers. The authors also suggest a possible Shandong glass provenance.

For other examples of different shape but presumably from the same workshop, Robert Hall, *Chinese Snuff Bottles IV*, No. 91; and *Chinese Snuff Bottles II*, No. 77, which is carved with stylized bamboo on the narrow sides and a convex snuff dish on each of the main faces.

133 | **Glass**

1850-1920
2 ⁷/₁₆ in. (6.2 cm.) high

Of eggplant shape, the opaque white bottle very finely painted in a mixture of pink and blue strokes or splashes, forming a very natural looking aubergine, the calyx formed by the application of molten green glass to the surface around the neck

1936-781 (CB. 279)

There are very few recorded glass snuff bottles in this shape, which was usually carved in nephrite. See *Snuff Bottles in the Collection of the National Palace Museum,* No. 115 for a matched set of ten nephrite bottles, and No. 112 for another matched set of ten bottles listed as glass, but with an uncanny resemblance to white nephrite with spinach-green nephrite calyxes and, in fact, included in the 'Jade' section of the catalogue.

The glass example illustrated by Hugh M. Moss in *Chinese Snuff Bottles,* No. 235, also has a glass calyx; however, in the example illustrated by Robert Hall in *Chinese Snuff Bottles,* No. 86, the bottle is white glass, but the calyx is made of carved green nephrite which was then applied to the neck. This same bottle is also shown by Robert Kleiner as No. 149 in *Chinese Snuff Bottles in the Collection of Mary and George Bloch,* where the author indicates that although both glass and nephrite examples may have come from the same workshop, the known glass examples have a flattened base, enabling them to stand, whereas all the nephrite examples taper naturally to a point.

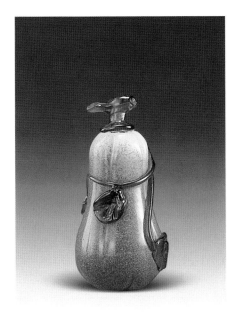

134 | **Glass**

1850-1900
1 ⁷/₈ in. (4.8 cm.) high

Shaped as a melon and painted in mottled yellow and orange with trailing green glass tendrils and leaves

1936-615 (CB. 278)

For another glass bottle of fruit shape with molten glass stems and leaves, see Humphrey K. F. Hui and Christopher C. H. Sin, *An Imperial Qing Tradition,* No. 141. It depicts a finger citron, but the tendrils and leaves are produced in the same manner.

A peach-shaped example is illustrated by Humphrey K. F. Hui, Margaret Polak, and Christopher C. H. Sin in *Hidden Treasures of the Dragon,* No. 151.

135 | **Glass**

1800-1900
3 ³/₈ in. (8.5 cm.) high

Naturalistically modeled and carved with scales and fins on the transparent top green layer, the interior of white glass mottled with aubergine spots

1936-970 (CB. 281)

A small group of glass bottles depicting fish is known. Most are of deep red glass, some use red glass overlay, and others blue glass overlay. Most have a split fan tail.

There appear to be only two recorded bottles of this type, which use green and milky white glass with aubergine or purple splashes and the more unusual rounded tail. The other was sold at Sotheby's, New York, The Dr. Paula Hallett Collection, 2 December 1985, lot 22 and dated to the eighteenth century.

For dark red glass examples, see Bob C. Stevens, *The Collector's Book of Snuff Bottles*, No. 180; Sotheby's, London, 24 April 1989, lot 337; and Sotheby's, New York, 1 July 1985, lot 61, formerly in the Collections of Gertrude Stuart and then Elizabeth and Ladislas Kardos.

For red overlay examples, see Hugh M. Moss in *Chinese Snuff Bottles*, No. 209; and *Chinese Snuff Bottles, A Miniature Art from the Collection of Mary and George Bloch*, No. 108.

136 | **Enamels on glass**

1723-1735, Yongzheng four-character seal mark in pink enamel on the base, and of the period
1 ³/₄ in. (4.5 cm.) high

Of octagonal shape with slightly swelling main faces, painted with two quail beneath chrysanthemum sprays on one side and three geese on a riverbank, another flying above, near peony on the other side, the faceted narrow sides each painted with a single stylized flower head, possibly mallow or camellia, alternately painted in pink and blue with stylized green foliage floral scrolls on a lemon-yellow ground, the cylindrical neck with blue *leiwen* on a yellow ground

1936-752 (CB. 230)

Literature: Edward Wenham, 'Antiques As Decoration'. *Arts & Decoration*, New York, Winter, 1928, illustrated p. 96.

For a thorough discussion of this rare group of enameled opaque glass bottles, see Hugh Moss, Victor Graham and Ka Bo Tsang, *The Art of the Chinese Snuff Bottle, The J & J Collection*, No. 185. The authors note that the unusual octagonal form unquestionably derived from European watches imported into China during the Kangxi to Qianlong periods, presumably reaching the Chinese Court in some quantities during the early Qing dynasty through the Jesuits.

The authors discuss the rarity of enameled glass bottles and draw the conclusion that the technical results of enamel on porcelain so far surpassed that of glass enameling that, regardless of the aesthetic outcome, the court enamelers stuck to the most technically competent results. They also suggest that there was a higher ratio of complete failures, or at least unacceptable results, that inhibited glass production.

The inclusion of the Yongzheng mark and the quality of the enameling, (sadly worn on the main faces however) firmly place this bottle as being of Imperial production and presumably the Imperial workshop situated inside the Palace, connected to the enameling workshops nearby.

The undecorated opaque glass bottle was sent to the enameling workshop for the addition of the color. At some point in the Yongzheng reign, the Emperor ordered the Imperial glassworks to be moved to his newly constructed palace, Yuanming Yuan, a few miles to the west of the capital, Beijing. At this time, it is impossible to be certain at which workshop this particular bottle originated. However, it is interesting to note information provided by the archives of the Imperial workshops from the Yongzheng period as quoted by Chang Lin-sheng 'Ch'ing Dynasty Imperial Enameled Glassware, *Arts of Asia*, May-June, 1991, p. 107, where the author mentions the submission of an opaque white glass bottle from the Yuanming Yuan to the Yongzheng Emperor. The Imperial response was positive but asked that the base be shaved (presumably the footrim) and that enamel colors be added.

There are very few surviving Imperial enameled opaque octagonal glass bottles, perhaps no more than ten. Most bear Qianlong marks and are usually decorated with European motifs. Surprisingly, the published example most similar to this one is not glass, but an exceptionally fine and rare enameled porcelain bottle, which was formerly in the collection of Joseph Baruch Silver, see Sotheby's, New York, 6 April 1990, lot 61; and Sotheby's,

New York, 19 September 2001, lot 238. (rescheduled to 15 October 2001 after the World Trade Center attacks). This rare and superb bottle has a Yongzheng mark, and is decorated with Chinese subject matter on the main faces, depicting birds perched on the bough of a tree, overhanging peonies springing from rockwork on one side, and bamboo, orchid, foxglove and *lingzhi* on the other. The faceted sides are similarly painted with stylized flower heads on a yellow ground, and it also has a band of *leiwen* around the cylindrical neck. Even the main faces have the addition of a dark blue enamel border, and the four-character mark is in pink enamel within a shaped panel on the base. In fact, if it were not for the difference in the material of these two bottles, it would be easy to surmise that they once formed part of a set from the same workshop.

The closest examples in glass all appear to date to the Qianlong period and most bear wheel-cut Qianlong marks. For two examples with Chinese-subject decoration, see Helen White, *Snuff Bottles from China, The Victoria and Albert Museum Collection*, pp. 134-135, pl. 59, and another illustrated by Bob C. Stevens, *The Collector's Book of Snuff Bottles*, No. 972. It depicts figures in a wooded landscape and is unmarked. Another is illustrated in *Masterpieces of Snuff Bottles in the Palace Museum*, No. 100, and is painted with two coiling *chilong* on a densely dotted ground to each side. It bears an incised Qianlong mark.

For two examples with European-subject decoration, see Hugh Moss, Victor Graham and Ka Bo Tsang, *op. cit.*, Vol. I, No. 185 and also illustrated by Bob C. Stevens, *op. cit.*, Nos. 977-978. It is painted with a European lady and child on each of the main faces, and with a European landscape scene dividing the floral octagonal panels on the narrow sides.

A fascinating comparison can be made with the decoration on a Qianlong-marked Imperial Beijing enamel and gilt-bronze octagonal two-tiered box and cover, made to hold a winter inkstone, which sold at Christie's, Hong Kong, 22-23 March 1993, lot 567. The cover was painted with geese and quail in a landscape setting very similar to this one, was octagonal and edged in blue enamel, and the sides painted with flowers on a yellow ground with further blue edging. It is very tempting to suggest that the makers of the Beijing Palace workshop box based their design on this bottle or another Yongzheng object of octagonal shape in the Palace collection.

The subject is also seen on a Yongzheng-marked *famille rose* porcelain cup now in the Chang Foundation, Taipei and illustrated by Soame Jenyns, *Later Chinese Porcelain, The Ch'ing Dynasty*, pl. XXXIV, fig. 1a.

137 | Enamels on glass

1730-1790, *Guyuexuan* iron-red mark on the base
2 ¼ in. (5.7 cm.) high

Of rounded shape, molded and painted in a continuous scene with four magpies and branches of a prunus above painted, but not molded, bamboo

1936-784 (CB. 231)

Literature: Edward Wenham, 'Antiques As Decoration', *Arts & Decoration*, New York, Winter, 1928, illustrated p. 96.

The most comparable example of this well-known group of *Guyuexuan* ('Ancient Moon Pavilion'), molded and enameled glass bottles is illustrated by Hugh Moss, Victor Graham and Ka Bo Tsang, *The Art of the Chinese Snuff Bottle, The J & J Collection*, No. 204. It is nearly identical in subject with slight variances in small details but is lacking the delightful addition of the painted bamboo on one side of this example.

The name *Guyuexuan* is to be found inscribed in iron-red on the foot of a large number of bottles of this type. The name has long been shrouded in mystery; however, the discovery by Hugh Moss of a bottle credibly dated to 1767 and bearing a maker's name Hu Xuan (the family name can be split into two components *gu* and *yue*) suggests that the term came about as a result of this enameler's works.

For another molded bottle also depicting magpies amidst prunus but less finely molded and detailed, see Humphrey K. F. Hui and Christopher C. H. Sin, *An Imperial Qing Tradition*, No. 178 from the collection of Christopher Sin; and also illustrated by Christie's, New York, November 27, 1991, lot 102. For a further example of this group, unmolded but painted with the same subject matter, see Robert Hall, *Chinese Snuff Bottles II*, No. 65.

The subject of prunus and magpies is a popular one. According to Hugh Moss, Victor Graham and Ka Bo Tsang, *op. cit.*, No. 204, this particular prunus is known as 'wax plum' because of its wax-like petals. Magpies are birds of joy or happiness and, depending on the number, they convey good wishes for each month of the year, each day of the month, etc. The combination of wax-plum blossoms and magpies forms a rebus *xi shang mei shao* 'happiness up to one's eyebrows.' It can also be from the rebus *xi que deng mei* which can be read as 'the announcement of good news'.

138 | **Enamels on glass**

1750-1820, *Guyuexuan* iron-red mark on the base
2 ⁵/₁₆ in. (5.9 cm.) high

Of ovoid shape, molded and then enameled in a continuous scene with an eagle standing on rockwork with bamboo below pine looking over its shoulder at a multi-colored cloud of vapor supporting the 'moon', which is inscribed in iron-red with the character *yue* 'moon'

1936-656 (CB. 232)

See the preceding bottle for a short description of the *Guyuexuan* group.

In Chinese, the words for 'hero' and 'eagle' have the same pronunciation. Thus an eagle often represents a hero. An eagle standing alone can form the rebus *Ying xiong du li*, meaning 'a hero of free and independent spirit'

Only one other example of this particular design appears to be published, see Sotheby's, New York, The Neal W. and Frances R. Hunter Collection, 15 September 1998, lot 15.

This bottle, like the preceding bottle, No. 137, has enameling on the molded or carved areas, as well as on the plain surface. For a discussion of this particular feature, see Hugh Moss, Victor Graham and Ka Bo Tsang, *The Art of the Chinese Snuff Bottle, The J & J Collection*, No. 202, where the authors note that this requires close cooperation between the glass and the enamel workshops. The design of the molding would have been meaningless without the enamel and therefore must be seen as a collaboration. Such a collaboration would have been unusual amongst private workshops and therefore a Palace workshop provenance is proposed.

139 | **Enamels on glass**

1780-1880
2 1/4 in. (5.7 cm.) high

Shaped as a double gourd with the lower section fluted, each lobe painted in *famille rose* enamels with one of the eight Daoist emblems on a tassel suspended from the upper gourd, below *ruyi* heads and a band of *leiwen* encircling the neck

1936-504 (CB. 229)

A similarly decorated bottle is illustrated in *Chinese Snuff Bottles*, No. 59. The same bottle is illustrated in *The Art of the Chinese Snuff Bottle, The J & J Collection*, No. 193. It too is lobed in eight sections, although of baluster shape rather than double gourd, and bears an unusual *Da Qing Nian Zhi* ('Made during the Qing dynasty') four-character mark. The authors suggest, persuasively, that some time between the Qianlong Emperor's abdication in 1795 and his death in 1799 would be a likely date of production.

They also argue convincingly for a strong link with the *Guyuexuan* group by comparing the tasseled decoration on other *Guyuexuan*-marked bottles in both glass and porcelain. A Palace attribution is also considered on stylistic comparison with other known later Palace enamels still in the Imperial Collection, Beijing, see *Biyanhu Shihua* (History of Snuff Bottles) pl. 44.

For another lobed baluster-shaped bottle decorated with the eight Buddhist emblems and bearing a *Guyuexuan* mark, see *Zhongguo Biyanhu Zhenshang* (Gems of Chinese Snuff Bottles), No. 107.

The tasseled decoration can be traced back to Ming dynasty ceramics, particularly those of the Jiajing reign (1522-1566). For various examples, see Christie's, 2 June 1994, lot 284, for jeweled objects on the neck of a *fahua meiping*, and Christie's, New York, 28 March 1996, lot 343, on the neck of a blue and white vase.

140 | **Enamels on glass**

1780-1880, Qianlong iron-red four-character mark
1 7/8 in. (4.8 cm.) high

Of double gourd shape, painted with a continuous design of rose or peony on the upper gourd, and chrysanthemum, morning-glory, pinks, peony and orchid on the lower gourd

1936-922 (CB. 228)

For another similar double gourd bottle with a continuous design of flowers on both the upper and lower sections and bearing a *Guyuexuan* mark, see Sotheby's, New York, The Neal W. and Frances R. Hunter Collection, 15 September 1998, lot 38.

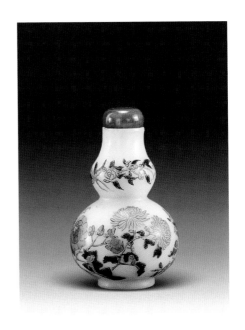

141 | Glass, overlay

1750-1800
2 ¹/₁₆ in. (5.3 cm.) high

Of oval shape, the yellow overlay carved with a dragonfly above finger-citrus on one side, and a spray of peach, pomegranate and finger-citrus on the other, on a realgar-like swirling transparent pale amber ground

1936-627 (CB. 274)

For another example of this fairly rare subject but with the addition of a blue overlay and a bat replacing the dragonfly of this bottle, see Christie's, New York, The Rachelle R. Holden Collection, 21 March 2000, lot 84.

In shape and style the bottle bears comparison with a well-known group of the multi-colored overlay bottles carved with butterflies and flowers, see *Snuff Bottles in the Collection of the National Palace Museum*, Nos. 309-311.

The peach, pomegranate and finger-citrus, *sanduo*, represent the 'three abundances': happiness, longevity and male offspring. See also another bottle in this collection, No. 191.

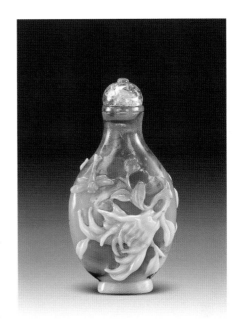

142 | Glass, overlay

1780-1850
2 ⁵/₈ in. (6.1 cm.)

Of rounded shape, carved through the variously beige-colored overlays in a continuous scene with a horse and buffalo below sterculia on one side, and a dog, a cockerel, a pig and a small building on the other, below pine, a goat and rockwork on one narrow side

1936-910 (CB. 268)

The subject, five of the twelve zodiac animals, suggests that this bottle once formed a set with others depicting the remaining animals, the rat, tiger, hare, dragon, snake, monkey, and goat.

143 | **Glass, overlay**

1750-1800
2 ⅜ in. (6 cm.) high

Of oval form, carved through the translucent amber overlay with two Imperial style descending dragons on a lemon-yellow ground, joined at their tails on each side and divided by mask handles on the shoulders

1936-766 (CB. 211)

Literature: Edward Wenham, 'Antiques As Decoration', *Arts & Decoration*, New York, Winter, 1928, illustrated p. 96.

For another translucent yellow overlay example carved with a *shou* character between the dragons, see Hugh M. Moss, *Snuff Bottles of China*, No. 221.

A milky-white glass bottle with red overlay dragons is illustrated by Robert Kleiner in *Chinese Snuff Bottles from the Collection of Mary and George Bloch*, No. 158, where it is attributed to the Beijing Palace workshops.

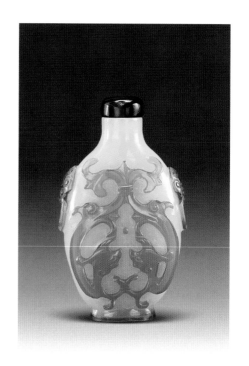

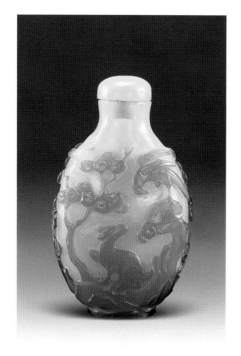

144 | **Glass, overlay**

1780-1850
2 ½ in. (6.3 cm.) high

Of ovoid shape, with the layer of transparent orange overlay on an opaque yellow ground carved in a continuous scene with a deer under pine on one side and a hawk on rockwork above a seated animal with a dog-like appearance, but presumably a bear, on the other

1936-540

The scene of a hawk or eagle above a bear is the symbol of a brave warrior. The bear in this example has been treated in a rather cursory manner by the craftsman who either misunderstood his brief or was simply unaware of the features of such an animal.

For a very similar example in cinnabar-red overlay on an opaque white ground, see Robert Hall, *Chinese Snuff Bottles II*, No. 103, where the bear also has an uncharacteristic dog-like appearance.

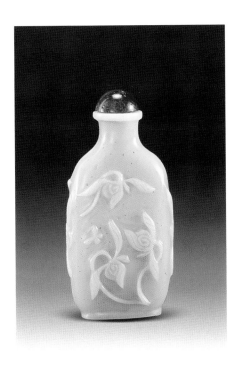

145 | Glass, overlay

1800-1850, Yangzhou Seal School
2 ³/₈ in. (6 cm.) high

Of rounded rectangular shape, carved with the layer of opaque white on lemon-yellow ground, orchid sprays on each of the main faces, a small butterfly to one side

1936-501 (CB. 215)

For a pear-shaped bottle with a very similar subject of loose flower sprays and two butterflies in pale turquoise-blue overlay on an opaque white ground, see Robert Hall, *Chinese Snuff Bottles IV*, No. 113. They are identified as lily sprays and it is suggested that it might have been intended as a gift for a troubled recipient. Whilst this might be the case, an identification as orchid seems more likely. For another example of rounded shape, see Christie's, New York, The Rachelle R. Holden Collection, 21 March 2000, lot 86. See also the discussion on orchids in the note under another bottle in this collection, No. 171.

146 | Glass, overlay

1780-1850
2 ⁷/₁₆ in. (6.2 cm.) high

Of rounded shape, the black overlay carved with a continuous scene of a crane above a deer and pine on one side and a hawk standing on pine above *lingzhi* and a dog-like animal, presumably a bear, on the other

1936-515 (CB. 214)

See bottle No. 144.

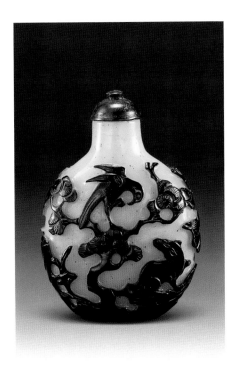

147 | Glass, overlay

1780-1850, Yangzhou Seal School
3 in. (7.6 cm.) high

Of cylindrical shape, carved through the pale red overlay in a continuous scene with two female Immortals amidst clouds below a crescent moon above, a scholar-warrior preparing for battle below a six-character inscription and seal

1936-921 (CB. 208)

Literature: Edward Wenham, 'Antiques As Decoration', *Arts & Decoration*, New York, Winter, 1928, illustrated p. 96.

The inscription is an auspicious idiom, *Da fu gui yi shou kao*, which can be read as 'extreme wealth, nobility and longevity'.

The seals read, *Ji Xiang*, an auspicious inscription.

This bottle bears comparison with another of different shape but identical color, signed by Li Junting and cyclically dated to 1823. It is illustrated by Robert Kleiner in *Treasures from the Sanctum of Enlightened Respect: Chinese Snuff Bottles from the Denis Low Collection*, No. 131. It certainly confirms a Yangzhou seal school attribution and perhaps even an attribution to the Li Junting workshops, if not to the master himself.

148 | **Glass, overlay**

1750-1800
2 ³/₄ in. (7 cm.) high

Of oval shape, very finely carved through the blue overlay with orchids and rockwork on one side, and two ducks amidst lotus and millet above waves on the other, divided by finely detailed lion-mask handles

1936-776 (CB. 20)

For a bubble-suffused bottle very similarly carved with orchids and rockwork but with a blue overlay of much paler tone, see Sotheby's, Honolulu, The Bob C. Stevens Collection, Part I, 7 November 1981, lot 50.

For another superb rendering of orchids and rockwork on a bottle of very similar shape, see Christie's, New York, The Reif Collection, 18 October 1993, lot 177.

For a discussion on early glass overlays pertinent to this bottle, see Hugh Moss, Victor Graham and Ka Bo Tsang, *The Art of the Chinese Snuff Bottle, The J & J Collection*, No. 363, where the authors note that the characteristics of the early overlays are 'impeccable formal integrity, vibrant color and superbly confident design and carving. The relief is usually well rounded and realistically three-dimensional.' This bottle bears all these traits.

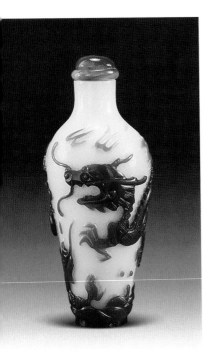

149 | **Glass, overlay**

1730-1790
2 ³/₄ in. (7 cm.) high

Of slender baluster shape, the blue overlay carved in a continuous scene with a four-clawed dragon chasing a flaming pearl amidst fire-scrolls, another dragon rising from breaking waves below

1936-938 (CB. 185)

For a red overlay bottle of similar design, see Helen White, *Snuff Bottles from China, The Victoria and Albert Museum Collection*, pl. 78, No. 5, which formed part of the Salting Bequest to the British Nation in 1910, and which the author dated between 1736-1850. For another of slightly more oval shape, carved through a sapphire-blue overlay with a *chilong* amidst scrolls above rocks, and bearing a wheel-cut Qianlong four-character mark on the oval foot, see Robert Hall, in *Chinese Snuff Bottles II*, No. 61; and, *ibid.*, No. 59 for another of more rounded shape.

The shape of this bottle with its high sloped shoulders and tapering cylindrical body is reminiscent of both Imperial clear glass and jade bottles from the reign of the Qianlong Emperor. For examples in jade, see Christie's, New York, The Reif Collection, 18 October 1993, lot 69; Robert Kleiner in *Chinese Snuff Bottles from the Collection of Mary and George Bloch*, No. 24. For a clear amethyst glass example, see Hugh Moss, Victor Graham and Ka Bo Tsang, *The Art of the Chinese Snuff Bottle, The J & J Collection*, No. 331.

150 | **Glass, overlay**

1750-1800
2 ¹/₂ in. (6.4 cm.) high

Of rounded shape, superbly carved through the blue overlay with a deer and stag on one side and two cranes on the other, each below peach and pine rising from rockwork with *lingzhi* on the narrow sides

1936-923 (CB. 194)

For a red overlay of similar shape and the same subject matter, see Robert W. L. Kleiner, *Treasures from the Sanctum of Enlightened Respect: Chinese Snuff Bottles from the Denis Low Collection*, No. 95. It is attributed to the Beijing Palace workshops, 1740-1800. Both bottles share a well-spaced comfortably-fitting composition.

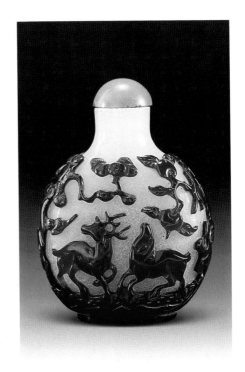

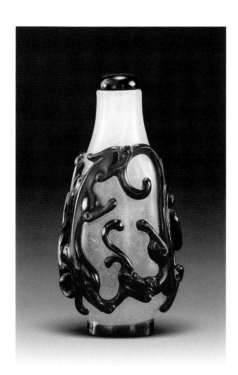

151 | Glass, overlay

1750-1820
2 ⁷/₈ in. (7.3 cm.) high

Of slender pear shape, delicately carved through the blue overlay with two coiling *chilong* on each side biting each other's tail

1936-924 (CB. 195)

For a similar bottle, differing only in the use of a clear glass ground rather than the semi-transparent ground of this example, see Robert Hall, *Chinese Snuff Bottles II*, No. 114, formerly in the Marian Mayer Collection. The author attributes the bottle to the Beijing Palace workshops, and dates it to 1710-95. He characterizes the group by the use of brilliant sapphire-blue overlay on a lightly crizzled clear glass in combination with the popular Palace motif of dragons carved with superb freedom.

For another example on a bubble-suffused ground but of rounded shape, see Hugh Moss, *Chinese Snuff Bottles*, No. 192. See also, Christie's, Hong Kong, The Louise and Christopher Randall Collection, 31 October 1995, lot 1885.

152 | Glass, overlay

1770-1850
2 ³/₄ in. (7 cm.) high

Of rounded rectangular shape, the pale blue overlay carved with prunus trees growing from rockwork over a swirling pink and white ground

1936-773 (CB. 258)

Literature: Edward Wenham, 'Antiques As Decoration', *Arts & Decoration*, New York, Winter, 1928, illustrated p. 96.

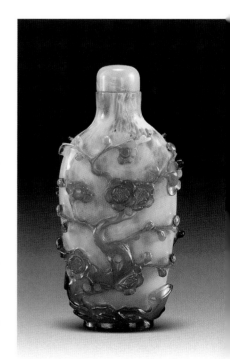

The combination of colors, blue on a pink and white ground, is highly unusual but surprisingly satisfying. The craftsman has made full use of the overlay to produce an exceedingly well balanced design.

For a smaller bottle with the same subject but in white overlay on a pink-blush ground, see Christie's, New York, The Reif Collection, 18 October 1993, lot 181; and another with blue overlay on a white ground sold at Sotheby's, London, The Baronesses Sapuppo and d'Essen Collection, 14 November 2000, lot 37. For a bottle of very similar shape and design but carved from a green overlay on a coffee-colored ground, see Robert Hall, *Chinese Snuff Bottles II*, No. 104.

For a smaller rounded bottle with a more unusual bubble-suffused ground depicting the same subject, see Sotheby's, New York, 17 March 1997, lot 47, formerly in the Arthur Loveless Collection, Seattle. For another red overlay opaque white glass bottle also depicting prunus, see Robert Kliener, *Treasures from the Sanctum of Enlightened Respect: Chinese Snuff Bottles from the Denis Low Collection*, No. 89.

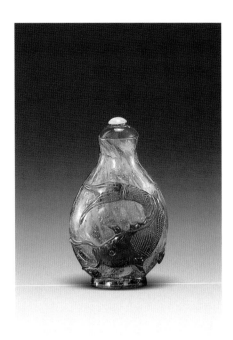

153 | Glass, overlay

1770-1830
1 ³/₄ in. (4.5 cm.) high

Of pear shape, the translucent blue overlay carved with a carp on each side on a swirling glass ground with mottled colored splashes including aventurine

1936-735 (CB. 246)

For a very similar bottle depicting two fish on each side, see Sotheby's, London, The Eric Young Collection, Part II, 13 October 1987, lot 47.

The single fish on each side of this bottle forms the rebus, *xijian dali,* which can mean 'happy to see good fortune'.

154 | Glass, overlay

1780-1850
2 ³/₁₆ in. (5.5 cm.) high

Of rounded shape, carved through the blue overlay with a boggle-eyed fan-tailed fish amongst fronds on each side above waves, the interior crizzled throughout

1936-771

Literature: Edward Wenham, 'Antiques As Decoration', *Arts & Decoration,* New York, Winter, 1928, illustrated p. 96.

For a bottle of similar type with the fish filling more of the surface, see Sotheby's, New York, The Neil W. and Francis R. Hunter Collection, 15 September 1998, lot 137.

Another with a crizzled clear glass ground, attributed to the Beijing Palace workshops, is illustrated by Robert W. L. Kleiner in *Chinese Snuff Bottles from the Collection of Mary and George Bloch,* No. 88.

155 | Glass, overlay

1780-1850
2 ¹/₂ in. (6.4 cm.) high

Of compressed baluster shape, the blue overlay carved with a continuous design of numerous joined fruit or floral roundels reminiscent of Japanese *mon* on the body and rounded shoulder, the base also unusually carved in overlay with a coiling dragon

1936-943 (CB. 187)

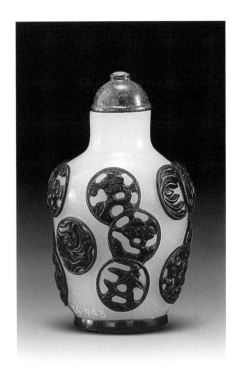

The various roundels each depict a single fruit, plant, flower, or insect. Some are independent roundels and others are joined at their edges. The single roundels are an orchid, a stylized peony or camellia, and a daisy or chrysanthemum. The conjoined single roundels include chrysanthemum, butterfly and melon; *lingzhi*, pomegranate and gourd; begonia, prunus and orchid; pomegranate, peach, and finger-citrus; lotus and peony; prunus, pine and bamboo.

For a very similar example in blue overlay but of slightly more cylindrical shape, see Robert Kleiner, *Treasures from the Sanctum of Enlightened Respect: Chinese Snuff Bottles from the Denis Low Collection*, No. 101, and previously

sold at Christie's, New York, 25 March 1998, lot 313. Another, formerly in The Dr. Paula Hallett Collection, sold at Sotheby's, New York, 2 December 1985, lot 25.

The design, which is clearly based on the Japanese *mon*, a noble floral crest, is found in porcelains of the Yongzheng and Qianlong periods and, though rare, obviously appealed to Imperial taste. See Christie's, Hong Kong, 30 April–2 May, 1995, lot 669, for a pair of Yongzheng-marked porcelain bowls with floral medallions in clusters and also an unmarked baluster jar with similar decoration, painted in *doucai* (contrasting) enamels in the Palace Museum, Beijing, illustrated in *Kangxi, Yongzheng, Qianlong - Qing Porcelain in the Palace Museum Collection*, p. 216, pl. 45.

Snuff bottles with this design, however, are quite rare. Another enameled glass example is illustrated by Robert Kleiner in *Chinese Snuff Bottles in the Collection of Mary and George Bloch*, No. 26; and another rare *doucai* porcelain example, sold at Sotheby's, New York, The Janos Szekeres Collection, 5 June 1987, lot 18.

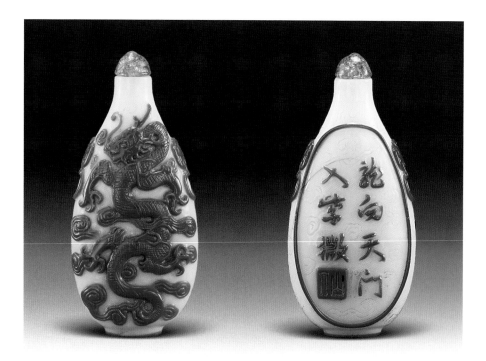

156 | **Glass, overlay**

1760-1840
3 in. (7.6 cm.) high

Of pear shape, carved through the blue overlay with an ascending three-clawed dragon amidst clouds on one side and a seven-character inscription followed by a seal within an oval panel on the other, the narrow sides and reverse panel lightly incised with cloud scrolls

1936-993 (CB. 189)

The inscription, *long xian tian men ru zi hui,* can be read as 'The dragon approaches the heavenly gate leading to the Purple Palace'. The seal *shan ren* can be read as 'recluse' or 'hermit'. The characters *zi hui* can also mean 'morning glory' as in a sunrise.

No comparable bottle appears to be published. A bottle of flattened cylindrical shape, carved through a single green overlay on an opaque white ground with orchids growing from rockwork, and a relief five-character inscription which can be read as 'the (reflection of the)

moon in the water is exceedingly pure and beautiful' followed by the name *Jiting,* is illustrated by Hugh Moss, Victor Graham and Ka Bo Tsang, *The Art of the Chinese Snuff Bottle, The J & J Collection,* No. 396.

In terms of quality of carving, depth of overlay, style of calligraphy and general aesthetic, it is similar to this example. Both it and Blair's are confident bottles, but do not fit comfortably into any particular group. Both do, however, bear hints of the Yangzhou Seal school.

157 | **Glass, overlay**

1840-1880
2 ³/₈ in. (6 cm.) high

Of rounded shape, the violet-blue overlay carved with a bat above a stylized *shou* character within a *leiwen* band on each side, the bats' wings partly forming the handles to the narrow sides which include a lozenge above a long-life Buddhist swastika

1936-553 (CB. 198)

For another example using the same colors but of slightly more simplistic design, see Sotheby's, Hong Kong, 3 November 1994, lot 846. It is dated 1780-1850, which may be correct at the tail end but it is unlikely to be a late Qianlong period piece. The carving of this example, while cruder, is certainly more vibrant.

158 | **Glass, overlay**

1840-1900
2 ³/₁₆ in. (5.6 cm.) high

Of rounded shape, carved through the blue overlay with confronted archaistic dragons forming a *shou* character on each side dividing fixed-ring handles

1936-663 (CB. 192)

For a multi-color glass example of finer quality, see Clare Lawrence, *Miniature Masterpieces from the Middle Kingdom, The Monimar Collection of Chinese Snuff Bottles*, No. 126.

159 | **Glass, overlay**

1750-1800
4 ³/₈ in. (11 cm.) high

Of tall slender tapering cylindrical shape, the red overlay carved in high relief with a seated lady looking upwards towards a bird perched on a swing hung from a branch of bamboo growing from rockwork on one side, and a four-line twenty-eight-character inscription to the other

1936-561 (CB. 178)

Provenance: The American Art Galleries, New York
The Elizabeth Andrews Collection, 8-9 February 1922, lot 35.
(See fig. 25 in the Introduction.)

Literature: Edward Wenham, 'Antiques As Decoration', *Arts & Decoration*, New York, Winter, 1928, illustrated p. 96.

This large overlay bottle appears to be the only one of its type published. The four-line poem of seven characters each can be read as:

(i) *Ren jian tian shang zhong qing chi*
(ii) *Xiang Guan di hen keng chi*
(iii) *(Ying Wu) bu zhi nong yi xu*
(iv) *Nan nan you yong (zang hua shi)*

Which can be translated as:
(i) Heaven and earth are filled with unrequited loves;
(ii) By the Xiang Hall, the echo of a bird's call emptily fills the branches
(iii) But a parrot does not understand the affairs of the heart -
(iv) Or the lovely chanting of the 'Poem of Faded Flowers'.

Xiang of line (ii) refers to a place in Hunan Province famous for growing a very special kind of bamboo with spots on the surface known as *Xiang Fei Zhu*. For an example of an enameled snuff bottle molded to imitate this particularly famous spotted bamboo, see *Snuff Bottles in the Collection of the National Palace Museum*, p. 93, No. 28. It bears a Yongzheng four-character mark and is of the period.

Zang hua shi of line (iv) is the name of a famous poem from the Chinese novel, *The Dream of the Red Chamber*.

For an early eighteenth century cinnabar lacquer panel with a black ground depicting the same subject of a lady with a parrot perched on a swing above her, see Sotheby's, Hong Kong, 28 October 1992, lot 252.

160 | **Glass, overlay**

1780-1850
1 ½ in. (3.8 cm.) high

Of pear shape, the overlay carved on each side with confronted descending *chilong* around a long-life symbol (swastika), the shoulders with lion-mask handles

1936-753 (CB. 170)

Literature: Edward Wenham, 'Antiques As Decoration', *Arts & Decoration*, New York, Winter, 1928, illustrated p. 96.

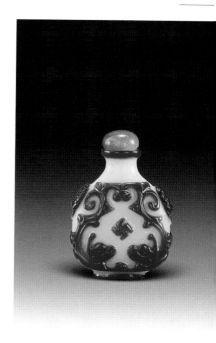

A small number of similar but rather cursorily carved red overlay bottles with opaque white grounds bearing wheel-cut Qianlong marks are recorded, see *Masterpieces of Snuff Bottles in the Palace Museum*, No. 74, and also *Snuff Bottles in the Collection of the National Palace Museum*, Nos. 289 and 291. The latter two are carved with *chilong*, the first is with chrysanthemum and crab apple. For a large number of floral decorated bottles, also with Qianlong marks, see *ibid.*, Nos. 280-282; Nos. 286-288; and No. 290.

See also Robert Kleiner, *Chinese Snuff Bottles in the Collection of Mary and George Bloch*, No. 158, for a slightly larger example, also carved with descending *chilong* but around a *shou* character. Kleiner attributes the bottle to the Qianlong reign and the Beijing Palace workshop, on stylistic grounds, particularly the finely carved lion-mask handles.

The bottles have tremendous charm, are usually of small size with an overlay rim around the neck, and most bear wheel-cut Qianlong four-character marks on the base. The designs tend to be quite simple and confined to *chilong*, archaistic motifs and floral scenes.

For another example with prunus and orchids, see Humphrey K. F. Hui and Peter Y. K. Lam, *The Imperial Connection*, No. 11. For a blue overlay bottle of larger size depicting five bats around a swastika, see Hugh Moss, Victor Graham and Ka Bo Tsang, *The Art of the Chinese Snuff Bottle, The J & J Collection*, No. 381, where it is noted that the swastika is an alternative form for the character *wan*, literally meaning 'ten thousand' but used in the sense of 'boundless.'

161 | **Glass, overlay**

1750-1800
2 ⁷⁄₁₆ in. (6.3 cm.) high

Of rounded shape, the red overlay carved in high relief with a continuous design of lotus growing from water

1936-764 (CB. 175)

For a similar bottle in blue overlay, with the addition of an eagle to one side, see Robert Kleiner, *Chinese Snuff Bottles from the Collection of Mary and George Bloch*, No. 105. The treatment of the curling edges of the lotus pads in both examples is very similar and a little idiosyncratic, possibly indicating the same workshop.

162 | **Glass, overlay**

1770-1830
2 ³/₈ in. (6 cm.) high

Of rounded shape, carved through the translucent red overlay with the eight horses of Mu Wang amidst pine, bamboo, *lingzhi* and rockwork

1936-917 (CB. 179)

For a red overlay bottle with four horses beneath pine and willow, see *Chinese Snuff Bottles* by Suzie and François Lorin, Fall 1997, No. 48.

For other examples of red overlays depicting the eight horses of Mu Wang, but all silhouetted on a plain ground, see Christie's, Hong Kong, The Louise and Christopher Randall Collection, 31 October 1995, lot 1924; and a blue overlay in *The Au Hang Collection of Chinese Snuff Bottles*, No. 69. See also another bottle in this collection, No. 193.

Mu Wang was a historical figure, the fifth sovereign of the Zhou dynasty, who was famed for his eight stallions.

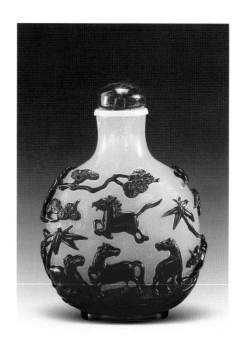

163 | **Glass, overlay**

1750-1800
2 ¹/₄ in. (5.8 cm.) high

Of rounded pear shape, the very finely detailed red overlay carved with a fish somersaulting from waves emitting a cloud of vapor which supports a temple on one side and a book on the other, one narrow side carved with *lingzhi* and rockwork, the other side with bamboo, all below a bat and a flying crane holding a scroll in its beak

1936-527 (CB. 172)

Literature: Edward Wenham, 'Antiques As Decoration', *Arts & Decoration*, New York, Winter, 1928, illustrated p. 96.

The various Daoist motifs on this bottle form rebuses representing longevity. For similar red overlay examples with Daoist symbolism, see Christie's, New York, 2 December 1993, lot 375; Sotheby's, New York, The Janos Szekeres Collection, 27 October 1986, lot 72; Sotheby's, New York, The Kardos Collection, 1 July 1985, lot 26; and Helen White, *Snuff Bottles from China, The Victoria and Albert Museum Collection*, pp. 190-191, pl. 3.

For a blue overlay bottle depicting the same subject but in a less three-dimensional format than this example, see Clare Lawrence, *Miniature Masterpieces from the Middle Kingdom, The Monimar Collection of Chinese Snuff Bottles*, No. 121.

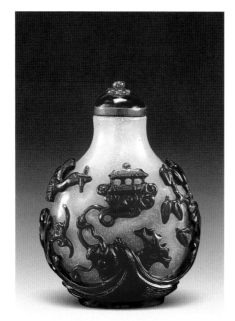

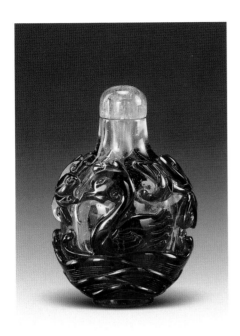

164 | Glass, overlay

1750-1820
2 ³/₁₆ in. (5.6 cm.) high

Of rounded shape, the red overlay carved in rounded relief with a continuous scene of two geese on a lotus pond

1936-756 (CB. 176)

For a similar example see Hugh Moss, *Chinese Snuff Bottles*, No. 184, where the birds are described as swans, which indeed these birds may also be. See also, Hugh Moss, Victor Graham, and Ka Bo Tsang, *The Art of the Chinese Snuff Bottle, The J & J Collection*, No. 382, where a bottle of slightly later date is illustrated which depicts a similar subject where the bird is described as a mandarin duck because of its frilly crest and tail feathers. These birds are a little unusual in having crests at the top of their heads and a pointed beak. The relief carving of this bottle is exceedingly deep and of its kind is amongst the finest.

See also Gerard Tsang and Hugh Moss, *Arts from the Scholar's Studio*, No. 56, where it is noted that 'the goose has become linked in Chinese thought with the famous calligrapher Wang Xizhi, who is said to have likened the supple line of their necks to the best brushstrokes in the art of calligraphy.' See also another bottle with a red overlay on a bubble-suffused ground with two geese on each side which sold at Christie's, New York, 3 June 1993, lot 334.

165 | Glass, overlay

1750-1820
2 ¹¹/₁₆ in. (6.7 cm.) high

Of ovoid shape, the red overlay finely carved with a continuous design of tree peonies growing from rockwork and carved in the style of Suzhou agates, a small sprig of begonia to one side

1936-774 (CB. 169)

Literature: Edward Wenham, 'Antiques As Decoration', *Arts & Decoration*, New York, Winter, 1928, illustrated p. 58 and p. 96. (See fig. 18 in the Introduction)

The vibrant cherry-red overlay is unusually thick and finely carved. The craftsman's use of negative space on each side of the bottle cleverly highlights and silhouettes the bending branches of the tree peony caught in a breeze.

The two most comparable red overlay examples both have semi-translucent yellowish-white or milky-white grounds, rather than the pure opaque white of this example, which adds clarity to the organization of the design. See *A Congregation of Snuff Bottle Connoisseurs*, No. 32, which depicts chrysanthemums on one side and an inscription in *hangshu* (running or grass script) reading *Yin jiu ji hua shi* which can be read as 'Drink wine while flowers bloom'. The bottle is attributed to the Beijing Palace workshops, 1736-1795. See also Hugh M. Moss, *Snuff Bottles of China*, No. 208, which is carved with tree peony growing from rockwork in a garden scene, with a bat above *lingzhi*, and branches to one side. The author dates the bottle 1750-1880.

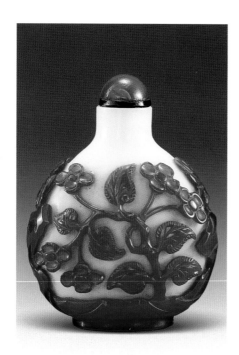

166 | **Glass, overlay**

1770-1830
2 ⁹/₁₆ in. (6.6 cm.) high

Of rounded shape, deeply carved through the semi-transparent cherry-red overlay with begonia on one main face and camellia on the other, divided by rockwork on the narrow sides

1936-582 (CB. 167)

For another bottle with a two-color overlay of pink and green depicting begonia in a basket, see Hugh Moss, Victor Grahm and Ka Bo Tsang, *The Art of the Chinese Snuff Bottle, The J & J Collection*, No. 392. The carving of this begonia, in particular the serrated edges of the leaves, is very similar to that example which is described as one of the 'transcendent masterpieces of the Qing art of glass carving.'

167 | **Glass, overlay**

1770-1830
2 ⁷/₈ in. (7.3 cm.) high

Of oval shape, carved with a *chilong* on one side and a bird-headed *chilong* on the other, mask fixed-ring handles on the shoulders

1936-926 (CB. 182)

For a bottle of very similar shape but carved with two *chilong* on each side, see Robert Hall, *Chinese Snuff Bottles II*, No. 46.

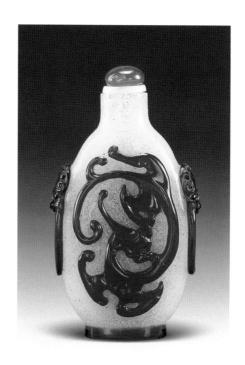

168 | **Glass, overlay**

1770-1820
2 ³/₈ in. (6.1 cm.) high

Of tapering baluster shape, delicately carved through the red overlay with a plump fan-tailed fish on each side dividing beribboned musical stones and *ji yang* character handles

1936-996 (CB. 180)

The characters *Ji Yang,* formed by the handles, form an auspicious idiom which can be read as 'good luck'.

For a bottle nearly identical in subject matter to this one, but of paler red tone on an opaque white ground and without the red overlay foot, see Sotheby's, New York, 27 June 1986, lot 261.

For another red overlay bottle depicting a large fan-tailed fish on each side, see Hugh Moss, Victor Graham and Ka Bo Tsang, *The Art of the Chinese Snuff Bottle, The J & J Collection*, No. 377. The fish on this example fit more comfortably on the space provided by a rectangular bottle and are distinctly more realistic than the J & J Collection example.

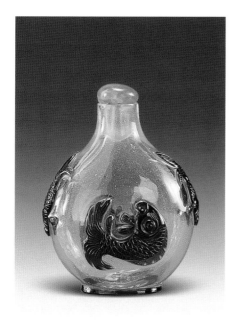

169 | **Glass, overlay**

1770-1850
2 ³/₁₆ in. (5.6 cm.) high

Of rounded shape, the clear colorless ground decorated in red with a single coiling carp on each side divided by a descending fish forming a handle on each of the narrow sides

1936-972 (CB. 181)

For another example of similar type see Hugh Moss, *Chinese Snuff Bottles*, No. 178.

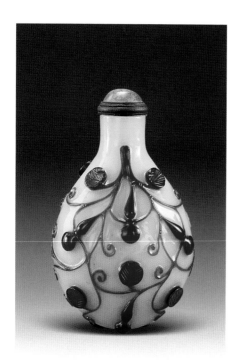

170 | **Glass, overlay**

1780-1850
2 ¹/₂ in. (6.4 cm.) high

Of rounded pear shape, carved through the red overlay with a continuous design of a meandering gourd vine, with three gourds forming the feet

1936-780 (CB. 171)

The design of gourds and tendrils was a popular one in snuff bottle production in a variety of media. The rebus formed by this combination, *Zisun wandai*, can be read as 'May you have ten thousand sons and grandsons'.

The most popular shape of bottle using the theme of gourds and tendrils was, quite naturally, a gourd itself. Most published examples of overlay glass with this design take this form. As is the case with this bottle, most of these have three feet formed from gourds trailing under the base, providing a satisfactory support.

For other gourd-shaped red overlay bottles, see Helen White, *Snuff Bottles from China, The Victoria and Albert Museum Collection*, pp. 169-170, No. 1, which entered the collection in 1903 in the Boone Bequest; Robert Kleiner, *Chinese Snuff Bottles in the Collection of Mary and George Bloch*, No. 154, attributed to the Palace workshops, 1715-1760; *A Congregation of Snuff Bottle Connoisseurs*, No. 34, dated to 1800-1850 but attributed to the Palace workshops; and *Zhongguo Biyanhu Zhenshang*, (Gems of Chinese Snuff Bottles), No. 65.

171 | Glass, overlay

1770-1830, Yangzhou Seal School
2 7/32 in. (5.9 cm.) high

Of rounded shape, carved through the red overlay with an orchid and a three-character inscription within a roundel on one side and a twenty-character inscription within a circle on the other

1936-757 (CB. 273)

The three-character inscription *Wang Wen Xiang* alongside the orchid, can be read as 'The fragrance of kingship and culture'.

The lengthy inscription on the other side is a four-line poem with five characters to each line:

(i) Yue dao tian xin chu
(ii) Feng lai sui mian shi
(iii) Yi ban (or gu) qing yi wei
(iv) Liao de shao ren zhi

This can be read as:
(i) The moon reaches the middle of the sky
(ii) as a wind picks up over the surface
(iii) It carries [the orchid's] clear pure scent:
(iv) only a few truly understand what this means

In poetry, the orchid has been associated with integrity in the face of slander since the pre-Han period. It is mentioned in the poetry of Qu Yuan in the 4th-3rd century B.C. It was also considered the flower of the Emperor, see Humphrey K. F. Hui and Peter Y. K. Lam, *The Imperial Connection*, No. 15, where the authors note that the Empress Dowager Cixi had a fondness for orchids and was nicknamed *laner*, translated as 'orchid child', as well as given the name *languinen*, meaning 'orchid beauty' in her position as an Imperial concubine of junior rank.

The orchid and the rock combined embody the virtues 'fragrant' and 'strong', see Marsha S. Weidner, *Views from the Jade Terrace*, p. 74, regarding the revered poet Sushi who wrote 'Spring and orchids are like a beautiful woman.'

For another bottle carved in high relief with orchids on one side and a poem about the moon and water on the other signed by Jiting, see Hugh Moss, Victor Graham and Ka Bo Tsang, *The Art of the Chinese Snuff Bottle, The J & J Collection*, No. 396.

172 | Glass, overlay

Dated *Jiashen er yue*, corresponding to the second month of 1824, Yangzhou Seal School
2 7/8 in. (6.7 cm.) high

Of rectangular shape, the pale red overlay carved with a female Immortal, probably Xiwangmu, Queen of the West, holding a whisk and standing between a long-tailed bird and a basket of peaches, below the four-character cyclical inscription on one side, and a drunken scholar, possibly Li Po, supported by an assistant with another assistant nearby holding a lantern, all below two flying bats and a crescent moon, on the other side

1936-513 (CB. 168)

Literature: Edward Wenham, 'Antiques As Decoration', *Arts & Decoration*, New York, Winter, 1928, illustrated p. 96.

Xiwangmu is usually depicted riding on the back of a large mythical bird. Her earliest incarnation is as an ancient Mother Goddess. She later evolved into the Daoist Queen of the West. Peaches of immortality grew in her celestial garden.

For another bottle carved in agate depicting Xiwangmu, see Hugh Moss, Victor Graham, Ka Bo Tsang, *The Art of the Chinese Snuff Bottle, The J & J Collection*, No. 160.

The rather comical nature of the drunken poet carried home by his dutiful assistant has been caught very well by the carver despite the rather cursory, medium quality carving of both the scene and the white ground.

173 | Glass, overlay

1800-1850, Yangzhou Seal School
2 3/8 in. (5.6 cm.) high

Of rounded shape, carved through the cinnabar brown overlay with loosely arranged objects and animals, with two squirrels, a dish of pomegranates, a wine ewer and cup, a bowl and spoon and a seal to one side, and two fish hanging from a branch, a basket of peaches, quail and millet, a Yixing teapot and the inscription on the other, fixed-ring handles on the narrow sides

1936-913 (CB. 233)

Literature: Edward Wenham, 'Antiques As Decoration', *Arts & Decoration*, New York, Winter, 1928, illustrated p. 96.

The inscription *Ping An* can be read as 'peaceful' or 'safe'. The seal reads *shou* for longevity.

For a red overlay bottle with a similar arrangement of assorted objects on an opaque white ground from the Hedda and Lutz Franz Collection, see *A Congregation of Snuff Bottle Connoisseurs*, No. 64, which is attributed to the Yangzhou School and dated 1800-1850.

See also Humphrey K. F. Hui and Christopher C. H. Sin, *An Imperial Qing Tradition*, No. 168, for a fascinating discussion on the plethora of puns to be found on this type of bottle with numerous auspicious objects and motifs.

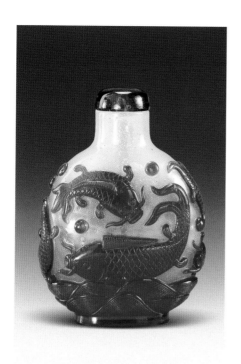

174 | **Glass, overlay**

1800-1900
2 ⅝ in. (6.3 cm.) high

Of rounded shape, the translucent pale red overlay carved with a continuous scene of seven fan-tailed fish amidst bubbles and above waves

1936-560 (CB. 177)

For a bottle with a similar subject of fish amidst bubbles and waves, see Robert Hall, *Chinese Snuff Bottles IV*, No. 116.

Two fish symbolize conjugal bliss and the joys of union.

175 | **Glass, overlay**

1840-1900
2 ⁷⁄₁₆ in. (6.1 cm.) high

Of rounded shape, the red overlay carved with stylized twin fish forming a *yin-yang* symbol at the center of each main side, a large *chilong* on each of the narrow sides, their trifurcated tails trailing around to the main faces

1936-678 (CB. 174)

For another glass bottle depicting a similar subject but in black overlay on a white ground and with a *shou* character replacing the *yin-yang* symbol, see Humphrey K. F. Hui, Margaret Polak, and Christopher C. H. Sin, *Hidden Treasures of the Dragon*, No. 23.

176 | **Glass, overlay**

1750-1820
2 ¹⁵/₁₆ in. (6.8 cm.) high

Of oval shape, the translucent lime-green overlay delicately carved with eight coiling *chilong*, a ninth forming the foot

1936-760 (CB. 267)

For a bottle of similar type with a pale green overlay of peony, see Sotheby's, New York, The Neal W. and Frances R. Hunter Collection, 15 September 1998, lot 128.

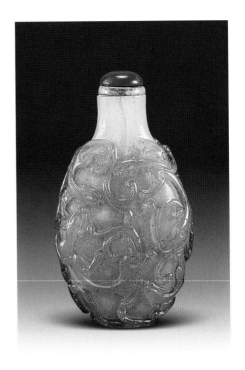

177 | **Glass, overlay**

1780-1870
2 ⁵/₈ in. (6.6 cm.) high

Of rounded shape, the green overlay carved with a tied lotus spray on one side and a grasshopper on a cabbage or beet leaf beneath a small butterfly on the other

1936-778 (CB. 221)

For a pale green overlay bubble-suffused bottle similarly carved on one side with a large lotus pad and flower growing from a pond, rather than tied as in this example, see *Chinese Snuff Bottles* by Suzie and François Lorin, Fall 1997, No. 52. For a baluster-shaped bottle carved with a grasshopper on one side and a praying mantis on the other, see Clare Lawrence, *Twenty-six Friendly Beasts*, (unnumbered), from the Eric Young Collection. For another green overlay depicting a praying mantis on a lotus pad, see *Zhongguo Biyanhu Zhenshang*, (Gems of Chinese Snuff Bottles), No. 78.

178 | Glass, overlay

1800-1880
2 ⁹/₁₆ in. (6.5 cm.) high

Of oval shape, carved with a cricket on a beet or cabbage on one side and a squirrel and grape vine on the other

1936-531 (CB. 220)

For a pale green overlay bottle depicting a similar scene of a cricket on a cabbage to one side, see Robert Hall, *Chinese Snuff Bottles II*, No. 109. The overlay on this example is much thicker and less well-carved than the Hall example, suggesting a different workshop, and a marginally later production date for this bottle. It is surprising that a subject as popular as the 'squirrel and vine', which signifies abundant progeny, is not found more often in snuff bottle production. For a red overlay example, see Sotheby's, Hong Kong, 28 October 1992, lot 326.

179 | Glass, overlay

1800-1880
2 ⁵/₁₆ in. (5.9 cm.) high

Of rounded shape, the black overlay carved with five bats, *wufu*, around a central stylized *shou* medallion on one side, and two birds in the branch of a prunus tree on the other

1936-765

Literature: Edward Wenham, 'Antiques As Decoration', *Arts & Decoration*, New York, Winter, 1928, illustrated p. 96.

The rebus on one side *Wufu qing shou* can be read as 'five bats extend good wishes on one's birthday'. The rebus on the other side formed by the magpies in a plum tree *Xi que deng mei* can be read as 'the announcement of good news'.

For another bottle from the Dodge Collection carved with the same depiction of five bats and a *shou* character on both sides on an opaque white ground, see Sotheby's, New York, 17 March 1997, lot 30. For another on a clear ground, see Robert Hall, *Chinese Snuff Bottles II*, No. 110.

See also a blue and white porcelain bottle painted with the same subject and bearing a Daoguang hallmark *Rui di tui tang zhi* ('Hall of retiring for contemplation in the far-sighted official's house'), illustrated in *Zhongguo Biyanhu Zhenshang* (Gems of Chinese Snuff Bottles), p. 114 (in the introduction to the porcelain section).

180 | **Glass, overlay**

1800-1880
2 ⁹/₃₂ in. (5.8 cm.)

Of rounded shape, with a single layer of white overlay on an opaque black ground, carved on one side with three figures enjoying a drink while seated in a boat being punted by a boy beneath overhanging pine; the reverse with a seated figure fanning a stove emitting a cloud of vapor while another figure carries hot wine into a building

1936-744 (CB. 260)

Literature: Edward Wenham, 'Antiques As Decoration', *Arts & Decoration*, New York, Winter, 1928, illustrated p. 58 and p. 96. (See fig. 18 in the Introduction)

The use of a white overlay on black is quite rare. It is more usual to see white overlay on blue. For another example depicting floral sprays rising from a rockwork, see Christie's, Hong Kong, The Louise and Christopher Randall Collection, 31 October 1995, lot 1891.

The scene may represent Su Dongpo's visit to the Red Cliffs.

181 | **Glass, overlay**

1780-1850, Yangzhou seal school
2 ¹¹/₃₂ in. (5.9 cm.) high

Of rounded rectangular shape, with a single layer of white overlay on a translucent red ground, delicately carved with a female figure seated at a moon window near convoluted rocks and tree sprays watching a butterfly, a seal to one side, the reverse with Huang Chengyan on his mule, an assistant nearby, below prunus and two flying birds, the two scenes divided by fixed-ring handles

1936-911 (CB. 254)

Literature: Edward Wenham, 'Antiques As Decoration', *Arts & Decoration*, New York, Winter, 1928, illustrated p. 96.

The seal can be read as *Ji Yang* or *Ji Xiang* an auspicious idiom.

For a nearly identical bottle in all respects, save the shape, and obviously produced by the same workshop, presumably at the same time, see *A Congregation of Snuff Bottle Connoisseurs*, No. 63, dated 1800-1850 and attributed to the Yangzhou School.

A bottle of identical shape and color, but carved with cats and cockerels, is illustrated by Robert Hall, *Chinese Snuff Bottles II*, No. 119, formerly from the Marian Mayer Collection. Another with a pale green overlay on a white ground, carved on one side with a lady holding a bird in a moon window encircled by rocks and plants, is illustrated by Hugh Moss, *Chinese Snuff Bottles: 6. Chinese Snuff Bottles from the Collection of the Rt. Hon. The Marquess of Exeter, K.C.M.G.*, p. 87, No. G.92.

Another bottle, carved through a pink overlay on an opaque white ground, also attributed to the Yangzhou seal school, from the Humphrey Hui Collection, bears the same seal *ji yang*. It is illustrated in *An Imperial Qing Tradition* by Humphrey K. H. Hui and Christopher C. H. Sin, No. 167.

Interestingly, all the bottles have identical mask handles with elongated rings carved in very low relief.

This bottle is a fine example of the Yangzhou seal school. The term refers to a group of glass overlay bottles following a distinctive style; usually carved in low relief, silhouetted on a ground of a different color, and often bearing seal marks or inscription in seal characters. Their attribution to Yangzhou is discussed in detail by Hugh Moss, Victor Graham and Ka Bo Tsang, *The Art of the Chinese Snuff Bottle, The J & J Collection*, Nos. 398-404. What began as strong circumstantial evidence in favor of this attribution appears to be confirmed by more recent discoveries of signed and dated bottles and also glass wares. A strong link was suggested by Gerard Tsang in an article in the *JICSBS*, June 1979, in his reading of the seal, *Xiaomei*, found on many of the bottles, which was the art name of a painter from Yangzhou called Wang Su (1794-1879) and confirmed by a bottle illustrated by Humphrey K. F. Hui, Margaret Polak, and Christopher C. H. Sin, in *Hidden Treasures of the Dragon*, No. 225, with the inscription *Xiaomei Wang Su Zuo*, ('Made by Wang Su') indicating that the artist was also a carver of overlay bottles.

Another bottle, made by Sun Shihua and illustrated by Robert Kleiner in *Chinese Snuff Bottles in the Collection of Mary and George Bloch*, No. 172, is carved with a scene of a huntsman on horseback followed by a dog. Above them, a wounded goose falls from the sky, pierced by the huntsman's arrow. The author notes that the subject is inspired by a painting by one of the 'eight eccentric' artists, Hua Yan, one of the most celebrated painters of Yangzhou. See also an article by Clare Lawrence in the *JICSBS*, Summer 1993, 'An

Analysis of the Seal School Group of Glass Snuff Bottles', pp. 10-11, where this observation was initially developed.

Many of the bottles of this group bear cyclical dates, mostly without reign marks, and are therefore open to interpretation based on a sixty-year cycle. Until the late 1980s the group was dated to the second half of the nineteenth century.

However, in 1991, this author handled an extraordinary pink-red overlay vase, almost 7 inches high, bearing a cyclical date *Dingchou* and a signature Li Shi. It came from the estate of Elizabeth Parke Firestone and sold at Christie's, New York, 22 March 1991, lot 504. This author interpreted the cyclical date as 'probably' corresponding to 1757, whilst drawing attention to the 'seal-school' snuff bottles, then generally dated to the late nineteenth century. A fax correspondence ensued between this author and Hugh Moss over the dating of this piece. Only after this piece came to light was Hugh Moss able to make the connection between the family name Li on the Firestone vase, and the Li Junting of known seal school bottles, and thus satisfactorily re-date the entire Yangzhou seal school production.

The Firestone vase itself bears stylistic characteristics of mid-to late eighteenth century glass, including delicacy of carving, quality of glass and overall aesthetic. The shape is not unlike a Qianlong-marked enameled glass vase illustrated by Hugh Moss, *By Imperial Command: An Introduction to Ch'ing Imperial Painted Enamels*, No. 66, from the Museé Guimet; in form, it can also be compared to a number of very fine Imperial porcelain vases of the Qianlong period, see *Qingdai taoci daguan*, pp. 272-275.

A date of 1817, however, is now considered the correct reading of the cyclical date on the Firestone vase.

Another snuff bottle illustrated by Robert Kleiner, *op. cit.*, pp. 256-258, No. 171, carved with white overlay on a turquoise ground and depicting a hermit and boy below a crane on one side and horses nuzzling beneath a tree on the other, which is dated *jimao* year corresponding to 1819, now provides a close link with the Firestone vase. An inscription on one side can be read as: 'A treasure of Mr. Li of Jingjiang, the twelfth month of the *jimao* year (1819) and a seal Junting'. It is another important documentary piece mentioning, as it does, the town of Jingjiang, twenty miles from Yangzhou and the maker's name of Li Junting.

The appearance of a *Shende Tang* - marked bottle of the Daoguang period (1820-1850), formerly owned by Clare Lawrence, which is obviously of the classic type attributed to the Yangzhou seal school, has further confirmed the reappraisal of the cyclical dates. See also Nos. 192 and 193.

182 | **Glass, overlay**

1780-1850, Yangzhou seal school
2 ³/₄ in. (7 cm.) high

Of rounded rectangular shape, the yellow overlay carved with four archaistic bronze vessels on each main face, two of elongated shape forming the handles on the narrow sides

1936-856 (CB. 207)

Literature: Edward Wenham, 'Antiques As Decoration', *Arts & Decoration*, New York, Winter, 1928, illustrated p. 96.

For a cinnabar-red overlay example, see Christie's, South Kensington, London, The Gerry P. Mack Collection, 4 October 1999, lot 173.

See also lot 127 in the same sale for a nephrite example, where each vessel is inscribed with the name of the type of bronze vessel it is copying.

See also another example with the colors reversed which sold at Sotheby's, Hong Kong, 28 October 1992, lot 314.

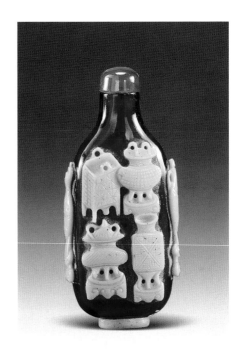

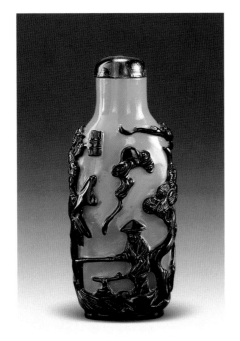

183 | **Glass, overlay**

1780-1850
2 ²⁷/₃₂ in. (7.2 cm.) high

Of cylindrical shape, carved with a boy on a buffalo playing a flute, ambling towards a figure seated in a small pavilion, another figure with bundles on a pole stretched across his shoulders, and a fisherman near pine below the sun and clouds

1936-532 (CB. 269 or 209)

The use of turquoise and black in combination is quite unusual in snuff bottle production, though strikingly effective. The rustic subject matter, however, was a very popular one, following the classical painting tradition. It depicts the four vocations, *Yu Qiao Geng Du*, represented by fisherman, woodcutter, farmer and scholar.

184 | **Glass, overlay**

1780-1850
2 7/16 in. (6.2 cm.) high

Of oval shape, carved on each side with two dragons and two cranes with archaistic bodies forming characters, the narrow sides with three joined rings

1936-925 (CB. 257)

The character formed on each side, *Ji*, can be read as 'auspicious'.

For a bottle of identical design, including the three interlocked rings on the narrow side, but carved with a blue overlay on a yellow ground, see Sotheby's, New York, 17 March 1997, lot 42. Another identical bottle in yellow glass is illustrated by Bob C. Stevens, *The Collector's Book of Snuff Bottles*, No. 170; and a two-color overlay of green and white on a transparent red ground is illustrated by Humphrey K. F. Hui and Christopher C. H. Sin in *An Imperial Qing Tradition*, No. 159, where the bird is identified as a phoenix and thus, in combination with the dragon, forms the rebus *longfeng chengxiang*, meaning 'auspicious omen presented by the dragon and phoenix'. These birds may have

been intended to represent phoenix but became crane-like somewhere in the process of production. All three bottles, including this one, must surely have been produced in the same workshop, which substituted colors to add variety to the output.

185 | **Glass, overlay**

1800-1880
2 3/8 in. (6 cm.) high

Of oval shape, the red overlay carved with chrysanthemums and prunus rising from rockwork on the main faces and a begonia on one narrow side and a daisy on the other

1936-920 (CB. 272)

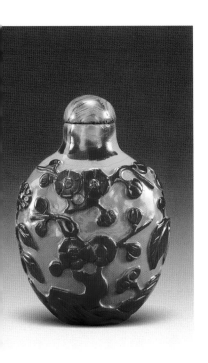

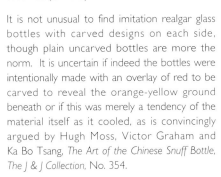

It is not unusual to find imitation realgar glass bottles with carved designs on each side, though plain uncarved bottles are more the norm. It is uncertain if indeed the bottles were intentionally made with an overlay of red to be carved to reveal the orange-yellow ground beneath or if this was merely a tendency of the material itself as it cooled, as is convincingly argued by Hugh Moss, Victor Graham and Ka Bo Tsang, *The Art of the Chinese Snuff Bottle, The J & J Collection*, No. 354.

For examples of carved realgar bottles, see Hugh Moss, Victor Graham and Ka Bo Tsang, *ibid.*, No. 354, attributed by design (seven Buddhist lions at play) as possibly Imperial, possibly Beijing Palace workshops, and dating between 1740-1820; Robert W. L. Kleiner,

in *Chinese Snuff Bottles from the Collection of Mary and George Bloch*, No. 109, formerly in the Gerd Lester Collection and carved with pomegranate and melons and dated 1800-1860.

Realgar (arsenic bisulphide) was an important though highly toxic substance used in Daoist alchemical practice.

Although it is generally accepted that these bottles imitate realgar, the possibility that they might imitate carved lacquer, bamboo or even hornbill should not be ruled out.

For another example carved with butterflies, see Christie's, Hong Kong, The Louise and Christopher Randall Collection, 31 October 1995, lot 1845.

186 | **Glass, overlay**

1750-1800
1 ²¹/₃₂ in. (4.2 cm.) high

Of rounded shape, a single layer of white, green, yellow and red overlay on a translucent ground neatly carved with a continuous design of lotus

1936-622 (CB. 250)

For a slightly larger version of this type of bottle, see Sotheby's, Hong Kong, 28 April 1997, lot 18.

For another bottle similar in style and subject, but carved from a single layer of yellow overlay on a clear blue glass ground, see Humphrey K. F. Hui, Margaret Polak, and Christopher C. H. Sin, *Hidden Treasures of the Dragon*, No. 120.

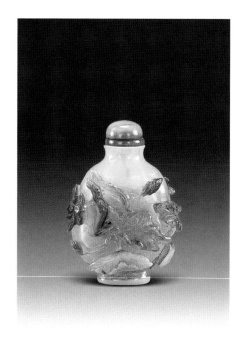

187 | **Glass, overlay**

1750-1800
2 in. (5 cm.) high

Of pear shape, decorated with a *chilong* carved from a multi-color overlay of swirling blue, green and yellow coiling around a *bi* disk on each side, the *bi* discs tied with tassels on the narrow sides

1936-624 (CB. 266)

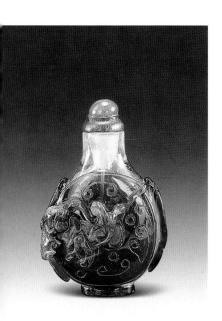

There is a group of these bottles, all with a double overlay carved with *bi* discs and coiling dragons as the main design, and with tassles on the narrow sides. See Bob C. Stevens, *The Collector's Book of Snuff Bottles*, No. 212. A similar bottle from the Eric Young Collection was sold as lot 48 at Sotheby's, London, 13 October 1987.

Another is illustrated in *An Imperial Qing Tradition* by Humphrey K. F. Hui and Christopher C. H. Sin, No. 157, where the authors suggest a possible attribution to the Guangzhou Imperial workshops, circa 1760. The argument for Guangzhou production is based on the now

well-known records of considerable orders for glass overlay bottles from the Court to the Imperial workshops at Guangzhou. See *Tributes from Guangdong to the Qing Court*, pp. 52-53.

This type of bottle is usually small, with deep carving, most commonly depicting a *chilong*, a popular Court subject.

For two more unusual examples, see Rachelle R. Holden, *Rivers and Mountains Far From the World*, No. 7; and Robert W. L. Kleiner, *Chinese Snuff Bottles from the Collection of Mary and Geroge Bloch*, No. 103.

188 | Glass, overlay

1770-1830
2 ⁷/₁₆ in. (6.1 cm.) high

Of rounded shape, the double overlay of red on white on a blue ground carved with a *chilong* emerging from a *bi* disc on one side, and a cloud vapor emerging from a *bi* disc on the other, the *bi* discs carved with c-scrolls and dots, tied tassel handles on the narrow sides

1936-761 (CB. 202)

See the preceding bottle, No. 187.

189 | Glass, overlay

1750-1820
2 ⁹/₁₆ in. (6.6 cm.) high

Of spade shape, the single layer of multi-colored overlay carved with various flower heads in red, pink, turquoise, yellow and violet issuing from green leafy branches rising from a woven basket forming the foot

1936-545 (CB. 244)

It is rare to find a six-colored overlay bottle. For multi-colored overlay bottles, three, four, or occasionally five, colors are more common.

For another similar bottle with five overlays, see *A Congregation of Snuff Bottle Connoisseurs*, No. 46, from the Lily and Y. B. Fung Collection. Though carved with only five overlays it bears similar characteristics of flowers rising from a basket which forms the foot. The authors note that the four species of flowers depicted on their bottle, peony, lotus, chrysanthemum and prunus, represent the four seasons of the year. This example also depicts four varieties of flowers, begonia, peony, magnolia or hibiscus, and probably orchid, though stylized. The exact significance of this grouping is uncertain.

For a slender pear-shaped bottle similarly carved with a five-color overlay of peony on a bubble-suffused ground, see Robert Kleiner, *The Bellis Collection*, No. 17.

190 | **Glass, overlay**

1750-1790
2 ¹¹/₁₆ in. (6.9 cm.) high

Of rounded shape, carved through overlay of red, green, blue and pink with a continuous scene of morning glory rising from rockwork on one side and peony on the other, two butterflies on one narrow side and a single butterfly above *lingzhi* on the other

1936-662 (CB. 237)

For other similar examples with flowers and rockwork in identical or nearly identical colors, see Christie's, Hong Kong, The Louise and Christopher Randall Collection, 31 October 1995, lot 1895; Hugh M. Moss, *Snuff Bottles of China*, No. 241; Sotheby's, New York, The Janos Szekeres Collection, 27 October 1986, lot 69; and Sotheby's, Hong Kong, 28 April 1997, lot 34.

191 | **Glass, overlay**

1750-1830
2 ³/₈ in. (5.6 cm.) high

Of rounded shape, with a wide mouth, the single layer of four-color overlay on an opaque white ground, finely carved in low relief with the *sanduo* ('three abundances'), peach, pomegranate and finger-citrus, growing from leafy branches

1936-629 (CB. 245)

The 'three abundances' represent happiness, longevity and male offspring.

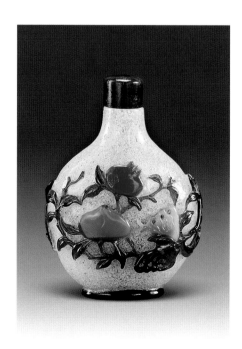

192 | Glass, overlay

1780-1830, Yangzhou Seal School
2 ¼ in. (5.7 cm.) high

Of rounded shape, with a double overlay of cinnabar-red on black on a white ground, decorated with a female Immortal punting a log boat with a stork at the prow beneath a crescent moon and a formation of five birds on one side; the reverse with a fisherman punting his craft below a full moon and a four-character seal-script inscription, alongside a vertical three-character inscription, the ground plane carved with breaking waves on both sides

1936-758 (CB. 234)

Literature: Edward Wenham, 'Antiques As Decoration', *Arts & Decoration*, New York, Winter, 1928, illustrated p. 96.

The horizontal four-character inscription *Yu Shi Zhen Chang* can be translated as 'Treasure collected by the Yu family'. The vertical three-character inscription *Jinyu Ting* can be read as 'Rain Today Pavilion' or 'Pavilion of Today's Rain'.

This bottle forms part of the well-known group of 'seal school' bottles produced in Yangzhou and usually dated to the first half of the nineteenth century. Many bottles of the school bear cyclical dates (sixty-year cycles) but, with two exceptions, no reign mark to establish the actual date. See bottle No. 181 for further discussion of the Yangzhou seal school.

Until the late 1980s, the whole school was ascribed to the second half of the nineteenth century, and the two known Qianlong-marked examples were simply considered as having apocryphal marks. However, the discovery of a glass bottle with the mark *Shende Tang* ('Hall for the Cultivation of Virtue'), a private hall of the Daoguang Emperor (1821-1850), has firmly established that the majority of these bottles date to the cycle which began in 1803 rather than 1863 as was previously believed.

Perhaps, then, the two Qianlong-marked bottles with identical cyclical dates, *bingwu* - 1784 or 1846 - are indeed of the Qianlong period and thus the earliest known bottles of this group.

The first, from the Rachelle R. Holden Collection, is illustrated in several publications, including Bob C. Stevens, *The Collector's Book of Snuff Bottles*, No. 1006, and in Rachelle R. Holden, *Rivers and Mountains Far from the World*, No. 95. A double overlay of cinnabar-red on black and white, it is carved with two boys on wading buffaloes on one side, and two fishermen hauling in their catch on the other.

The second example sold at Sotheby's, New York, June 1, 1994, lot 671, is also illustrated in the *JICSBS*, Autumn 1994, p. 23, fig. 2. With overlays of russet on black on a turquoise-blue

ground, it is carved with scenes similar to those on the Holden bottle, although the color of the glass, the shape, and the placement of the inscriptions all differ. While these bottles are obviously linked to each other, how do they relate to the rest of the Yangzhou school? The Holden bottle is certainly more like the Princeton bottle, sharing identical colors and a similar river scene. The bottle sold at Sotheby's is more like some other published bottles, including a rare triple overlay bottle illustrated by Hugh M. Moss, *Snuff Bottles of China*, No. 233, and now part of the Holden Collection, see Rachelle R. Holden, *op. cit.*, No. 126.

The motif on the second Holden bottle, No. 126, is similar to that of an example now in the Bloch Collection and illustrated by Robert Hall in *Chinese Snuff Bottles*, No. 43, and in *Chinese Snuff Bottles, A Miniature Art from the Collection of Mary and George Bloch*, No. 134. It has a three-character seal, *Jinyu Tung* previously erroneously read as *Qi Yu Ting* ['Breath of Rain Pavilion']. It would appear, therefore, that both these bottles were made for the same (private?) pavilion, presumably connected to the Yu Family.

A third bottle, formerly in the Ko Collection, and purchased in Tianjin in 1941, also depicts boys on buffaloes and bears the pavilion name, *Jinyu Ting*. It is attributed to the school of Li Junting, 1780-1840, and was illustrated by Hugh Moss in an advertisement in the *JICSBS*, Winter 2000, back cover.

The Bloch bottle can also be linked to the *Shende Tang*-marked example sold at Sotheby's, New York, October 3, 1980, lot 18, with identical overlay colors, although carved with fish in lotus ponds; and another in the Bloch collection illustrated by Robert Kleiner, *Chinese Snuff Bottles, A Miniature Art from the Collection of Mary and George Bloch*, No. 135, using identical color overlays which depicts a figure punting a craft to one side.

193 | **Glass, overlay**

1780-1850, Yangzhou Seal School
2 ³/₈ in. (6.1 cm.) high

Of rounded shape, carved through red and black overlays with a continuous scene of the eight horses of Mu Wang near rocky outcrops under *wutong* trees and clouds, below a crescent moon on one side and the sun on the other

1936-947 (CB. 271)

For another bottle of this school, see Robert Kleiner, *Chinese Snuff Bottles in the Collection of Mary and George Bloch*, No. 182, where the author notes that this type of bottle

> ...belongs to a distinctive sub-group of Yangzhou snuff bottles, all of which are carved in an unusually deep relief, often using the cinnabar-red overlay. They are usually carved with a double overlay of colors and are often characterized by carved billowing clouds around the shoulders.

For other bottles of this group with different subject matter, see Bob C. Stevens, *The Collector's Book of Snuff Bottles*, No. 255, from the Chicago Natural History Museum; and Christie's, The Louise and Christopher Randall Collection, Hong Kong, 31 October 1995, lot 1908.

194 | **Glass, overlay**

1780-1850
2 7/16 in. (6.2 cm.) high

Of rounded shape, the double overlay of beige on blue carved with seven scholars seated or standing on rocky outcrops amidst pine and small buildings, one raising a wine glass or vessel, another playing a *qin*, the others conversing or contemplating, the lower blue layer carved with a bamboo grove and small buildings amidst rockwork and pine, leaf lappets at the neck

1936-785 (CB. 203)

This bottle belongs to a distinctive group, all with double overlay decoration, carving in deep relief, and a collar of pendant plantain leaves.

Two stylistically similar bottles are illustrated by Hugh Moss in *Chinese Snuff Bottles: 6. Chinese Snuff Bottles from the Collection of the Rt. Hon. The Marquess of Exeter, K.C.M.G.*, p. 91, No. G.107 and p. 95, No. G.115.

For other examples of this type, see Robert Kleiner, *Chinese Snuff Bottles in the Collection of Mary and George Bloch*, Nos. 164 and 165; and, *Chinese Snuff Bottles, A Miniature Art from the Collection of Mary and George Bloch*, No. 121.

According to Gerard Tsang and Hugh Moss, writing in *Arts from the Scholar's Studio*, under No. 118, 'The Seven Sages of the Bamboo Grove were a group of scholars of the late 3rd century A.D. who gathered together to enjoy music, poetry, elegant conversation, contemplation and the wine that so often inspired them. They were ministers of state, philosophers, poets, calligraphers and musicians, and the group has since been used to symbolize the elegant gatherings of creative minds, becoming a popular subject in later Chinese art.'

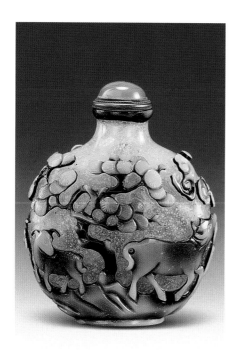

195 | **Glass, overlay**

1800-1880
2 ¹/₂ in. (6.4 cm.) high

Of rounded shape, with a double overlay of white on black on a bubble-suffused ground, carved in a continuous scene with a horse under pine on one side and a bullock and goat under pine, clouds, and a crescent moon on the reverse

1936-768 (CB. 252)

This bottle belongs to a small group, all carved in deep relief through overlays of white on black, or black on white, usually on a snowstorm ground.   Most are decorated with animals under trees, usually pine. This bottle is probably the largest and most complicated in imagery, but all have similar carving of the animals, trees and rockwork.

For other examples, see Bob C. Stevens, *The Collector's Book of Snuff Bottles*, No. 226, carved with a boy clutching a branch of prunus; No. 227, with a spotted deer beneath pine; No. 231, also with a spotted deer and a bird, but with a black on white overlay on a dark blue ground; and Hugh Moss, *Chinese Snuff Bottles: 6. Chinese Snuff Bottles from the Collection of the Rt. Hon. The Marquess of Exeter, K.C.M.G.*, p. 92, No. G.108, white on black overlay carved with a deer and a crane amidst *lingzhi* and pine trees.

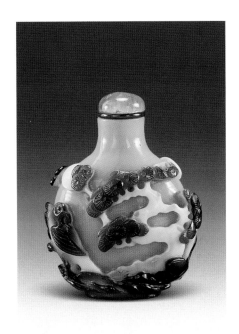

196 | **Glass, overlay**

1820-1880
2 ⁷/₁₆ in. (5.3 cm.) high

Of rounded shape, the double overlay of green on white on a pink ground carved in high relief with a continuous scene of two birds of prey standing on rockwork below pine

1936-762 (CB. 255)

For a very similar bottle, in both subject matter and color, see Sotheby's, London, The Eric Young Collection, Part III, 24 April 1989, lot 291.

Another bottle, with the same unusual combination of colors and depicting a landscape framed by pine and *wutong* trees, is illustrated by Humphrey K. F. Hui and Christopher C. H.

Sin in *An Imperial Qing Tradition,* No. 160. In both cases, the overlays are relatively deep and well carved. Another bottle from the same workshop, identical in color and very similar in subject, is illustrated in *A Congregation of Snuff Bottle Connoisseurs,* No. 55.

197 | **Glass, overlay**

1770-1850
2 $^{9}/_{16}$ in. (6.5 cm.) high

Of pear shape, carved through the black on white overlay to the dark blue ground with two confronted birds below lotus on one side, and a Pekinese dog near rockwork with two doves perched near a chrysanthemum on the other side

1936-909 (CB. 270)

Literature: Edward Wenham, 'Antiques As Decoration', *Arts & Decoration*, New York, Winter, 1928, illustrated p. 96.

For three almost identical bottles, see Sotheby's, London, Chinese Snuff Bottles from the Stone Picking Studio (*Cai Shi Xuan*), 21 June 1995, lot 19; Sotheby's, London, Collection of the Baronesses Sapuppo and d'Essen, 14 November 2000, lot 27; and Rachelle R. Holden, *Rivers and Mountains Far from the World*, No. 48.

Bottles from the same group but with different subject matter are illustrated by Hugh Moss, *Chinese Snuff Bottles: 6. Chinese Snuff Bottles from the Collection of the Rt. Hon. The Marquess of Exeter, K.C.M.G.,* pp. 92-93, No. G.113, carved with a continuous design of three goats, an inscription, and a tethered horse with an inscription. See also Sotheby's, Hong Kong, *Important Chinese Snuff Bottles from the Kaynes-Klitz Collection, Part II,* 30 October 1990, lot 22, carved with two goats and two monkeys under a peach tree on one side, and a cat chasing a butterfly on the other.

198 | Glass, overlay

1780-1850
2 ⁵/₈ in. (5.9 cm.) high

Of oval form, the three-color overlay of green on yellow on red very delicately carved in a continuous scene with four fan-tailed fish amidst lotus and fronds on an opaque white ground

1936-618 (CB. 238)

This extraordinary bottle makes full use of the three overlay colors of green, yellow and red. The yellow has been used to brilliant effect on the lotus pod to one side and also forms a subtle silhouette around the fish and lotus leaves.

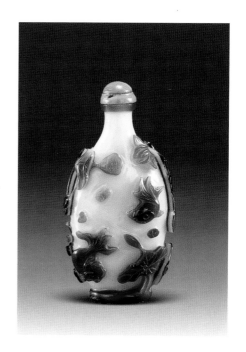

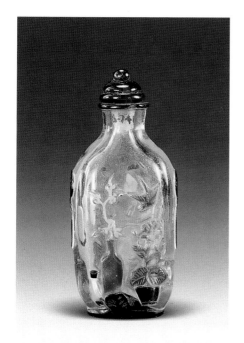

199 | Glass, overlay

1780-1850, Yangzhou Seal School
2 ⁷/₁₆ in. (6.2 cm.) high

Of rounded rectangular shape, the yellow, pink, brown, green and blue overlay on a clear ground carved with a stork, a butterfly, a dragonfly above lotus on one side, and a long-tailed bird above flowers growing in vessels on the other side, mask fixed-ring handles below the shoulders on the narrow sides

1936-741 or 743 (CB. 248)

For a discussion on the rarity of clear glass ground bottles of this school, see an article by Clare Lawrence 'An Analysis of the Seal School Group of Glass Snuff Bottles', *JICSBS*, Summer 1993, p. 4, where she notes that of the five hundred bottles she examined, fewer then ten percent had a clear ground.

For another example of pear shape, using very similar colors and also depicting birds, insects and flowers, see Humphrey K. F. Hui and Christopher C. H. Sin, *An Imperial Qing Tradition*; No. 165.

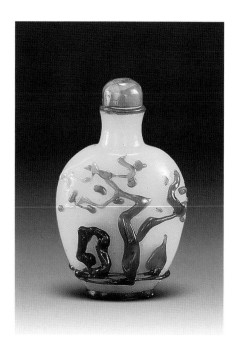

200 | **Glass, overlay**

1870-1930
2 ⁵/₁₆ in. (5.8 cm.) high

Of rounded spade shape with a slightly flaring neck, the single layer of blue, green and pink overlay forming a continuous scene of a pink blossoming tree above rockwork on one side, and bamboo above rockwork on the reverse, all on an opaque white ground

1936-738 (CB. 239)

This type of overlay bottle comes from a rather curious group. This distinctive school of glass decoration achieved its results by applying molten glass to the surface of the bottle and 'trailing' it to form the design. The use of trailed glass for decoration is not seen in early bottles, and appears only in the second half of the nineteenth century. On this example, the simple techniques of pressing and 'trailing' the glass have produced very competent rockwork and bamboo. It is possible that the inspiration for the unusual use of 'trailing' glass came from Europe, in particular, English glasswares of the Victorian period.

For another example, of double-gourd shape, overlaid in identical colors with a design of lotus, and also trimmed in blue at the neck and foot, see Robert Hall, *Chinese Snuff Bottles*, No. 46. That bottle would appear to be from the same workshop as the Blair example.

Porcelain Bottles

201 | **Porcelain**

1700-1735, Kangxi/Yongzheng
3 ³/₄ in. (9.5 cm.) high

Of inverted teardrop shape, painted with meandering scrolling hibiscus flower heads on a dense foliage-laden stem, all on a minutely black-dotted green ground

1936-1031 (CB. 353)

A very similar flask with a black ground was sold at Christie's, Hong Kong, 29-30 October, 1995, lot 716, where comparisons were drawn with a well-known group of similarly enameled black-ground Imperial dishes with Yongzheng marks. This example is painted with the more classic *famille verte* palette of the late Kangxi period but could easily date to the reign of the Yongzheng Emperor.

A third example with molded decoration and a black ground is illustrated by Helen White, *Snuff Bottles from China, The Victoria and Albert Museum Collection*, pl. 116, No. 4.

202 | **Porcelain**

1736-1795, Qianlong four-character iron-red seal mark within double lines and late in the period 2 ³/₁₆ in. (5.6 cm.) high

Of octagonal shape, with rounded convex main faces, each painted with peony and chrysanthemums below yellow flowers, possibly nandina, mulberry or jujube, all within gilt circular surrounds on a ruby ground, the narrow faceted sides painted with stylized floral decoration, probably depicting begonia and daisy, which continues to the waisted neck

1936-835 (CB. 340)

The octagonal shape and raised circular panels of this bottle are obviously derived from the earlier Beijing enamel and glass bottles, themselves based on imported European watches. See an octagonal glass bottle in this collection, No. 136.

For a nearly identical bottle in all but color, see Hugh Moss, Victor Graham and Ka Bo Tsang, *The Art of the Chinese Snuff Bottle, The J & J Collection,* No. 209. The authors discuss at length the mystery of the late development (ca.1780) of porcelain snuff bottle production at Jingdezhen, the main Imperial porcelain factories in Jiangxi province. To paraphrase, the conclusions drawn were as follows:

(i) That the inherent qualities of porcelain, translucency and sonority, are mostly missing in the confines of such a small object as a snuff bottle.

(ii) That enameled glass or metal bottles, could be made in the Beijing Palace workshops and bore many features indistinguishable from the porcelain examples. This left little incentive in the early years to order from the distant Southern province.

(iii) Enamel and glass production was as advanced at the Palace, if not more so, than any porcelain production at Jingdezhen. By the time porcelain snuff bottle production was perfected in Jingdezhen, perhaps a decade or so later, quantity rather than quality was more usually the order of the day.

(iv) As a result of a decline in Palace enameling, at least by the 1760s, bottle production in Jingdezhen may have been instigated.

(v) The nationwide spread of the snuff-taking habit may not have taken place until the second half of the 18ᵗʰ century, limiting local demand at Jingdezhen.

(vi) That the kilns at Jingdezhen were of a type not well suited for the production of such small intimate objects, much smaller than even the tiniest of Imperial productions such as pen rests, brush pots, water droppers, cricket cages, bird feeders and miniature models. Jingdezhen was set up for mass production on a large scale for the most part.

(vii) Snuff bottle production had started and developed as a Beijing Palace operation, and thus the technical knowledge necessary to production was based there.

For another porcelain example with a plain ground and iron-red decoration on the edges and narrow sides, see Robert W. L. Kleiner, *Treasures from the Sanctum of Enlightened Respect: Chinese Snuff Bottles from the Denis Low Collection,* pp. 158-159.

For other similar examples, with differences in borders or the addition of a poem to the reverse, see Hugh Moss, *JICSBS,* June 1976, p. 4, No. 1, in an article 'Porcelain Snuff Bottles in the Collection of Alex S. Cussons'; *A Congregation of Snuff Bottle Connoisseurs,* No. 101; and Sotheby's, Hong Kong, 3 November 1994, lot 1026.

For a similar design on a set of Jiaqing-marked bottles, see *Snuff Bottles in the Collection of the National Palace Museum,* No. 90.

203 | **Porcelain**

1736-1795, Qianlong four-character iron-red seal mark in line within a rectangle and a further Qianlong seal at the end of the poetic inscription, late in the period
2 7/16 in. (6.2 cm.) high

Of quatrefoil shape, painted on one side with chrysanthemum growing from blue rockwork, the other side with a twenty-eight-character inscription and two seals, a simple whorl band at the foot and stylized floral decoration at the neck and narrow sides

1936-856 (CB. 341)

The twenty-eight-character inscription constitutes four lines of poetry, each line consisting of seven characters. They can be read as:

(i)   *(Qiu yu) fei fei bi xian zi*
(ii) *(Xian qing) jin ri bu (dong li)*
(iii) *Bu zhi leng ye han ____ li*
(iv) *Kai dao xi feng di ji zhi*

This can be translated as:
(i)   Autumn rains are heavy and bring life to the green moss
(ii) At ease and clear-headed he walks the Eastern fence
(iii) No one knows why in the chilly night or cold morning
(iv) These several stems of flowers (chrysanthemums) have bloomed in the West wind

The poem is followed by two iron-red seals reading: *Qian* and *Long*

The reference to *Dong li* ('East fence') in the second line is a clear reference to the famous Jin dynasty poet Tao Yuanming (real name Tao Qian, died A.D. 427), who composed poems about chrysanthemums and who planted them in profusion after his early retirement, particularly at the East fence.

This bottle falls into a well-known group of Imperial bottles painted with a floral scene on one side and a poem on the other, all produced during the latter part of the reign of the Qianlong Emperor and into the reign of his successor Jiaqing. However, this bottle appears to be the only example depicting chrysanthemums.

The most comparable published example is illustrated in *Snuff Bottles in the Collection of the National Palace Museum*, p. 114, No. 74. It is also of quatrefoil shape but with peony rather than chrysanthemum, and also has a twenty-eight-character poem followed by the seals *Qian* and *Long* with a Qianlong four-character seal mark on the base, which is unusual for this group. The Taipei bottle forms part of a boxed set of twenty ordered by the Imperial Court, perhaps as gifts to Court officials. Bottles of this type generally fall into three categories as far as the marks are concerned:

1. Qianlong seal marks on the base and Qianlong seal after the poem.

2. Jiaqing seal marks on the base and Qianlong seals after the poem.

3. Jiaqing seal marks on the base and other seals after the poem.

Those of the first category were probably produced late in the Qianlong Emperor's reign.

Those in the second category date to between 1796, when the Qianlong Emperor abdicated in favor of the Jiaqing Emperor, and his death in 1799.

The third category dates to post 1799, after the death of Qianlong.

This bottle falls into the first category.

For an example of rounded shape that falls into the first category, and interestingly, the only other bottle of this 'poem and flower group', which has a thin pink-ground-band of classic scroll on the foot, see Christopher C. H. Sin and Humphrey K. F. Hui, *An Imperial Qing Tradition*, No. 1, and also illustrated by Humphrey K. F. Hui and Peter Y. K. Lam, *The Imperial Connection, Court Related Chinese Snuff Bottles*, No. 105. See also *Snuff Bottles in the Collection of the National Palace Museum*, Nos. 81 and 82, for two rectangular examples painted with peony.

For an example of the second category, see *ibid.*, No. 83 (boxed set of twenty); and *ibid.*, No. 85 for circular examples (boxed set of twenty). Another example is illustrated by Robert Kleiner, *Chinese Snuff Bottles from the Collection of John Ault*, No. 121, and also illustrated on the front cover of the *JICSBS*, Spring 1987.

A sub-group to the three categories exists which are also of quatrefoil shape but are painted on both sides with floral decorations and omit the poem altogether. All appear to be marked Jiaqing in iron-red. For examples, see *Snuff Bottles in the Collection of the National Palace Museum*, No. 78, and No. 91 (set of five); and another in *Masterpieces of Snuff Bottles in the Palace Museum*, No. 163.

Linked with this group are bottles that bear the same characteristics of floral decoration on each side, but are of a different shape. See *Snuff Bottles in the Collection of the National Palace Museum*, No. 77, of spade shape and marked Qianlong; and *ibid.*, No. 76 of rounded rectangular shape and marked Jiaqing.

Finally, one other bottle is published which obviously forms part of the same group, but is painted with a different subject. See *Chinese Snuff Bottles, A Miniature Art from the Collection of Mary and George Bloch*, No. 141. It is painted with female figural scenes to each side and bears a Jiaqing mark.

204 | Porcelain

1736-1795, Qianlong four-character iron-red seal mark in a line and late in the period
2 ⁷/₁₆ in. (6.6 cm.) high

Of tapering baluster shape, painted on one side with a court official and two boys, the official holding a gilt *ruyi* scepter, one boy holding a paintbrush, the other holding three round objects, all on a garden terrace, the other side painted with numerous flowers including chrysanthemum, peony, camellia, magnolia, hibiscus, begonia, sweet olive and cockscomb, the narrow sides painted in iron-red with stylized scrolling foliage and flower heads

1936-863 (CB. 322)

A number of quite similar Imperial bottles are published. They usually have either iron-red Qianlong seal marks or iron-red Jiaqing seal marks.

The Blair example, however, appears to be unique in the use of a figural panel on one side rather than the use of flower panels on both sides.

It is interesting to note in this example that the lower part of the gilt surround to the panels on each side is truncated by an iron-red floral scroll, a feature to be found only on the Qianlong-marked examples.

In all the Jiaqing examples, the panels extend fully to the foot, as is also the case with some Qianlong-marked examples (see the following bottle, No. 205). This helps to build a chronology for their production. The panel designs actually fit more comfortably in the larger format suggesting that, at some point very late in the Qianlong reign, the use of the iron-red border below was dropped for aesthetic reasons.

For two similar Qianlong-marked examples with iron-red borders below the panels, see Robert Kleiner, *Chinese Snuff Bottles in the Collection of Mary and George Bloch*, No. 192; and Christopher C. H. Sin and Humphrey K. F. Hui, *An Imperial Qing Tradition*, No. 2. It is also published by Humphrey K. F. Hui and Peter Y. K. Lam in *The Imperial Connection - Court Related Chinese Snuff Bottles*, No. 106.

For Qianlong-marked examples without the lower iron-red border below the main panels, see Robert Hall, *Chinese Snuff Bottles III*, No. 60; Robert W. L. Kleiner, *Chinese Snuff Bottles from the Collection of John Ault*, No. 119; and the following bottle in this collection, No. 205.

For Jiaqing-marked examples, see Robert Kleiner, *ibid.*, No. 122; *Snuff Bottles in the Collection of the National Palace Museum*, No. 89 (a boxed set of ten); and also Alexander Brody, *Old Wine into Old Bottles, A Collector's Commonplace Book*, pp. 100-101 and p. 157, No. 100.

For a rare Jiaqing-marked bottle with a figural scene on each main face and *famille rose* floral decoration on the narrow sides, see Sotheby's, Hong Kong, 28 October 1992, lot 450.

In shape and decoration, this bottle probably relates most closely to the more stylized floral bottles illustrated in *Snuff Bottles in the Collection of the National Palace Museum*, No. 93 (boxed set of ten).

For a discussion of the subject of the floral decoration, 'the legendary nine flowers of autumn', see Humphrey K. F. Hui and Christopher C. H. Sin, *op. cit.*, No. 2. The nine flowers include marigold, chrysanthemum, yellow hibiscus, begonia, aster, cockscomb, Joseph's coat, rose mallow and sweet olive. The motif is traditionally named *Jiu qiu tu* ('nine autumn painting') or *jiu qiu tong qing* ('nine autumn festival'). It is very likely that this bottle depicts the same subject. Most of the flowers listed do appear on the Blair bottle but one cannot rely on the botanical accuracy of each artist.

205 | **Porcelain**

1790-1820, Qianlong four-character iron-red seal mark in a line and possibly late in the period
2 ¹⁷/₃₂ in. (6.4 cm.) high

Of elongated spade shape, painted on each side in *famille rose* enamels with various flowers including cockscomb, peony, chrysanthemum, daisy, sweet olive, hibiscus, aster and others issuing from rockwork, the narrow sides with begonia and scrolling foliage

1936-992 (CB. 331)

See the preceding bottle in this collection, No. 204. This bottle obviously forms part of the group as a whole.

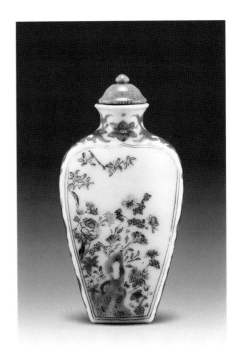

206 | **Porcelain**

1780-1820, both with Qianlong four-character iron-red seal marks and possibly late in the period
a - 2 ⁷/₁₆ in. (6.2 cm.) high
b - 2 ¹¹/₁₆ in. (7 cm.) high

Of tapering rectangular shape with waisted cylindrical necks, painted with alternate oval figural and floral panels on an underglaze blue ground with gilt floral decoration and floral roundels, the feet differing slightly, the neck and foot ring of the shorter bottle polished down and with a paler seal mark

144a - 1936-889-1 (CB. 329)

144b - 1936-889-2 (CB. 329)

For a very similar single bottle, without the addition of flower head roundels on the shoulders, see Christie's, New York, The Rachelle R. Holden Collection, 21 March 2000, lot 30. In that example the depiction was of solitary scholars in a landscape which had a long tradition in Chinese history, see Wen Fong, *Images of the Mind*, pp. 238-239. Traditionally, the recluse was a literati who renounced the civil service to devote himself to self-cultivation and an untrammeled life. The Blair example, though depicting one solitary scholar, also depicts two single figures of ladies, one holding a *qin*, the other a wrapped gift, and also a figure of a boy, either dancing or performing martial arts. This bottle may depict various scholarly accomplishments, if the ladies and boy are read as satellite figures to the single male scholar.

For another, see *A Congregation of Snuff Bottle Connoisseurs*, No. 96, where the authors note that the British Museum Collection has a similar example.

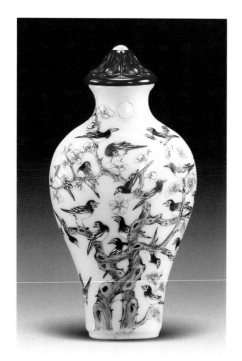

207 | **Porcelain**

1790-1820, Qianlong four-character iron-red seal mark and possibly late in the period
3 in. (7.5 cm.) high

Of baluster shape, painted in a continuous scene with thirty magpies amidst the branches of two prunus trees, one with greenish-white flowers, the other with pink flowers, below a moon

1936-857

For two bottles similarly decorated with thirty magpies in the branches of a blossoming tree, see Hugh M. Moss, *Snuff Bottles of China*, Nos. 310-311. Both are of cylindrical shape and one bears a Jiaqing iron-red mark.

Magpies can be read as a symbol of jubilation.

See also another bottle in this collection, No. 218.

208 | **Porcelain**

1770-1820, Qianlong four-character mark in iron red
2 ¼ in. (5.8 cm.) high

Of spade shape, painted on one side with the arrival of a lady on a small boat at a bank with the Daoist Immortals, holding various attributes, and on the other side with warrior figures, the narrow sides with underglaze-blue floral decoration which continues on the neck

1936-557 (CB. 322)

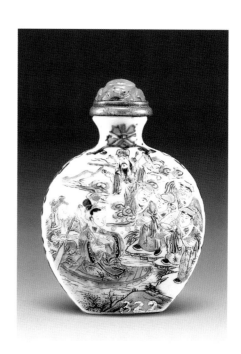

209 | Porcelain

1790-1830, Qianlong four-character underglaze blue seal mark
2 1/4 in. (5.7 cm.) high

Of spade shape, painted on each side with nine cranes beneath pine near *lingzhi* and rockwork, the narrow sides with underglaze blue and gilt floral decoration

1936-860 (CB. 323)

Although bottles of this shape with underglaze blue borders and narrow sides are well recorded, no others depicting numerous cranes appear to be published.

For other related examples, see Sotheby's, London, 21 June 1995, lots 128 and 129 from the Collection of The Stone Picking Studio (*Cai Shi Xuan*), both with Qianlong seal marks; Robert W. L. Kleiner, *Chinese Snuff Bottles in the Collection of Mary and George Bloch*, No. 196, where the author notes that 'The flattened shape with a flared neck appears to have been a popular one with the Court. Numerous nephrite snuff bottles of this shape remain within the Imperial collections in the National Palace Museum, Taiwan, *Catalogue*, Nos. 171-173.'

For further discussion of this group produced in Jingdezhen from the later part of the eighteenth century onwards, see Hugh Moss, Victor Graham and Ka Bo Tsang, *The Art of the Chinese Snuff Bottle, The J & J Collection*, No. 11.

210 | Porcelain

1796-1820, Qianlong six-character underglaze blue mark in a line
2 7/16 in. (6.2 cm.) high

Of spade shape, painted on each side in *famille rose* enamels with numerous boys holding lanterns on a terrace, a white elephant lantern held to the center of one side, a Buddhistic lion lantern on the other, with a dragon lantern beyond, the narrow sides with floral scrolling

1936-994 (CB. 324)

For another more rounded bottle depicting a similar scene, see the Humphrey K. F. Hui and Christoper C. H. Sin, *An Imperial Qing Tradition*, No. 7. The authors note that the scene depicted is known as *Baizi tu* 'Painting of One Hundred Boys'. According to legend, the Duke of Chou, Wen Wang (1231-1135 B.C.) had ninety-nine children of his own and adopted another to make one hundred sons. The design is based on a famous painting by the Song artist Su Hanchen.

See also another bottle illustrated by Hugh Moss, *Chinese Snuff Bottles: 6. Chinese Snuff Bottles from the Collection of the Rt. Hon. The Marquess of Exeter, K.C.M.G.*, p. 33, No. C.20, depicting a similar scene with men rather than boys.

The depiction of dragon, elephant and lion lanterns clearly suggests that the subject is a Buddhist festival.

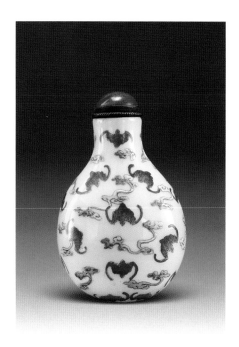

211 | **Porcelain**

1790-1880, Qianlong four-character iron-red seal mark
2 ³/₁₆ in. (5.4 cm.) high

Of rounded pear shape, painted with eighteen iron-red bats amidst yellow, purple and white cloud swirls and five more bats, *wufu,* around the mark

1936-872 (CB. 367)

Provenance: Almost certainly the American Art Galleries, New York
      The Elizabeth Andrews Collection, 8-9 February 1922, lot 354

For a bottle of ovoid shape painted with fourteen bats holding beribboned auspicious symbols and peaches amidst clouds, see Hugh Moss, Victor Graham and Ka BoTsang, *The Art of the Chinese Snuff Bottle, The J & J Collection,* No. 224. The authors agree on a date of between 1830–1890 based on the enamels used. Whilst this example might be as late as 1880 or thereabouts, a date earlier in the range seems more likely based on the high quality of the enamels and the shape which is identical to many bottles with Daoguang marks. The fact that this bottle is also unable to stand without support ties it to the J & J example.

Two other examples, identical in shape and decoration, one from the J. B. Speed Museum, Louisville, Kentucky, the other from the Bernice Straus Hasterlik Collection, both called Qianlong period, sold at Sotheby's, New York, 17 March 1997, lot 409 and Sotheby's, New York, 17 September 1996, lot 126, respectively. The fact that both bottles sold very well would suggest that more than one bidder was convinced by the rather loosely-painted Qianlong mark which is very similar to the mark on this example.

212 | **Porcelain**

1796-1820, Jiaqing four-character iron-red seal mark and of the period
2 ½ in. (6.3 cm.) high

Of rectangular shape, one side painted with two ladies conversing near a window where a gentleman sits playing a *qin*, the other side with the same gentlemen standing on a rock by a lake below two women on a pavilion terrace, the narrow sides with underglaze blue and gilt floral decoration

1936-991 (CB. 334)

For a bottle of identical shape depicting the same subject, scenes from *The Romance of the West Chamber (Xixiang Ji),* see Hugh Moss, Victor Graham and Ka Bo Tsang, *The Art of the Chinese Snuff Bottle, The J & J Collection,* No. 211. The authors note that the story was written in the Yuan dynasty by Wang Shifu but in a long tradition of earlier literary compositions.

The two ladies depicted are Cui Yingying and her maid, Hongniang. The gentleman is Zhang Junrui, a scholar in love with Cui Yingying.

For another bottle of more rounded shape but depicting similar interior scenes with balustrades highlighted in iron-red and yellow enamel and also with underglaze blue and gilt decoration on the narrow sides, see Robert W. L. Kleiner, *Chinese Snuff Bottles from the Collection of John Ault,* No.123. It is obvious that they form part of the same large group of Imperial bottles.

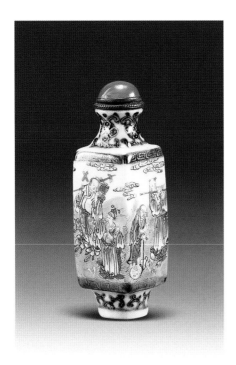

213 | **Porcelain**

1796-1820, Jiaqing four-character iron-red seal mark and of the period
2 ⁷/₁₆ in. (6.3 cm.) high

Of tall rectangular shape, painted in *famille rose* enamels with the eight Daoist Immortals, two on each face, on a green wave ground between gilt underglaze blue floral decoration at the waisted neck and foot

1936-620 (CB.335)

See Robert W. L. Kleiner, *Chinese Snuff Bottles in the Collection of Mary and George Bloch*, No. 203, for the most comparable published example. It too is of rectangular shape with a continuous Daoist scene set between underglaze blue and gilt borders, and bears a Jiaqing four-character iron-red seal mark on the base. It depicts Lu Dongbin directing a demon with a girl on his back towards an official seated at a desk.

For another example from the Alex S. Cussons Collection, see Sotheby's, Hong Kong, 3 May 1995, lot 625, painted with figures in a garden setting. For another of the same type but octagonal and illustrating a historical scene, see Humphrey K. F. Hui and Peter Y. K. Lam, *The Imperial Connection, Court Related Chinese Snuff Bottles*, No. 110. It is also illustrated by Christopher C. H. Sin and Humphrey K. F. Hui in *An Imperial Qing Tradition*, No. 4.

For other examples which fall into this grouping, see Rachelle R. Holden, *Rivers and Mountains Far from the World*, No. 109. Another with a Qianlong mark is illustrated by *A Congregation of Snuff Bottle Connoisseurs*, No. 96, from the Tuyet Nguyet Collection.

214 | **Porcelain**

1796-1820, Jiaqing six-character iron-red mark in a line and of the period
1 ⁷/₈ in. (4.8 cm.) high

Of square shape, painted on one side with a gentleman and a lady seated at a table, he drinking, whilst another lady looks on from a nearby moon window, the other side with the same gentleman, either resting against a table or in a drunken stupor, with the same lady approaching him, underglaze blue floral decoration on the neck and lotus on the narrow sides

1936-641-2 (CB. 336)

This bottle forms a pair with the following bottle in this collection, No. 215. The young male figure depicted is the same on each bottle.

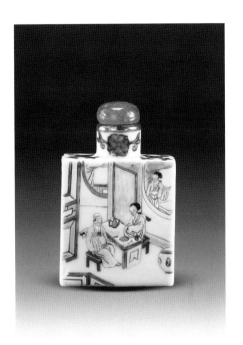

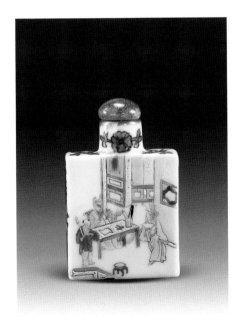

215 | **Porcelain**

1796-1820, Jiaqing six-character mark in iron red in a line and of the period
1 ⁷/₈ in. (4.8 cm.) high

Of square shape, painted on one side with a sleeping figure at a table dreaming, a thought bubble portraying a snake emerging from his head, a figure with a whisk standing nearby, the other side with the same figure, now awake, standing before a seated official and his assistant in an interior, underglaze blue floral decoration on the neck and lotus on the narrow sides

1936-641-1 (CB. 336)

This bottle forms a pair with the preceding bottle in this collection, No. 214.

216 | **Porcelain**

1796-1820, Jiaqing four-character iron-red seal mark and of the period
2 ³/₈ in. (6 cm.) high

Of quatrefoil shape, both sides painted with courtly scenes, one depicting a presentation with a dignitary seated in a yoke-back chair at a desk, another official holding a scepter and another a cloth, with a figure in iron-red approaching, the other side with two boys attending to another figure seated in a horse-shoe back armchair, the narrow sides with floral scrolling, probably begonia

1936-936 (CB. 333)

For a bottle of spade shape, similarly painted on one side with a scholar gentleman seated in an interior assisted by two youthful attendants, see *Zhongguo Biyanhu Zhenshang*, (Gems of Chinese Snuff Bottles), No. 196.

217 | **Porcelain**

1795-1820, Qianlong four-character seal mark in a line
2 ³/₁₆ in. (5.5 cm.) high

Of spade shape, with lightly molded border, painted with floral sprays growing from rockwork on each side including hibiscus, chrysanthemum, sweet olive, begonia, aster and peony, the narrow sides with formalized floral scrolling in iron-red

1936-934 (CB. 321)

See No. 204, for a discussion of the possible subject of the floral decoration, 'the legendary nine flowers of autumn' and flower-decorated bottles in general.

218 | Porcelain

1850-1900
2¹¹/₁₆ in. (6.8 cm.) high

Of cylindrical shape, painted in a continuous scene with thirty magpies amidst prunus and above camellia

1936-546 (CB. 348)

The Chinese term for magpie, *xiqiao*, means literally 'bird of happiness', and it is regarded as a bird of good omen. Thirty magpies expresses a wish for happiness every day of the month.

For a similar example depicting twelve magpies, 'happiness every month of the year', see Humphrey K. F. Hui, Margaret Polak and Christopher C. H. Sin, *Hidden Treasures of the Dragon*, No. 70.

See also bottle No. 207.

219 | Porcelain

1800-1850, Qianlong four-character iron-red seal mark in an oval
2 ³/₈ in. (6 cm.) high

Of spade shape, delicately painted on each side with two melons at the center on a floral leafy ground surrounded by four butterflies at the cardinal points facing the center, all on a yellow ground

1936-865

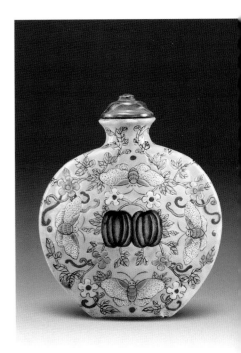

A nearly identical unmarked bottle from the Janos Szekeres Collection was sold by Sotheby's, New York, 27 October 1986, lot 6.

For another bottle of melon shape also depicting fruiting melon vines, see Robert W. L. Kleiner, *Chinese Snuff Bottles from the Collection of Mary and George Bloch*, No. 229, where the author suggests that the delicacy of painting and the tones of the enamels are entirely consistent with a Jiaqing dating.

Another sold at Sotheby's, Hong Kong, 5 May 1994, lot 1563.

The floral and leaf decoration on this bottle is identical to the decoration molded on a Jiaqing period bottle in this collection, No. 246.

Hugh Moss illustrates an iron-red ground bottle from the Russell Mullin Collection in *Chinese Snuff Bottles: 5*, fig. 18, and notes that a similar bottle on a yellow ground is in the Linda Riddell Hoffman Collection.

Melons with butterflies form the rebus *Guadie mianmian* ('May you have numerous descendants').

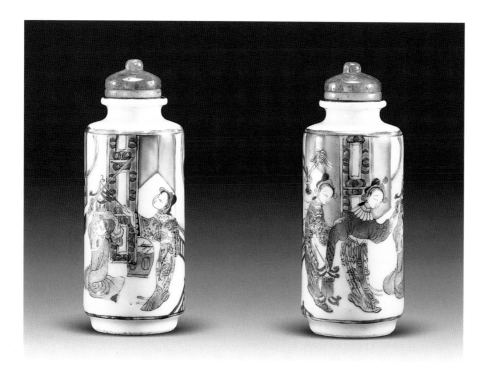

220 | **Porcelain**

1821-1850, Daoguang six-character iron-red seal mark in reserve and of the period
2 ³/₄ in. (6.9 cm.) high

Of cylindrical shape, finely painted in delicate *famille rose* enamels in a continuous scene with three elegant ladies in long-sleeved robes, one holding a sword, another a musical stone suspended from a rod above the head of a kneeling man, all set in a courtly interior

1936-506 (CB. 346)

This appears to be a unique bottle. The courtly scene may well be taken from one of the popular novels of the day, like the *Dream of the West Chamber.* Peculiar to this particular scene are the vertical areas of red, green and white panels. Initially they appear to be a form of latticework often seen in interiors. This may indeed be what they are supposed to represent, however, on close inspection of the panel directly behind the kneeling figure, it becomes obvious that the artist who painted them believed he was actually painting banners hanging from the ceiling. As represented, the banner hangs in front of a barrel-shaped seat but does not touch the floor. The white rectangular areas, which were meant to be open slots, do not allow a view beyond and must therefore be read as white areas of cloth.

For a Jiaqing-marked bottle of baluster shape, also showing interior scenes, see *Zhongguo Biyanhu Zhenshang,* (Gems of Chinese Snuff Bottles), No. 151. It depicts the same latticework.

221 | Porcelain

1821-1850, Daoguang four-character iron-red seal mark in a line and of the period
2 ⁷/₄ in. (6.2 cm.) high

Of rounded shape, painted in *famille rose* enamels with Europeans hunting in a wooded landscape, one side with a caped figure watching two others shoot a fox with rifles, the other side with two figures and their kill slung on a pole between them, another gentleman crossing a bridge nearby

1936-916

For another bottle of very similar shape and muted color scheme but depicting fisherman, see Robert Kleiner, *Treasures from the Sanctum of Enlightened Respect: Chinese Snuff Buttles in the Denis Low Collection*, No. 148. It bears a *Jian an ya zhi*, ('Made for the small temple of good health') and is dated to between 1800-1850.

222 | Porcelain

1821-1850, Daoguang four-character iron-red seal mark and of the period
2 ⁷/₁₆ in. (5.8cm.) high

Of large rounded shape, painted in the *famille rose* palette with a young man, a rifle slung over his shoulder, leading a black and white dog on one side, the reverse with a gentleman leading a Bactrian camel with a pack slung between its humps

1936-940

This bottle relates to a small group of bottles, mostly Daoguang-marked, depicting similar scenes. For the most likely interpretation of this unusual scene, see Humphrey K. F. Hui and Peter Y. K. Lam, *The Imperial Connection, Court Related Chinese Snuff Bottles*, No. 115, where the authors suggest that it is a historical rendering of the hunting trip called *Qiuli* or 'autumn hunting'. It began under the reign of the Kangxi Emperor and continued until the early nineteenth century. Between 1740 and 1745 the Qianlong Emperor ordered the painters at the Royal Painting Academy to illustrate this event.

Another example is illustrated in *Chinese Snuff Bottles, A Miniature Art from The Collection of Mary and George Bloch*, No. 153, of slightly different shape. For another cylindrical bottle painted in underglaze blue and copper-red with a continuous scene of a mounted Manchu official on a camel led by a groom, see *A Congregation of Snuff Bottle Connoisseurs*, No. 109.

For an example where the figure leading the dog is riding on horseback, see Sotheby's, Hong Kong, 29 April 1992, lot 410.

223 | **Porcelain**

1821-1850, Daoguang four-character iron-red seal mark and of the period
2 ¹/₄ in. (5.7 cm.) high

Of rounded shape, painted in *famille rose* enamels on one side with two scholars playing *weiqi* with an attendant nearby, and on the other with a boy and his buffalo approaching a man raising a whisk

1936-616

Bottles of this shape bearing Daoguang marks are plentiful. The subjects vary enormously from birds and floral scenes to mythical dragons and a wide variety of genre scenes like this one. For an example depicting a gathering of literati which includes sages playing *weiqi*, see *Chinese Snuff Bottles and Jade Carvings from the Douglas, Gnam and other Collections*, The Chinese Porcelain Company, p. 22, No. 29. For an example with children at play, see Robert Kleiner, *Treasures from the Sanctum of Enlightened Respect: Chinese Snuff Buttles from the Denis Low Collection*, No. 144, and the same author in *Precious Playthings: Important Chinese Snuff Bottles from the Mack Collection*, No. 39, portraying a woodcutter in a landscape on one side.

224 | **Porcelain**

1850-1900, Qianlong four-character iron-red seal mark
2 in. (5 cm.) high

Of rounded shape, painted in *famille rose* enamels with peony and daisy growing from rockwork below magnolia and another tree spray, possibly prunus, around the iron-red and gilt lion-mask fixed-ring handles at the shoulders

1936-990 (CB. 342)

For an identically shaped bottle painted with children at play dated to the Republic period (1912-1949), see Sotheby's, Hong Kong, 2 May 1996, lot 1231. The conservative dating in the Sotheby's catalogue is probably a result of the unusual placement of handles on a form normally left plain, and the very fine condition of the enamels. A date between 1850-1900 seems much more likely for both bottles.

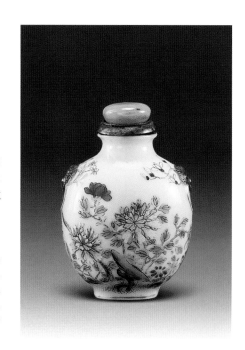

225 | **Porcelain**

1821-1850, Daoguang six-character iron-red seal mark and of the period
2 ⅛ in. (5.4 cm) high

Of compressed baluster shape, painted in a continuous scene with two five-clawed dragons contesting a flaming pearl amidst cloud and fire-scrolls above breaking waves, original stopper painted with a five-clawed dragon and a pearl

1936-861 (CB. 362)

For a pair of white-glazed Daoguang-marked bottles called 'Table bottles' on account of their large size, both in height and in girth, see Humphrey K. F. Hui, Margaret Polak and Christopher C. H. Sin, *Hidden Treasures of the Dragon*, No. 296.

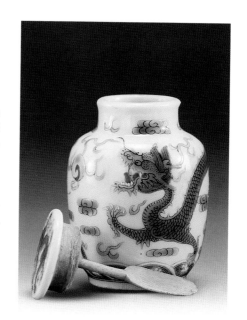

226 | **Porcelain**

1821-1850, *Tui Si Tang* three-character iron-red hallmark to the base, Daoguang

2 ⁵⁄₁₆ in. (5.6 cm.) high

Of rounded shape, painted on each side with two birds perched in an autumnal tree, possibly maple, above chrysanthemum and rockwork

1939-982

The mark *Tui Si Tang* can be read as the 'Hall of reflection'.

For an identical bottle, see Robert Kleiner, *Chinese Snuff Bottles from the Collection of John Ault*, No. 148, where the author notes that the bottle is painted like many Daoguang-marked bottles, with the black stippling of the grass being particularly indicative of the group.

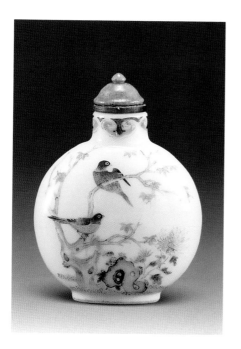

The shape of this bottle, gently rounded as it is, is highly successful. The omission of molded handles to the sides adds purity to the line, distinctly lacking in some bottles of this period.

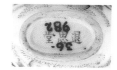

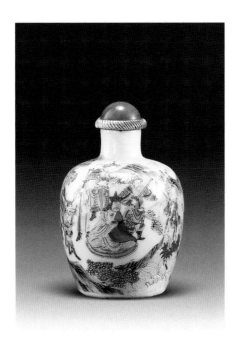

227 | **Porcelain**

1821-1880, *Fu Qing Tang* three-character iron-red mark
1 ⁷/₈ in. (4.9 cm.) high

Of compressed baluster shape, painted in a continuous scene with a sword-wielding lady (White Snake) on a boat surrounded by demons arriving at a promontory on which sits a monk and other figures heralding their arrival amidst frothy waves

1936-1050 (CB. 343)

The hallmark *Fu Qing Tang* can be read as 'Hall of good fortune and blessing'.

The subject is from the classic *Bai She zhuang* (White Snake Story). The figure in the prow of the boat is in fact the 'white snake' in the guise of a woman. She has fallen in love with a human and is shown arriving at Jinshan (near Nanjing) to meet him. However a protective monk is on hand to warn the man of troubles ahead. With her demonic powers, the white snake will inundate the temple with floodwaters. However, the monk will finally win the battle between them.

228 | **Porcelain**

1821-1890, Yongzheng pale blue enamel six-character seal mark
2 ³/₄ in. (7 cm.) high

Of baluster shape, delicately painted in primarily black, yellow and iron-red with five cockerels variously walking or scratching in the earth

1936-1016

For a similar example of five cockerels on a cylindrical bottle bearing a Guangxu mark, see Christie's, New York, The Rachelle R. Holden Collection, 21 March 2000, lot 13. For another example of *meiping* shape, with a *wan shang* ('play and appreciate') mark to the base, see Sotheby's, New York, 17 March 1997, lot 390.

The design of five roosters calls to mind the term *wugong* ('five Lords') which can be interpreted as a generic term referring to high positions. In Chinese lore, cockerels are a symbol for advancement by rank. A bottle like this may have been given as a gift to offer congratulations on a promotion.

For further discussion, see an article by Ka Bo Tsang, 'The Chicken and its Manifold Meanings,' *JICSBS*, Autumn 1993, pp. 4-17.

229 | **Porcelain**

1800-1850, Qianlong four-character seal mark
2 in. (5 cm.) high

Of spade shape, painted with peony sprays rising from blue Taihu rockwork on one side and the three stellar gods below pine on the other, the narrow sides with iron-red and gilt floral scrolling

1936-935

For an iron-red decorated spade-shaped bottle with similar peony sprays on one side, see *A Congregation of Snuff Bottle Connoisseurs*, No. 90. It bears a Qianlong Imperial poem on the reverse with the cyclical date *dingyou* corresponding to 1777.

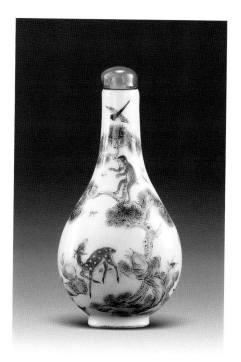

230 | **Porcelain**

1800-1850
2 ³/₄ in. (7 cm.) high

Of pear shape, painted in *famille rose* enamels with a magpie in flight above a monkey in the branches of a pine grasping for bees, with a deer amidst rockwork and *lingzhi* on one side, three further magpies on prunus branches and flower sprays on the other

1936-1037 (CB. 339)

Due to the belief that deer live to a great age, they have become a longevity symbol. As it is also believed to be the only animal able to find the sacred fungus of immortality, *lingzhi*, deer became a very popular subject. The deer with a bird, bee and monkey forms the rebus *julu fenghou*, which can be read as 'may you receive high rank and profit.'

231 | **Porcelain**

1820-1880
2 ¹/₈ in. (5.4 cm.) high

Of *meiping* shape, painted on a celadon ground with three geese on a riverbank near millet, a fourth goose flying above

1936-1053 (CB. 358)

For a blue and white porcelain bottle of tapering cylindrical shape painted with a similar scene, see Robert W. L. Kleiner, *Chinese Snuff Bottles from the Collection of Mary and George Bloch,* No. 228. See also Humphrey K. F. Hui, and Christopher C. H. Sin, *An Imperial Qing Tradition;* No. 21, and *Zhongguo Biyanhu Zhenshang,* (Gems of Chinese Snuff Bottles), No. 213.

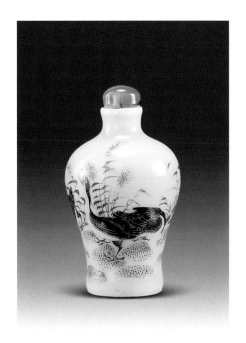

232 | **Porcelain**

1790-1850, indecipherable two-character iron-red seal mark in reserve
2 ³/₈ in. (6 cm.) high

Of spade shape, painted on each side with slightly varying scenes of Chinese buildings and walled gardens in a landscape

1936-667

233 | **Porcelain**

1820-1880, Qianlong four-character iron-red seal mark
2 ¹¹/₁₆ in. (6.9 cm.) high

Of double gourd shape, painted in bright enamels with a dense floral ground including chrysanthemum, morning glory, lotus, peony, daisy, pinks and magnolia

1936-887 (CB. 319)

For another rare *mille-fiore* double gourd bottle, of rounded rather than flattened shape, see Bob C. Stevens, *The Collector's Book of Snuff Bottles*, No. 300 from the collection of Edward Choate O'Dell.

234 | **Porcelain**

1850-1900, Qianlong four-character blue enamel seal mark
2 ²⁷/₃₂ in. (7.2 cm.) high

Of cylindrical shape, painted in a continuous scene with five variously colored five-clawed dragons contesting flaming pearls amidst fire-scrolls on an incised white-glazed wave ground

1936-1038 (CB. 344)

For a bottle of identical shape, painted with eight variously colored dragons on an incised white ground, see Christie's, New York, 2 June 1994, lot 425. Incised white grounds are seen on ceramic wares for both the export and the domestic market.

For a rectangular porcelain bottle painted with mythical animals on an incised white ground, see *Snuff Bottles in the Collection of the National Palace Museum*, No. 96.

During the Daoguang period, the Court continued its intense interest in ceramic snuff bottle production of the previous several decades. Taste, however, changed radically, generally favoring painted enamels over molded porcelain, and surface decoration over elaborate form.

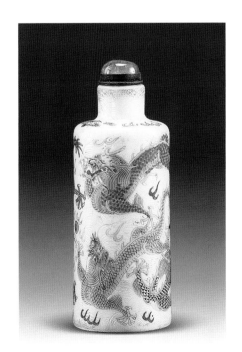

235 | Porcelain

1850-1900, Qianlong two-character iron-red mark
2 ⁹/₁₆ in. (6.6 cm.) high

Of rectangular shape, painted with alternate raised panels of chrysanthemum and peony divided by poem panels, all reserved on a molded dotted blue enamel ground with stylized gilt flower heads

1936-886 (CB. 327)

One poetic inscription *Dao chu hua fei pian* can be read as 'flower petals fly everywhere'. The other can only be partly read, the third and fifth characters being illegible *Xiang feng (?) Jin (?)*. It can mean 'fragrant wind' and 'splendid'.

236 | Porcelain

1800-1880, Qianlong four-character iron-red seal mark
2 ¼ in. (5.4 cm.) high

Of spade shape, painted in *famille rose* enamels with numerous boys, fifty on one side and forty-six on the other, all on a terrace, the boys holding a wide variety of shaped lanterns including fish, an elephant and a Buddhistic lion

1936-837 (CB. 326)

For a very similar bottle in the collection and a discussion of the subject, see No. 210.

The presence of fish, elephant and lion lanterns would indicate that the subject is a Buddhist festival.

237 | Porcelain

1850-1900
1 ⁷/₈ in. (4.7 cm.) high

Of rounded form and small size, painted with a river landscape on one side and five scholars unrolling a scroll painting centered by a *yin-yang* symbol on the other, above a pierced spreading foot, the shoulder with two pierced beribboned balls and the remnants of two Buddhistic lions, original stopper

1936-868 (CB. 355)

This extremely fragile and delicate bottle forms part of a well-known group. Three other bottles, similar in fragility, pierced at the foot, and with delicate molding to the shoulders, though differently decorated, are illustrated by Helen White, *Snuff Bottles from China, The Victoria and Albert Museum Collection*, pl. 118, Nos. 1, 2 and 3.

Another bottle from the same workshop, dated 1820-1880, was sold at Sotheby's, Hong Kong, 3 May 1995, lot 626.

For a blue and white example with Buddhistic lions on the shoulders but no beribboned balls and with pierced cash to the foot, see Robert Kleiner, *Precious Playthings: Important Chinese Snuff Bottles from the Mack Collection*, No. 43. It is dated to the 1770's.

The stopper on this bottle is unquestionably the original. It is pale green, glazed on the underside of the stopper and on a cylinder which neatly fits inside the neck of the bottle. The glaze is identical to the glaze on the pierced foot.

238 | Porcelain

1800-1850
2 ⁵/₁₆ in. (6 cm.) high

A double bottle formed as two pea-pods, enameled in colors with a lady on each face, the four ladies holding attributes of a plum blossom, book, fan and a large disc, possibly a drum or tambourine

1936-631

For a very similar example, dated Daoguang, see Sotheby's, London, 19 June 1981, lot 135.

Another, also depicting the same subject of four maidens, was sold at Christie's, London, The Ko Family Collection, Part II, 12 June 1972, lot 47.

For a bottle of similar shape in this collection, see No. 329.

239 | Porcelain

1880-1900, a set of twelve bottles, each bearing an iron-red character from the twelve earthly branches of the cyclical dating system
2 ⁵/₈ in. (6.6 cm.) high

Each painted in *famille rose* enamels with either floral scenes or floral and bird scenes

1936-1055 to 1066 (CB. 352)

Literature: Edward Wenham, 'Antiques As Decoration', *Arts & Decoration*, New York, Winter, 1928, illustrated p. 58.

The twelve earthly branches of the cyclical dating system, *zi, chou, yin, mao, chen, si, wu, wei, shen, you, xu and hai*, are usually used to represent the twelve animals of the zodiac: rat, ox, tiger, hare, dragon, serpent, horse, sheep, monkey, cock, dog, and boar. However, the earthly branches are also sometimes used, though more rarely, to represent the twelve fruit and flowers of the months: prunus, peach, peony, cherry, magnolia, pomegranate, lotus, pear, mallow, chrysanthemum, gardenia, and poppy. Although the depictions on the bottles themselves do not strictly adhere to this format, it is the most likely reason for their use.

The most comparable bottle, though more finely painted and bearing a Jiaqing iron-red mark, is illustrated in *A Congregation of Snuff Bottle Connoisseurs*, No. 99. It too is painted in polychrome enamels on a square bottle of rectangular section.

240 | Porcelain

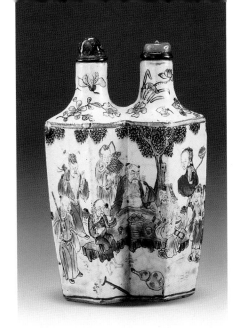

1820-1880, a Buddhist endless knot in iron-red on each base
2 ³/₄ in. (7 cm.) high

Two tapering trapezoidal bottles joined at one angle, painted in a continuous scene with the eight Daoist Immortals and the three Stellar Gods seated and standing around rockwork tables below pine, the sloping shoulders with a variety of flower sprays

1936-569 (CB. 337)

Literature: Edward Wenham, 'Antiques As Decoration', *Arts & Decoration*, Winter, 1928, illustrated p. 59.

For an almost identical example with crackled glaze, see Christie's, London, The Ko Family Collection, Part II, 12 June 1972, lot 26.

241 | Porcelain

1800-1850
2 ³/₁₆ in. (5.6 cm.) high

A double porcelain bottle, each section of cylindrical shape, painted in *famille rose* enamels with Zhong Kui, the Demon Queller, on horseback leading his sister in her wheeled chariot, one demon pushing it, and two others leading the group

1936-1028

For a rounded bottle depicting the same subject and bearing a Daoguang mark, see Sotheby's, London, 6 June 1988, lot 6.

242 | Porcelain

1880-1920, *Jing Shan Tang Zhi* four-character iron-red hallmark
2 ⁹/₁₆ in. (6.5 cm.) high

Of slender ovoid shape, painted in *famille rose* enamels with a wooded mountainous landscape, one side with two figures seated at a stone table, the other side with a lone figure crossing a bridge, all between a variety of brightly enameled bands at the neck and foot

1936-980

The hallmark *Jing Shan Tang Zhi* can be read as: 'Hall where goodness is respected.'

243 | **Porcelain, molded**

1780-1820, Qianlong six-character iron-red seal mark in a line and possibly late in the period
2 ⁵/₁₆ in. (5.9 cm.) high

Of flattened shield shape, each side molded and painted in the *famille rose* palette with a design repeated on each main face, iron-red bat above a tree growing from rockwork and frothy waves, the narrow sides painted with a formalized floral scroll over a lightly incised ground of scrolling foliage or *chilong*

1936-842 (CB. 446)

This and the following bottle, No. 244, are from the same workshop, and both have the design repeated on each main face. Other bottles are recorded with peach trees rising from rocks and waves on one side only, and bamboo, narcissus, *lingzhi*, and rockwork (identical to those of No. 244) on the other. For examples, see *A Congregation of Snuff Bottle Connoisseurs*, No. 107; and *Snuff Bottles of China* by Hugh Moss, No. 294.

For an identical example of this model, see Bob C. Stevens, *The Collector's Book of Snuff Bottles*, No. 293. For a slightly different example with a nearly identical subject but an alternate disposition of the peach tree to the left, more obviously breaking waves and a larger bat on the right side, see Hugh Moss, *Chinese Snuff Bottles: 5*, p. 72, fig. 82, and another illustrated by Robert Kleiner in *Chinese Snuff Bottles in the Collection of Mary and George Bloch*, No. 195, where the author suggests that the inclusion of scattered petals floating amidst waves is an allusion to marriage. Peaches, too, are symbolic of both longevity and marriage.

Another example similar to these, but painted directly on the biscuit with a predominantly yellow ground, is illustrated by Robert W. L. Kleiner, *Chinese Snuff Bottles from the Collection of John Ault*, No. 134.

It is most unusual, and rather puzzling, to find the incised scrolling (or possibly *chilong*) under the *famille rose* decoration on the narrow sides of this bottle.

244 | Porcelain, molded

1780-1820, Qianlong six-character underglaze blue mark in a line and possibly late in the period
2 ³/₈ in. (6.1 cm.) high

Of flattened shield shape, molded and painted identically on each side with narcissus, bamboo and *lingzhi* sprays, peony and rockwork, the narrow sides and waisted neck painted in underglaze blue and gilt with floral decoration

1936-841 (CB. 447)

See the preceding bottle, No. 243.

For an almost identical example, see Robert Kleiner, *Chinese Snuff Bottles in the Collection of Mary and George Bloch*, No. 194, where the author notes that the reign mark has the inverted 'S'-shape element in the *Qian* character suggesting it was made to order for the abdicated Qianlong Emperor. This particular element is difficult to discern on the Blair bottle.

See also, *ibid.*, No. 192 and No. 197, for further discussion of the protocol of reign marks.

See another illustrated by Hugh Moss, in *Chinese Snuff Bottles: 5*, p. 73, fig. 83.

245 | Porcelain, molded

1796-1820, Jiaqing four-character iron-red seal mark and of the period
2 ³/₄ in. (7 cm.) high

Of double-gourd shape, molded over the entire body in low relief and painted with a continuous design of gourds, leaves and scrolling tendrils, supported on a shallow oval foot

1936-849 (CB. 456/444)

This and the following bottle, No. 246, are quite similar. However, this example is unquestionably of a higher quality in terms of the ceramic and painting. The delicate subtleties of soft molding are made all the more apparent by the overall placement of the gourds and leaves. In the hand it is also markedly more comfortable to hold and feels more delicate.

Only a few examples of this type appear to be published; see Sotheby's, New York, The Janos Szekeres Collection, 27 October 1986, lot 13; and possibly another (neck reduced and heavily rubbed) illustrated by Hugh Moss, *Chinese Snuff Bottles: 6. Chinese Snuff Bottles from the Collection of the Rt. Hon. The Marquess of Exeter, K.C.M.G.*, p. 40, No. C.42.

This example can also be associated with Imperial Qianlong-marked bottles of double-gourd shape with painted fruiting gourds and iron-red bats which might be considered a precursor; see Robert Kleiner, *Chinese Snuff Bottles in the Collection of Mary and George Bloch*, No. 193.

246 | **Porcelain, molded**

1796-1820, Jiaqing four-character iron-red seal mark and of the period
3 in. (7.6 cm.) high

Of double-gourd shape, molded and painted in the *famille rose* palette with a continuous design of gourds, flower heads and trailing foliage with five and six-petal leaves, the oval base with the mark raised from the ground by four molded gourds forming the feet of the bottle

1936-579

Provenance: The American Art Association The Anderson Galleries Inc.
New York, *The Ton-Ying Collection*, 24-25 January 1930, lot 220
(See fig. 33 in the Introduction.)

See the preceding bottle, No. 245.

On this bottle, the four lower gourds extend below the base edge to form feet; it may have been made as a table bottle. For other examples of high-relief gourd-footed bottles, see Sotheby's, New York, The Dr. Paula Hallett Collection, 2 December 1985, lot 125; Bob C.

Stevens, *The Collector's Book of Snuff Bottles*, No. 281; Sotheby's, London, 10 February 1976, lot 51; and Hugh Moss in *Chinese Snuff Bottles: 5*, p. 66, fig. 63.

A fruiting gourd vine symbolizes a wish for numerous descendants.

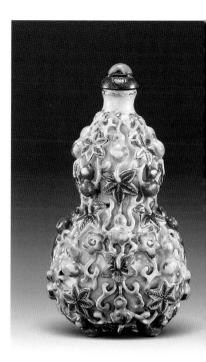

247 | **Porcelain, molded**

1796-1820, Jiaqing four-character iron-red seal mark and of the period
3 in. (7.7cm.) high

Of spade shape, molded in low relief with a continuous scene from the *Romance of the Three Kingdoms* epic, *Cao Chuan Jie Jian*, depicting archers on a crenellated city wall firing at canopied boats on a swirling waterway below

1936-574

The epic *Romance of the Three Kingdoms*, story here depicted, *Cao Chuan Jie Jian*, ('grass boat borrows arrows'), is very finely wrought. The man in the prow of the boat is a historical figure, Zhuge Liang (181-234 A.D.). He was the chief of staff of one kingdom's army, and he battled against General Cao Cao (155-220 A.D.). He is depicted on the ramparts of the city wall.

Zhuge Liang's forces need arrows for warfare. His army has only three days to complete its mission. He devises a simple but effective plan to feign an attack on his opponents using boats with thick straw roofs. However, he needs the west wind to blow in a favorable direction in order for his scheme to be successful. On the last night available to him, the wind turns in his direction and he sends his fleet of straw-roofed boats in a dummy attack. As planned, his opponent fires massive salvoes of arrows. These are 'collected' by his foes for re-use against Cao Cao.

248 | Porcelain, molded

1796-1820, Jiaqing four-character iron-red seal mark and of the period
2 ⅞ in. (7.3 cm.) high

Of ovoid shape, molded and painted in a continuous scene in *famille rose* enamels with three of the Daoist Immortals in a tree raft approaching the remaining five Daoist Immortals standing on a promontory amidst dense rockwork

1936-929

Literature: Edward Wenham, 'Antiques As Decoration'. *Arts & Decoration*, New York, Winter, 1928, illustrated p. 96.

A number of identically molded bottles are published, though differing slightly in enamel colors and strength of molding. This example is probably one of the finest. See *Chinese Snuff Bottles*, No. 94; Sotheby's, New York, 3 October 1980, lot 112; another illustrated in *Chinese Snuff Bottles, A Miniature Art from The Collection of Mary and George Bloch*, No. 161; and one sold at Sotheby's, New York, The Gerry P. Mack Collection, 25 October 1997, lot 275.

249 | **Porcelain, molded**

1796-1820, Jiaqing four-character iron-red seal mark and of the period
2 ⁹/₁₆ in. (6.5 cm.) high

Of spade shape, finely molded and painted in bright enamels in a continuous scene with a scholar gentleman and lady on a pavilion terrace extending to a lotus pond to one side, and two ladies and a gentleman on boats cutting lotus to the other

1936-968 (CB. 417)

For two other nearly identical examples, see Robert W. L. Kleiner, *Chinese Snuff Bottles from the Collection of John Ault*, No. 128, which is also marked with an iron-red Jiaqing four-character seal mark and attributed to the Imperial Jingdezhen workshops. Another is illustrated by Hugh Moss, *Chinese Snuff Bottles: 6. Chinese Snuff Bottles from the Collection of the Rt. Hon. The Marquess of Exeter, K.C.M.G.*, p. 47, No. C.60, with an illegible seal but dated by the author to the Jiaqing reign. A third example (possibly the Ault bottle) was sold at Sotheby's, Hong Kong, The Kaynes-Klitz Collection, Part I, 16 November 1989, lot 125.

This bottle belongs to a large group of porcelains molded in high relief with fine details and delicate enameling. Most bear Jiaqing marks, though some have Qianlong marks or no mark at all. This suggests that the group may have been produced after Qianlong's abdication in 1795 but before his death in 1799.

The shape and general aesthetics of these bottles bear close similarities to a small group of Imperial ivory bottles attributed to the Palace workshops during the reign of the Qianlong Emperor. On the ivory examples, the subject is always carved in high relief with rounded sculpted forms and usually depicted on a wave ground. Similarities in the shape of the neck and the square format of the seal mark, further solidify the connections. It seems likely, therefore, that the porcelain bottles, which are slightly larger, were produced as indirect copies of those in ivory.

For a simple enameled bottle, delicately painted with the same subject on each side and also marked Jiaqing, see Sotheby's, New York, 1 July 1985, lot 194.

Lotus gathering had a long-established tradition, and can be found described in many Chinese poems and paintings. In the cool calm of dawn, a literatus would drift out on a lotus pond, gather some buds and blooms, and take them back to his study.

250 | Porcelain, molded

1796-1820, Jiaqing four-character iron-red seal mark and of the period
2 ⁵/₁₆ in. (5.9 cm.) high

Of baluster shape, molded in relief and painted in a continuous scene with figures in a canopied boat on one side, possibly depicting Su Dongbo's visit to the Red Cliffs, and the Northern Song poet Mi Fu, painting calligraphy on rockwork with an assistant nearby on the other side, all between *ruyi* lappets at the foot and shoulder and *leiwen* band at the neck

1936-957

This is a most unusual shape and size for this type of bottle. Most examples are either spade or flattened ovoid in shape and usually of larger size. The design on this example seems cramped within the confines of the border decorations, though still displaying a sensitivity of modeling and dexterity of enameling expected of this group.

For a bottle of larger size with identical decoration, see Rachelle R. Holden, *Rivers and Mountains Far from the World*, No. 151.

For other similar bottles, see Hugh Moss, *Chinese Snuff Bottles: 6. Chinese Snuff Bottles from the Collection of the Rt. Hon. The Marquess of Exeter, K.C.M.G.*, p. 51, No. C.70; The Joseph Grimberg Collection of Snuff Bottles, *Arts of Asia*, November-December, 1993, p. 94, No. 35; and *Chinese Snuff Bottles, A Miniature Art from the Collection of Mary and George Bloch*, No. 160.

The Northern Song dynasty poet Mi Fu (1050-1107) was also a famous calligrapher and painter. He was born in Taiyuan, Shanxi Province, and was famous for his love of strangely shaped stones.

The Song dynasty poet Su Dongbo (1036-1101), also known as Su Shi, wrote his famous 'Prose Poem of the Red Cliffs', *Chibi Fu*, after two trips there with guests in 1082. Mi Fu and Su Dongpo were considered two of the four 'Song Masters.'

251 | **Porcelain, molded**

1796-1820, Jiaqing four-character seal mark in iron-red and of the period
2 ³/₈ in. (7 cm.) high

Of spade shape, molded and painted in a continuous scene and a masted ship and foreigners approaching a promontory with various Immortals, animals and attributes

1936-638

The subject presented here is *Ba man jin bao* 'eight barbarians bearing tributes'.

For two other bottles with identical subjects, also marked Jiaqing, see Christie's, South Kensingston, London, The Gerry P. Mack Collection, 4 October 1999, lot 5; and Hugh Moss, *Snuff Bottles of China*, No. 293. For a plain porcelain bottle painted with a similar subject, also bearing a Jiaqing mark and of Imperial type related to this bottle, see Sotheby's, Hong Kong, 3 May 1995, lot 599.

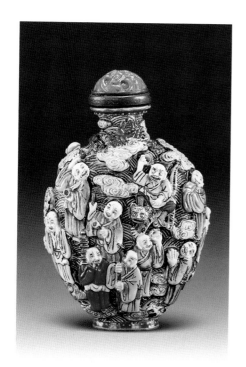

252 | **Porcelain, molded**

1796-1820, Jiaqing four-character iron-red seal mark and of the period
2 ⁷/₈ in. (6.7 cm.) high

Of spade shape, molded in high relief and painted in bright *famille rose* enamels with the Eighteen *Luohan* amidst clouds and waves

1936-623

For a discussion of the *luohan* (also called *arhan* or *arhat*), Buddhists who attain enlightenment but who remain on earth as teachers, see Hugh Moss, Victor Graham and Ka Bo Tsang, *The Art of the Chinese Snuff Bottle, The J & J Collection*, No. 227.

See also No. 272 in this collection.

253 | **Porcelain, molded**

1796-1820, Jiaqing four-character iron-red seal mark and of the period
2 ⁵/₈ in. (6.7 cm.) high

Of oval shape, molded and painted with the 'one hundred antiques': various vessels and stands, lanterns, a wrapped *qin* and games, on a white-glazed ground

1936-876

The collection has two almost identical bottles of this type; however, the addition of a white glaze to the diaper ground of this bottle and the use of a wider range of primary enamels add clarity to this example, missing on the other.

For very similar bottles, also marked Jiaqing, see Sotheby's, Hong Kong, 28 October 1992, lot 451; and Rachelle R. Holden, *Rivers and Mountains Far from the World*, No. 133, where the author notes the large number of rebuses hidden in the design. These include the vase and *ruyi* scepter which form the rebus *ping'an*

ruyi meaning 'may you be safe and may your wishes come true'.

See C. A. S. Williams, *Outlines of Chinese Symbolism and Art Motives*, p. 228, for a discussion of the 'one hundred antiques', where the author states they are 'a miscellaneous collection of emblematic forms comprising the Eight Treasures, *babao*, the Four Treasures, symbols of the four fine arts: music, chess, calligraphy and painting, in addition to many representations of sacrificial vessels, flowers, and other small decorative motifs.'

254 | **Porcelain, molded**

1796-1820, Jiaqing four character iron-red seal mark and of the period
2 $^{15}/_{16}$ in. (7.4 cm.) high

Of rounded rectangular shape, molded and painted in *famille rose* enamels with a continuous design of the *bajixiang*, the Eight Buddhist Emblems, on a ground of meandering flower heads on stylized clouds painted in *grisaille* over a white ground, the neck with a band of *leiwen* beneath a circle of raised dots, above a shoulder band of formalized *lingzhi* heads which are echoed at the base above a band of dots

1936-536

For a very similar bottle, with slightly paler enamels, see Robert W. L. Kleiner, *Chinese Snuff Bottles from the Collection of Mary and George Bloch*, No. 225.

The Eight Buddhist Emblems consist of the wheel of the law, the conch shell, the umbrella, the vase, the lotus, the double fish, the canopy and the endless knot.

255 | **Porcelain, molded**

1796-1820, Jiaqing, indecipherable four-character iron-red seal mark
2 $^{1}/_{2}$ in. (6.4 cm.) high

Of oval shape, molded and painted in bright enamels with nine Buddhistic lions chasing beribboned balls on an incised wave ground between *ruyi* lappets, below a band of *leiwen* at the neck and another above a chevron band at the foot

1936-882

The design of this bottle is almost certainly based on Imperial ivory models, such as No. 98 in this collection.

For a similar enameled example, see Sotheby's, New York, The Janos Szekeres Collection, 27 October 1986, lot 15.

256 | **Porcelain, molded**

1821-1850, Jiaqing four-character iron-red seal mark and possibly late in the period
2 ³/₄ in. (7 cm.) high

Of ovoid shape, molded in low relief and enameled in bright *famille rose* colors with a continuous battle scene from the *Romance of the Three Kingdoms* showing archers on a crenellated city wall shooting arrows down at straw-canopied boats on the swirling waterway below

1936-897

For a similar but finer bottle and a full discussion of the subject, see No. 247.

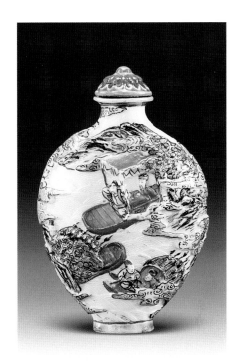

257 | **Porcelain, molded**

1830-1880, Qianlong two-character mark in iron-red
2 ⁷/₈ in. (7.3cm.) high

Of ovoid shape, molded in relief and painted with a continuous scene of boys at play on a terrace supervised by elegant ladies, various figures holding peaches

1936-577

Rachel R. Holden, in *Rivers and Mountains Far from the World*, illustrates a nearly identical scene in higher relief, No. 130.

The subject of elegant courtly scenes with the addition of children was a popular one. As many ladies and children are holding peaches or vases with peach sprays, this bottle was perhaps made as a birthday presentation gift.

See also Louise Cort and Jan Stuart, *Joined Colors: Decoration and Meaning in Chinese Porcelain*, p. 57, where the authors note:

> A woman's status depended on giving birth to a boy, and the higher rank her son obtained, the greater her own authority. Domestic interiors and garden scenes of mothers and children were popular in the early eighteenth century, when new enamel colors and shading techniques promoted figure painting.

258 | Porcelain, molded

1780-1850
2 ³/₄ in. (7 cm.) high

Of large spade shape, molded and painted in *famille rose* enamels, an elegant courtyard garden with a central figure of a lady with two large feathers in her hat, assisted by other female figures, the other side with the same central figure seated at a raised dais, presiding over the judgement of two figures kneeling before her, all surrounded by halberd-bearing and sword-wielding soldiers and other officials

1936-521

For other examples, see Hugh Moss, *Chinese Snuff Bottles: 6, Chinese Snuff Bottles from the Collection of the Rt. Hon The Marquess of Exeter, K.C.M.G.*, p. 48, No. C.68, where the reverse is described as a mythological scene; Hugh Moss, *Chinese Snuff Bottles: 5*, p. 52, fig. 20, described as not being of fine quality in molding or enameling; Sotheby's, New York, 3 October 1980, lot 113; Sotheby's, London, 13 October 1981, lot 56; and another was illustrated by John G. Ford, *Chinese Snuff Bottles, The Edward Choate O'Dell Collection*, pl. 62.

We cannot readily identify the lady with the two large feathers in her headdress, but she appears in a number of scenes on snuff bottles, usually in a courtly setting. Though it seems highly unlikely, there might be a connection between this figure and another that usually forms part of *Ba man jin bao*, 'eight barbarians bearing tributes'. One of the barbarians is usually depicted with such a headdress. For an example in this collection, see bottle No. 251.

259 | **Porcelain, molded**

1796-1820, Jiaqing
2 ³/₁₆ in. (5.7 cm.) high

Of ovoid shape, molded in high relief in a continuous scene with two females in a canopied boat passing a swimming demon to one side and further Immortals on a promontory to the other

1936-967 (CB. 407)

For a nearly identically molded bottle, see Robert Kleiner, *Treasures from the Sanctum of Enlightened Respect: Chinese Snuff Bottles from the Denis Low Collection*, No. 152, where the author discusses this classic series of lacquer-and ivory-inspired Imperial bottles.

The subject of this and the following bottle in this collection, No. 260, is the same, though the disposition of the figures varies slightly. The scene may well represent the 'White Snake Story', see another bottle in this collection, No. 227. The only problem with this particular attribution of the subject is the appearance around the bottle of other Immortals not necessary to the story. For another identical example also called the story of 'White Snake,' see Robert Hall, *Chinese Snuff Bottles IV*, No. 69.

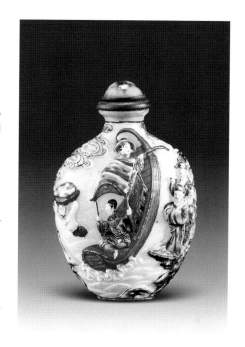

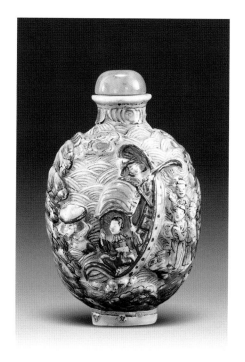

260 | **Porcelain, molded**

1796-1820, Jiaqing four-character iron-red seal mark and of the period
2 ⁵/₈ in. (6.8 cm.) high

Of ovoid shape, molded in high relief in a continuous scene with a female Immortal in a canopied boat passing a swimming demon to one side and further Immortals on a promontory to the other

1936-900

The subject is identical to the preceding bottle in this collection, No. 259.

261 | **Porcelain, molded**

1800-1850, indecipherable two-character iron-red seal mark
2 ³/₈ in. (7 cm.) high

Of ovoid shape, molded and painted in the *famille rose* palette with ten deer in a rocky landscape with pine and *lingzhi*

1936-902

This appears to be the snuff bottle maker's response to the well-known Imperial porcelain 'Hundred Deer' vases. The colors used on this bottle echo the Tang blue-green style enamels used on the Imperial vases. For an example see Sotheby's, Hong Kong, 1 November 1999, lot 398.

For another bottle similarly depicting deer in a landscape but on a molded diaper ground, see Sotheby's, London, The Baronesses Sapuppo and d'Essen Collection, 14 November 2000, lot 167.

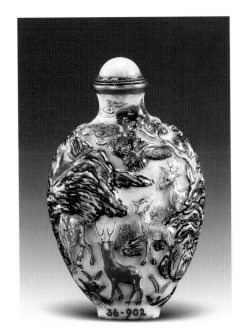

262 | **Porcelain, molded**

1800-1850, indecipherable iron-red seal mark
3 in. (7.7 cm.) high

Of rounded rectangular shape, molded in high relief and painted in *famille rose* enamels with the eight Daoist Immortals amidst clouds on a green and black wave ground, centered on one side by Shoulao, and on the other by a female Immortal, all between molded *ruyi*-head bands at the foot and shoulder, and a *leiwen* pattern at the neck

1936-576

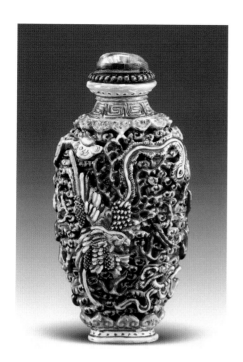

263 | Porcelain, molded

1796-1820, Jiaqing four-character iron-red seal mark and of the period
3 in. (7.7 cm.) high

Of ovoid shape, molded in relief and painted in bright *famille rose* colors with a descending three-clawed dragon on one side, and a phoenix on the other, all on a swirling cloud ground between *ruyi*-head lappets, a band of *leiwen* at the neck

1936-562

See a very similar enameled example illustrated by Hugh Moss in *Chinese Snuff Bottles: 5*, p. 54, No. 26.

264 | Porcelain, molded

1800-1880, indecipherable iron-red seal mark
2 ¹⁵/₁₆ in. (7.5 cm.) high

Of ovoid shape, molded and painted in a continuous scene with a descending three-clawed dragon on one side, and a phoenix on the other side, all on a colorful swirling cloud ground between *ruyi*-head lappets, and *leiwen* pattern at the neck

1936-580

265 | Porcelain, molded

1800-1880, Qianlong four-character iron-red seal mark
3 in. (7.6 cm.) high

Of tapering baluster shape, molded and painted in *famille rose* colors, with a phoenix on one side and a three-clawed dragon contesting a flaming pearl on the other, all on a dense colorful cloud ground with gilt highlights

1936-898

For a very similarly modeled example of more rounded and less tapering shape, partially white-glazed and partly left in the biscuit, see Robert Hall, *Chinese Snuff Bottles IV*, No. 64.

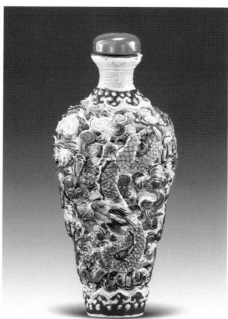

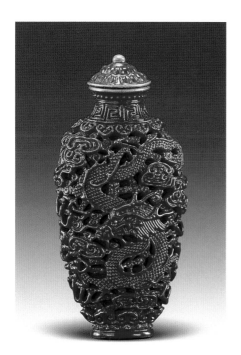

266 | **Porcelain, molded**

1796-1820, Jiaqing four-character gilt seal mark and of the period
2 ¹⁵/₁₆ in. (7.5 cm.) high

Of rounded rectangular shape, molded and glazed red in imitation of cinnabar lacquer with a phoenix on one side and a dragon on the other, all amidst dense clouds, matching stopper

1936-518

For an identical bottle see Robert Hall, *Chinese Snuff Bottles II*, No. 17.

267 | **Porcelain, molded**

1795-1820
2 ⁷/₁₆ in. (6.3 cm.) high

Of ovoid shape, molded and covered in a turquoise glaze with the eight Daoist emblems, *ba bao*, on a dense floral ground between *ruyi* lappets at the shoulder and foot, and *leiwen* at the neck

1936-906

For a similar turquoise-glazed bottle with the addition of painted black lines to imitate the matrix of turquoise, see Robert W. L. Kleiner, *Chinese Snuff Bottles from the Collection of John Ault*, No. 130, where the author notes that despite having no reign mark, its similarity in quality and style to Jiaqing marked examples leaves us in no doubt as to its date. He also suggests that unmarked examples, (like this one) were made for private sale.

See also Hugh Moss, Victor Graham and Ka Bo Tsang, *The Art of the Chinese Snuff Bottle, The J & J Collection*, No. 235 for a white enameled example and a discussion of possible Imperial attribution.

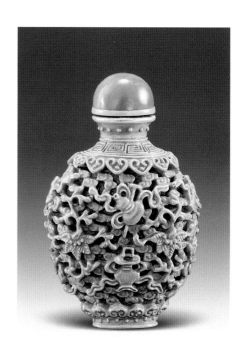

268 | Porcelain, molded

1796-1820, Jiaqing four-character iron-red seal mark and of the period
2 ¹⁵/₁₆ in. (7.4 cm.) high

Of ovoid shape, molded in relief with a descending three-clawed dragon to one side and a phoenix to the other, all on a swirling cloud ground between *ruyi*-head lappets, and a band of *leiwen* at the neck

1936-570 (CB. 380 or 400)

The chrysanthemum design of the stopper and its high quality make it very likely that this is the original. See the discussion of such stoppers on lacquer and ivory bottles under No. 102 in this collection.

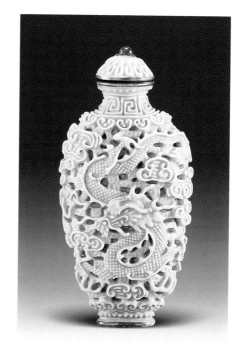

269 | Porcelain, molded

1796-1820, Jiaqing
2 ¹/₂ in. (6.4 cm.) high

Of oval shape, molded with nine Buddhistic lions chasing beribboned balls on a wave ground, covered overall in a white glaze

1936-628

The design of this bottle is almost certainly based on Imperial ivory models. For an example, see No. 98.

For another bottle identically molded but enameled, see No. 255 (reverse illustrated).

For another example, see Sotheby's, New York, The Janos Szekeres Collection, 27 October 1986, lot 15.

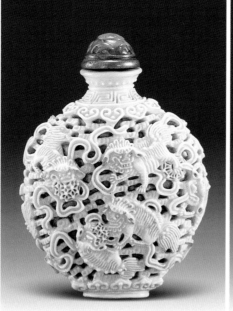

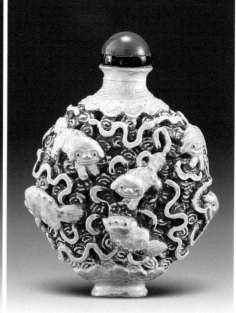

270 | **Porcelain, reticulated**

1796-1820, Jiaqing four-character iron-red seal mark and of the period
2 ⅜ in. (6.2 cm.) high

Of rounded shape, molded and reticulated with nine Buddhistic lions chasing beribboned balls on a crisply carved cloud ground, covered overall in a white glaze

1936-930

For a very similar bottle with a coral-red glaze and gilt highlights, also with a Jiaqing mark, see Robert W. L. Kleiner, *Chinese Snuff Bottles from the Collection of Mary and George Bloch*, No. 223. Their derivation from Imperial ivory bottles is discussed.

271 | **Porcelain, molded**

1850-1900, Qianlong four-character seal mark
2 ¾ in. (6.8 cm.) high

Of rounded shape, molded with nine yellow Buddhistic lions chasing beribboned balls on an iron-red wave ground

1936-903

For a similar bottle, also with a Qianlong mark but covered in a creamy glaze, see Sotheby's, New York, The Bernice Straus Hasterlik Collection, 17 September 1996, lot 143.

272 | **Porcelain, molded**

1800-1900
2 ⅜ in. (6 cm.) high

Of oval form, molded in high relief in a continuous scene of the Eighteen *Luohan* amidst clouds and waves below a dragon at the neck

1936-549 (CB. 410 or 491)

For a bottle similarly molded but painted with bright enamels, see Hugh Moss, Victor Graham, and Ka Bo Tsang, *The Art of the Chinese Snuff Bottle, The J & J Collection*, No. 240. The authors note that the source of the design is easily found in the Imperial ivories of the Qianlong period, where the subject was a popular one.

For a discussion of the Eighteen *Luohan*, see *ibid.*, No. 227.

273 | Porcelain, reticulated

1800-1900, Qianlong incised four-character mark
2 ⁵/₁₆ in. (5.9 cm.) high

Of rounded shape, the outer layer molded and pierced revealing the plain bottle within, decorated with the Eighteen *Luohan* standing amidst cloud scrolls, the bottle left in the biscuit

1936-955

It would seem that no identical bottle has been published, although it forms part of a well known group of molded monochrome bottles, some of which are reticulated. For a white glazed bottle molded in relief with the Eight Daoist Immortals on a wave ground, see Rachelle R. Holden, *Rivers and Mountains Far from the World*, No. 89.

Nos. 272 and 274 in this collection are decorated with similar subjects, the Eighteen Buddhist *Luohan* and the Eight Daoist Immortals respectively, but the reticulation on this bottle gives it a totally different appearance. For another reticulated bottle, molded and carved with the emblems of the Eight Daoist Immortals, see Hugh Moss, Victor Graham, and Ka Bo Tsang, *The Art of the Chinese Snuff Bottle, The J & J Collection*, No. 235, where the authors discuss molded porcelain bottle production.

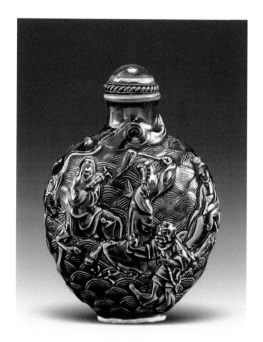

274 | Porcelain, molded

1800-1900
2 ⁵/₈ in. (6.6 cm.) high

Of rounded shape, finely molded in high relief with the *Ba Xian*, the Eight Daoist Immortals, amidst breaking waves, a small building on a promontory on one shoulder; all under a thick unctuous deep blue glaze which stops neatly above the foot

1936-700

275 | Porcelain, molded

1850-1900, *Yu Yao Jian Zhi* raised molded mark
2 ⁷/₁₆ in. (6.2 cm.) high

Of rounded rectangular shape, molded on each side in high relief with an ascending full-faced five-clawed dragon centered by a flaming pearl amidst swirling clouds, the eyes picked out in black, a molded chrysanthemum stopper

1936-1047

The mark *Yu yao jian zhi* can be read as 'Imperial ware made under supervision'

276 | Porcelain, molded

1770-1820, Qianlong four-character iron-red seal mark
2 ¹³/₁₆ in. (7.1 cm.) high

Of cylindrical shape, molded in low relief and gilt in a continuous scene with two five-clawed dragons amidst cloud scrolls above breaking waves, *ruyi* lappets at the neck

1936-543

For an identical bottle, also bearing a Qianlong mark but dated to the Jiaqing period, see Robert Kleiner, *The Bellis Collection*, No. 29, formerly in the Collections of Arthur Loveless, Bob Stevens and Eric Young.

277 | Porcelain, molded

1800-1880, indecipherable four-character iron-red mark
2 ⁷/₁₆ in. (6.2 cm.) high

Of ovoid shape, molded and painted in a continuous scene with nine iron-red dragons on a white-glazed wave ground between turquoise bands at the foot and neck

1936-878

Literature: Edward Wenham, 'Antiques As Decoration', *Arts & Decoration*, New York, Winter, 1928, illustrated p. 96.

The chrysanthemum design of the stopper and its high quality make it very likely that it is the original.

The reverse of this bottle bears the unusual feature of depicting the underside of one dragon's head, showing its throat rather than the upper side with the eyes.

For other examples with very similar modeling but undecorated, see Robert W. L. Kleiner, *Chinese Snuff Bottles from the Collection of Mary and George Bloch*, No. 224, dated to the Jiaqing period (1796-1820); and Humphrey K. F. Hui, Margaret Polak and Christopher C. H. Sin, *Hidden Treasures of the Dragon*, No. 25 which is dated to the Tongzhi period (1862-74).

278 | Porcelain, molded

1790-1850
2 ¹/₄ in. (5.7 cm.) high

Of lobed spade shape, imitating a purse, molded with a winged dragon on each side amidst cloud scrolls and two *lingzhi* sprays at each shoulder, the two-legged winged dragons clutching *lingzhi* in each claw and another in their mouths

1936-625

Literature: Edward Wenham, 'Antiques As Decoration', *Arts & Decoration*, New York, Winter, 1928, illustrated p. 96.

This is a most unusual bottle from a two-piece mold and no other example appears to be published.

Stylistically it might be compared with a group of molded pouch-shaped bottles painted in iron-red and blue enamel, see Robert W. L. Kleiner, *Chinese Snuff Bottles from the Collection of John Ault*, No. 160. The Ault example has underglaze blue floral borders with gilt highlights indicative of a Jiaqing date.

279 | Porcelain, molded

1790 -1830, Qianlong four-character iron-red seal mark and possibly late in the period
2 ³/₄ in. (7 cm.) high

Of rounded shape, molded and painted in a continuous scene with two fan-tailed fish amidst aquatic fronds on a pale blue wash ground with dark blue areas

1936-895

Although other bottles molded with a single fish on each side are known, this bottle, with the addition of molded fronds and seaweed, and different shades of underglaze blue, appears to be unique. The high quality of the painting and molding are quite different from the other published examples and suggest a possible Qianlong production date.

For other molded fish bottles, see Hugh Moss, *Chinese Snuff Bottles: 6. Chinese Snuff Bottles from* the Collection of the Rt. Hon. The Marquess of Exeter, K.C.M.G., pp. 38-39, No. C.34, probably the most comparable example in terms of background color imitating water; Helen White, *Snuff Bottles From China, The Victoria and Albert Museum Collection*, pp. 258-259, No. 1; and Christie's, New York, The Reif Collection of Chinese Snuff Bottles, 18 October, 1997, lot 13.

280 | **Porcelain, molded**

1821-1850, indecipherable iron-red seal mark, Daoguang
3 in. (7.6 cm.) high

Of ovoid shape, molded in relief with Liu Hai with his arms raised holding his string of cash and standing on rockwork, the other side with his mythical toad seated on blue rockwork near bamboo emitting a spume of vapor from its mouth

1936-610

For a depiction of the same subject on an agate bottle, see Christie's, London, South Kensington, The Gerry P. Mack Collection, 4 October 1999, lot 84.

See C. A. S. Williams, *Outlines of Chinese Symbolism and Art Motives*, p. 403, where the author notes 'Liu Hai was said to have been a Minister of State during the 10th century A.D. It was claimed that he had a mystical three-legged toad that would take him anywhere he wanted to go. Every so often, the creature escaped down a well, and Liu Hai had to fish him out with a line baited with gold coins.'

281 | **Porcelain, molded**

1800-1860, Qianlong four-character gilt seal mark
2 ³/₄ in. (7 cm.) high

Of rounded rectangular form, molded and painted with the animals of the zodiac and a tree in a rocky landscape, the background pale blue with dark blue mottling

1936-646

The twelve zodiac animals, *Shi er shu xiang* or *Shi er sheng xiao*, comprise the rat, ox, tiger, hare, dragon, snake, horse, sheep, monkey, rooster, dog, and pig.

The rather arbitrary choice of horizon on this bottle leaves the ox floating, somewhat surprisingly, in the sky alongside the dragon.

A number of bottles are published with almost identical molding even though all differ somewhat in enameling. See Robert Hall, *Chinese Snuff Bottles IV*, lot 74, with a robin's egg ground; and Rachelle R. Holden, *Rivers and Mountains Far from the World*, No. 75, where the author fully discusses the Chinese zodiac tradition. That bottle is covered in a dark glaze simulating bronze. This example uses both gilt and dark brown imitating bronze on the lower half, and a lavender-blue with darker blue splotches suggestive of robin's egg for the upper portion of the background.

282 | **Porcelain, molded**

1795-1880, Qianlong four-character iron-red seal mark
2 1/4 in. (5.7 cm.) high

Of moon-flask shape, molded with a European watch face on each side with misplaced Roman numerals in the center and misplaced Arabic numerals surrounding them, all on a finely dotted turquoise ground with gilt floral highlights

1936-859 (CB. 364)

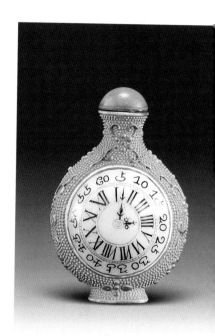

The design of this bottle is based on a European pocket watch but, interestingly, the artist was conversant neither with the placement of Roman numerals nor the Arabic numbers, as evidenced by the misplacement, by one position, of each.

European watches were probably introduced at Court by the Jesuits, and gathered much favor from the Kangxi period onwards. The fascination with them quickly spread into the production of snuff bottles, where their unusual basic outline, often octagonal, was transplanted to glass and enamel bottles.

This example, with its Qianlong iron-red mark, probably dates to no earlier than the last years of the eighteenth century and probably later. The use of a faux shagreen (shark skin) surround is unusual. Shagreen is a material not generally found on watches. It is more commonly found on small cases for calling cards or needles.

For a porcelain bottle, also molded as a European pocket watch, but of a higher quality and dated to the Qianlong period, see Robert W. L. Kleiner, *Chinese Snuff Bottles from the Collection of Mary and George Bloch*, No. 221. It was originally purchased in Beijing in May 1926, by H. G. Beasley and sold at Sotheby's, London, 2 July 1984, lot 5.

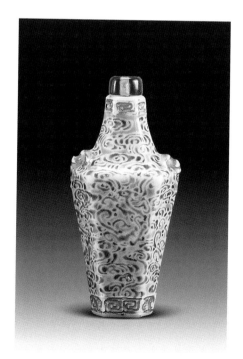

283 | **Porcelain, molded**

1800-1900
2 1/2 in. (6.3 cm.) high

Of tapering hexagonal shape with tall sloping shoulders, painted with four stylized blue enamel *chilong* amidst swirling clouds on a lime-green ground, gilt lion masks on the shoulders between bands of *leiwen* at the neck and foot

1936-1051

This bottle's shape and decoration are exceedingly rare for a snuff bottle, and it is most likely a miniature interpretation of a ceramic vase of Jingdezhen production.

284 | **Porcelain, molded**

1850-1900
2 ³/₈ in. (6.1 cm.) high

Of ovoid shape, molded in low relief on each side with two confronted *chilong* in a band around the center between lappets above the foot and c-scrolls and raised bosses at the shoulder and neck

1936-891 (CB. 308)

This bottle seems to have been made in imitation of overlay glass. For blue glass overlay bottles decorated with a design of scrolls and dots like these, see Sotheby's, Hong Kong, 28 April 1997, lot 26; and *Chinese Snuff Bottles*, by Suzie and François Lorin, Fall 1997, No. 53.

For ceramic bottles with this type of decoration, see Christie's, London, The Ko Family Collection, 14 June 1971, lot 90; and *Chinese Whispers* by Robert Hall, No. 7.

285 | **Porcelain, molded**

1820-1880
3 in. (7.6 cm.) high

Modeled as a crouching lion biting a large brocade ball held between its front paws, the eyes picked out in black enamel, the glaze with a light overall crackle

1936-985 (CB. 479)

Provenance: The Anderson Galleries, New York
The Suvale & Voron, Inc. dissolution sale, 2-4 April 1929, lot 21.
(See fig. 32 in the Introduction.)

For another model, see Robert Hall, *Chinese Snuff Bottles III*, No. 67, where the author suggests that this type is probably the earliest of a series of similarly molded Buddhistic lion bottles, and characterized by superb modeling. For another, similarly crackled, see Suzie and François Lorin, *Chinese Snuff Bottles*, No. 10.

286 | Porcelain, molded

1850-1900
3 in. (7.6 cm.) long

Modeled as a squirrel with tail tucked to one side and crouching on a grapevine, the whites of the eyes left in the biscuit, the pupils picked out in black enamel

1936-984 (CB. 498)

Literature: Edward Wenham, 'Antiques As Decoration,' *Arts & Decoration*, New York, Winter, 1928, illustrated p. 96.

For an identical model, dated to between 1796-1830, see Robert Hall, *Chinese Snuff Bottles*, No. 63. For an enameled example of slightly different design, see The Chinese Porcelain Company, New York, *Chinese Snuff Bottles from the Fernhill Park Collection*, No. 20.

For two other examples of the same subject but with a different design and enameled with very glassy enamels, see Hugh Moss, Victor Graham and Ka Bo Tsang, *The Art of the Chinese Snuff Bottle, The J & J Collection*, Nos. 243-244. The authors discuss the origins of the model and likely production dates as late as the 1940s. This example, of course, cannot post date 1928, when it was illustrated in *Arts & Decoration*. Stylistically, this bottle and No. 287, could be dated to the 1850s. The hand-carved details of the fur and leaves are certainly not suggestive of later mass production.

287 | Porcelain, molded

1850-1900
2 ¹/₂ in. (6.4 cm.) high

Modeled as a squirrel with tail tucked to one side and crouching on a grapevine

1936-997 (CB. 476)

Provenance: The Anderson Galleries, New York
The Suvale & Voron, Inc. dissolution sale, 2-4 April 1929, lot 31.
(See fig. 32 in the Introduction)

For a nearly identical bottle, see Sotheby's, New York, The Neal W. and Frances R. Hunter Collection, 15 September 1998, lot 169.

288 | **Porcelain, Molded**

1796-1820, Jiaqing six-character iron-red seal mark with a gilt surround, and of the period.

3 ³/₁₆ in. (8.1 cm.) high

Molded in the form of a gnarled prunus trunk with blossoming branches, against which grow a branch of pine, a spray of bamboo, with the addition of a *lingzhi* fungus, and covered overall with a crackled white glaze

1936-575

Several bottles from two-piece molds, similar in subject and form to this and to No. 289, are recorded. For an extensive discussion of this group, see Hugh Moss, Victor Graham and Ka Bo Tsang, *The Art of the Chinese Snuff Bottle, The J & J Collection*, Nos. 238 and 239. The authors suggest that if the demand for this particular group was large enough, two or more molds might have been made for the same design, allowing several workers to produce them simultaneously. This would account for the variations to be found on the entire group. Obviously, some of the changes were intentional and simply a development of the model, particularly the addition of a bat on the following bottle, No. 289, and the broadening of the surface to accept it. They also suggest that the ivory tone of the glaze may point to an

ivory prototype. This bottle can be directly compared to the unmarked example illustrated, *ibid.*, No. 238. It is of a creamier tone than this bottle and has the addition of brown enamel or iron oxide to highlight minor areas of the design.

The pine, bamboo and prunus have been known collectively since the Song dynasty as 'The Three Friends of Winter' because each retains its vigor during the harshest months of the year. In the cold season, when most plants are dormant, the bamboo and pine remain green, and the prunus is the first to bloom. This type of resistance to the elements is much admired by the Chinese, and the 'Three Friends of Winter' are represented in every field of Chinese art.

289 | **Porcelain, molded**

1796-1820, Jiaqing
3 ⁷/₃₂ in (8.2 cm.) high

Molded in high relief as the flowering trunk of a gnarled prunus tree, with a branch of pine, bamboo and a *lingzhi* fungus, on rocky ground, one side with a swooping bat

1937-569 (CB. 459)

Though unmarked, this bottle clearly dates to the same period as the preceding bottle, No. 288, which has a Jiaqing mark. This bottle is unquestionably the more finely molded of the two, and arguably has the finest enameling of the entire group, with the possible exception of one in the Hedda and Lutz Franz Collection, illustrated by Robert Hall in *Chinese Whispers*, No. 1.

Most published examples are more like this bottle than No. 288, and usually have the addition of a bat to the design. See Hugh Moss, Victor Graham and Ka Bo Tsang, *The Art of the Chinese Snuff Bottle, The J & J Collection*, No. 239; Hugh Moss, *Chinese Snuff Bottles: 5*, p. 67, fig. 68; Sotheby's, London, 3 March 1987, lot 61, from the Eric Young Collection. Another, also from the Young Collection, which sold at Sotheby's, London, 13 October 1987, lot 3, bears close resemblance to this example and

has a six-character Jiaqing mark. See also Hugh Moss, *Chinese Snuff Bottles: 6. Chinese Snuff Bottles from the Collection of the Rt. Hon. The Marquess of Exeter, K.C.M.G.*, p. 41, No. C.40; and *Chinese Applied Art*, pl. IV, case G.

290 | **Porcelain, molded**

1820-1880
3 ⁵/₈ in. (9.2 cm.) high

Modeled as a curled lotus leaf, budding stalks growing on one side and an insect on the veined pad on the other, covered overall with a white, lightly crackled glaze

1936-958 (CB. 462)

This and the following bottle, No. 291, are nearly identical.

For a bottle possibly from the same mold, see Robert W. L. Kleiner, *Chinese Snuff Bottles from the Collection of Mary and George Bloch*, No. 240. It also has a crackled glaze, which the author suggests is in imitation of the *ge* glazes of the Song dynasty, but which appears simply to be due to the nature of the 'soft' paste used.

There is an earlier ivory example in the same collection, *ibid.*, No. 186, and another ivory example was sold at Sotheby's, London, 21 June 1995, lot 164.

291 | **Porcelain, molded**

1850-1900
3 ³/₄ in. (9.5 cm.) high

Modeled as a curled lotus leaf, buds rising from stalks on one side and an insect on the veined pad on the other, covered overall in a white heavily crackled glaze

1936-961

With the exception of the heavy crackle, this bottle is identical to the preceding one, No. 290 (reverse illustrated).

292 | **Porcelain, molded**

1850-1900
3 ¹/₃₂ in. (7.7 cm.) high

Modeled as a curled lotus leaf, with pods and buds on one side and trailing tendrils on the other forming the neck, some crackle to surface

1936-960 (CB. 461)

For an identical bottle, possibly with its original stopper, see Sotheby's, The Gerry P. Mack Collection, 25 October 1997, lot 315. Another is illustrated by Clare Lawrence, *Miniature Masterpieces from the Middle Kingdom, The Monimar Collection of Chinese Snuff Bottles*, No. 94. This particular form of bottle is also found enameled in a variety of tones of green with the lotus buds highlighted in other colors. For an example, see Sotheby's, London, 21 June 1995, lot 134.

293 | **Porcelain, molded**

1800-1850
2 in. (5.1 cm.) high

Modeled as a curled lotus leaf, veined on all sides, one side with lotus pads and a pod

1936-892 (CB. 474)

This bottle is one of a group made in porcelain and primarily painted on the biscuit in simple enamels depicting lotus leaves. Most, unlike this example, have the start of the pod veins at the center of the bottle on one side and fanning out from this point. This example, however, has the veins extending down from the mouth of the bottle.

For other examples, see *Snuff Bottles in the Collection of the National Palace Museum*, No. 97, under a green glaze; Clare Lawrence, *Miniature Masterpieces from the Middle Kingdom, The Monimar Collection of Chinese Snuff Bottles*, No. 94, under a white glaze; and Sotheby's, London, 21 July 1977, lot 15, under a vari-colored glaze.

294 | **Porcelain, molded**

1850-1900
2 ¹/₂ in. (6.4 cm.) high, without stopper

Of natural gourd shape, molded and painted with trailing foliage and smaller gourds in iron-red, green and black, one gourd molded almost in the round hanging from the upper bulb, the stopper original

1936-840

A fruiting gourd vine symbolizes a wish for numerous descendants. For two more lavishly molded and enameled gourd bottles in this collection, see Nos. 245 and 246.

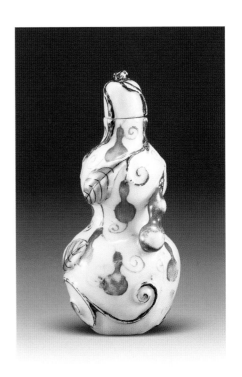

295 | **Porcelain, molded**

1820-1880
2 ⁷/₁₆ in. (6.2 cm.) high

Molded in medium relief as a butterfly with out-stretched wings and symmetric markings picked out in enamels and gilt, the wing edges with green feathery details, spur marks polished on the base

1936-846

This bottle is very rare. Only three (or possibly five) identical examples appear to be published. One is illustrated in *Chinese Snuff Bottles, A Miniature Art from the Collection of Mary and George Bloch*, No. 186 (in which the author refers to the Princeton example); another sold at Sotheby's, Hong Kong, 3 November 1994, lot 1030; and a third was sold at Sotheby's, Hong Kong, 4 November 1996, lot 213.

Two others, which just might be the same as the bottles already listed, were auctioned in the 1970's. One was sold at Sotheby's, London, The Mrs. A. M. Robertson Collection, 24 June 1975, lot 184; the other was also sold at Sotheby's, London, 18-19 January 1971, lot 69.

A porcelain butterfly bottle, of slightly different shape and less well-defined molding, is illustrated by Robert Hall in *Chinese Snuff Bottles II*, No. 3; and also illustrated by Bob C. Stevens, *The Collector's Book of Snuff Bottles*, No. 350.

It is somewhat surprising that such a popular subject as the butterfly, appearing as it does with such frequency in paintings on silk, paper and porcelains, was not used more often as a regular shape for bottles. Possibly the slightly awkward form made it uncomfortable to carry.

296 | **Porcelain, molded**

1750-1795
2 ⁵/₈ in. (6.6 cm.) high

Modeled as a standing lady wearing floral turquoise-ground robes and a dark blue surcoat with gilt and enamel borders, holding a folded fan in her left hand and a floral spray at her chest in the other, the head pierced for the stopper, now replaced

1936-884

For an identical figure and two others from a set of three, see Sotheby's, London, 7 June 1990, lots 277-279. The three bottles entered the Bloch Collection, and are illustrated by Robert Kleiner, in *Chinese Snuff Bottles in the Collection of Mary and George Bloch*, pp. 318-320, No. 207. The three figures are listed as a mandarin, his lady and a female attendant. The latter figure is identical to this one. Each of the female figures holds a floral spray in one hand and a fan in the other, whilst their facial features are identical.

A pair of figures, identical to the mandarin and his lady, from the Chester Beatty Collection, Dublin, was illustrated on the cover of *Arts of Asia*, March-April, 1988.

Robert Kleiner, *ibid.*, p. 320, suggests that the Princeton example, here illustrated, was probably once part of the Chester Beatty group.

No other figures of comparable quality in modeling and enameling are recorded.

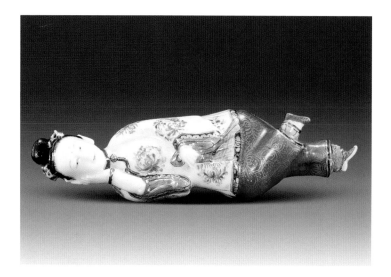

297 | **Porcelain, molded**

1770-1820
3 ¹⁵/₁₆ in. (10 cm.) long, including stopper

Molded as a recumbent lady with one leg crossed and her right hand held at her cheek, her short white coat painted with chrysanthemum sprays, her iron-red pants delicately gilt with a honeycomb cell pattern with further chrysanthemum sprays, the slipper of her left foot forming the stopper

1936-578 (CB. 456 or 482)

In modeling, this bottle is almost identical to the following bottle in this collection, No. 298. The enameler has simply used a different color scheme. Perhaps they once even formed part of a set.

For similar molded but differently enameled examples, see *A Congregation of Snuff Bottle Connoisseurs*, No. 112 from the Lilly B. Y. and Y. B. Fung Collection; Robert W. L. Kleiner, *Chinese Snuff Bottles from the Collection of John Ault*, No. 135, where the author suggests that this group was inspired by ivory medicine figures of reclining ladies; and the same author, *The Bellis Collection*, No. 63.

See also, two examples sold by Sotheby's, Hong Kong, 5 May 1994, lot 1562; and 3 November 1994, lot 1022.

298 | **Porcelain, molded**

1770-1820
4 in. (10.1cm.) long, including stopper

Molded in the form of a reclining lady, her head resting on her right hand while she lies with legs crossed, wearing a pale blue jacket with a floral design, and iron-red trousers delicately gilt with flower heads, her hair drawn up in a coiled chignon, the slipper of her left foot forming the stopper

1936-572 (CB. 458 or 484)

See the preceding bottle in this collection, No. 297.

299 | **Porcelain, Molded**

1770-1820
4 in. (10.9 cm.) long, including stopper

Molded as a reclining lady propping her head on her right hand, with crossed legs, wearing a pale blue jacket lightly decorated in pale black with stylized flower heads, her trousers decorated in black on green with further flower heads, the slipper of her left foot forming the stopper

1936-571

This bottle differs slightly in modeling from the two previous examples in having the head tipped more dramatically to one side and in the treatment of the left sleeve and the silk cloth held in her left hand. Otherwise, the similarities are striking.

For a similar molded example with different enamels, see *A Congregation of Snuff Bottle Connoisseurs*, No. 113.

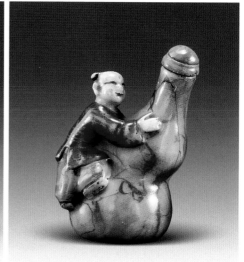

300 | **Porcelain, molded**

1770-1820
2 in. (5.2 cm.) high

Molded as a recumbent caparisoned elephant, its head turned to one side, a *gu*-shaped beaker resting on its saddle-cloth and a boy sitting astride its hind quarters clutching the vase

1936-869

An elephant supporting a vase on its back forms the rebus *taiping youxiang*, meaning 'peace in the country, prosperity prevails'.

It is unusual to find a snuff bottle in the form of a recumbent elephant with a vase on its back and also a small boy. The majority of published examples omit the boy. This design was a popular one at Court, and Imperial works of art in the form of vases, decorative sculptures and holders for symbolic objects such as sprigs of coral, etc. are still to be found in and around the Forbidden City.

For a similarly molded elephant, without the boy, see Hugh Moss, Victor Graham and Ka Bo Tsang, *The Art of the Chinese Snuff Bottle, The J & J Collection,* No. 237. See also Rachelle R. Holden, *Rivers and Mountains Far from the World,* No 58; and Hugh M. Moss, *Chinese Snuff Bottles: 5,* p. 56, fig. 34 and p. 57, fig. 35, a standing version from the Seattle Museum of Art. Also see Sotheby's, London, 14 November 2000, Chinese Snuff Bottles from the Collection of the Baronesses Sapuppo and d'Essen, lot 145.

301 | **Porcelain, molded**

1790-1850
2 ¹/₁₆ in. (5.3 cm.) high

Modeled as a boy clambering up the side of a large *faux bois* double gourd

1936-871

Stylistically similar to the preceding bottle, No. 300, it is presumably from the same workshop, although this bottle is probably of a slightly later date. The marbled coloring of the gourd is close to the treatment of the elephant on the preceding bottle, just as the coloring of the boy's jacket echoes the vase on the elephant's back.

For other examples of boys clutching double gourds, see Robert Hall, *Chinese Snuff Bottles II,* No. 15, formerly in the collection of Marian Mayer; *Chinese Snuff Bottles, A Miniature Art from the Collection of Mary and George Bloch,* No. 159; Bob C. Stevens, *The Collector's Book of Snuff Bottles,* No. 353; and *A Congregation of Snuff Bottle Connoisseurs,* No. 301.

302 | **Porcelain, molded**

1770-1820
3 in. (7.6 cm.) high

Porcelain, molded as the Daoist Immortal, Liu Hai, standing with his right leg slightly raised, his foot resting on the back of his mythical toad, wearing a robe with floral decoration on a turquoise ground and open at his chest, a string of cash slung over his shoulder, his back with a tiger-skin apron at the waist

1936-893

Provenance: Almost certainly the American Art Galleries, New York
The Ton-Ying Collection, 29-30 January 1926, lot 15

Literature: Edward Wenham, 'Antiques As Decoration', *Arts & Decoration*,
New York, Winter, 1928, illustrated p. 58. (See fig. 18 in the Introduction.)

For a nearly identical model using more subdued colors, see Robert W. L. Kleiner, *Chinese Snuff Bottles from the Collection of Mary and George Bloch*, No. 226, formerly in the Paula Hallett Collection and sold at Sotheby's, New York, 27 June 1986, lot 2.

For other models, see Humphrey K. F. Hui and Christopher C. H. Sin, *An Imperial Qing Tradition*, No. 43, formerly in the collection of Gerry P. Mack; and *A Congregation of Snuff Bottle Connoisseurs*, Nos. 114 and 115.

See also the following bottle in this collection, No. 303.

303 | **Porcelain, molded**

1790-1820
3 ¹/₁₆ in. (7.8 cm.) high

Modeled as the Daoist Immortal, Liu Hai, painted primarily in iron-red and green over a white glaze, with touches of pink, aubergine and gilt, his floral decorated robe open at his chest, a string of cash around his neck, his mythical three-legged toad climbing at his front, the reverse with a tasselled stone suspended from the string of cash and hanging above his tiger-skin apron

1936-885

Provenance: The American Art Galleries, New York
The H. A. E. Jaehne Collection,
10-12 April 1923, lot 120, sold at
$52.50.
(See fig. 28 in the Introduction.)

A large number of bottles exist depicting this Daoist figure, and quality varies enormously; generally, it declined as the nineteenth century progressed. This example, with its superb high-relief molding and finely executed enameling, is amongst the finest and earliest of the group. Most of these bottles are dated to the reign of the Jiaqing Emperor, but this example may even be slightly earlier.

The modeling and enameling on this bottle can be favorably compared to much larger figures from Jingdezhen which are generally accepted as dating to the late Qianlong and early Jiaqing periods, see David Howard and John Ayers, *China for the West*, Nos. 644-648.

Of the many published snuff bottles of this group, the most comparable example is illustrated by Bob C. Stevens, *The Collector's Book of Snuff Bottles*, No. 314. It is similar in modeling, but the use of enamels is more liberal, particularly on the robe.

See Hugh M. Moss, *Chinese Snuff Bottles: 5*, pp. 60-61, figs. 49 and 50; Clare Lawrence, *Miniature Masterpieces from the Middle Kingdom, The Monimar Collection of Chinese Snuff Bottles*, No. 87 for another similar example though not so finely molded and more cursorily painted; Sotheby's, New York, The Janos Szekeres Collection, 27 October 1986, lot 7.

A later, though similar, model, painted predominantly in underglaze blue, is illustrated by Robert W. L. Kleiner, *Chinese Snuff Bottles from the Collection of John Ault*, No. 193. The author suggests a Tongzhi date (1862-1874). An identically molded bottle, covered entirely in a crackled white glaze is illustrated by Humphrey K. F. Hui, Margaret Polak, and Christopher C. H. Sin in *Hidden Treasures of the Dragon*, No. 195.

304 | **Porcelain**

1780-1820. Qianlong four-character seal mark in iron-red, and probably late in the period.

2 ³/₁₆ in. (5.6 cm.) high

Of spade shape, painted on each side with a pair of confronted five-clawed dragons contesting a flaming pearl amidst dense cloud scrolls

1936-874 (CB. 366)

Most bottles decorated in iron-red with dragons bear nineteenth century reign marks or apocryphal Qianlong marks. The mark on this example, a Qianlong four-character seal mark in iron-red, though clumsily written, appears genuine by the sheer quality of the remaining iron-red decoration and the porcelain body. The shape, too, suggests a late eighteenth century attribution.

For later examples, see Sotheby's, London, 24 April 1989, lot 344; and Robert Hall in *Chinese Snuff Bottles III*, No. 61.

305 | **Porcelain**

1800-1850

2 ⁵/₈ in. (6.7 cm.) high

Of squared rectangular shape, each side decorated in iron-red with boys at various playful pursuits on a terrace within canted oval panels surrounded by leafy floral tendrils

1936-981 (CB. 369)

For a bottle of similar design and shape, bearing an iron-red Jiaqing mark and attributed to the Imperial kilns at Jingdezhen, see Clare Lawrence, *Miniature Masterpieces from the Middle Kingdom, The Monimar Collection of Chinese Snuff Bottles*, No. 97. As in this example, the boys' topknots are picked out in black enamel.

306 | **Porcelain**

1850-1900, Qianlong four-character seal mark
2 ³/₄ in. (7 cm.) high

Of rectangular shape and square section, delicately painted in a continuous scene with a five-clawed dragon on each face contesting a flaming pearl at the corners with the dragon on the next panel, three dragons descending and one ascending

1936-1001 (CB. 368)

This bottle is somewhat similar to the preceding bottle, No. 305. On both, black enamel is used sparingly to highlight part of the decoration; in this case, the eyes of the dragons. The shape and spacing of the design, however, are less successful.

307 | **Porcelain**

1820-1850
2 ⅞ in. (7.3 cm.) high

Of pear shape, each face decorated in iron-red enamel with Zhong Kui, the Demon Queller, shown on one side dressed as an official and on the reverse, as a warrior

1936-649-1

For a discussion of the popularity of this subject in the nineteenth century, see an article by Daphne Lange Rosenzweig, entitled 'Re-Interpreting the Recent Past: Nineteenth Century Chinese Life and Art', *JICSBS*, Spring 1999, pp. 33-34, figs. 10-12.

For a rounded rectangular bottle showing Zhong Kui as both scholar and warrior, see The Chinese Porcelain Company, New York, *Chinese Snuff Bottles from the Fernhill Park Collection*, No. 13. That bottle bears the hallmark *Shen de Tang Zhi* ('Made for the Hall for the Cultivation of Virtue'), a mark used on porcelain pieces made for the Daoguang Emperor.

Other bottles with the same subject are illustrated by Hugh M. Moss in *Chinese Snuff*

Bottles: 6. Chinese Snuff Bottles from the Collection of the Rt. Hon. The Marquess of Exeter, K.C.M.G., No. C.11; Humphrey K. F. Hui, Margaret Polak and Christopher C. H. Sin, *Hidden Treasures of the Dragon,* No. 173; and *The Au Hang Collection of Chinese Snuff Bottles,* No. 273.

308 | **Porcelain**

1800-1850
2 ⁷/₈ in. (7.3 cm.) high

Of pear shape, painted with Zhong Kui, the Demon Queller, on one side dressed as an official and on the other dressed as a warrior

1936-649-2

See the preceeding bottle in this collection, No. 307.

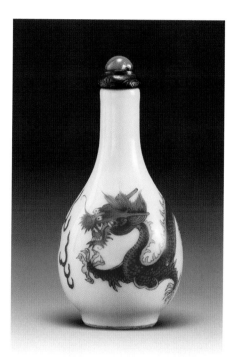

309 | **Porcelain**

1820-1880
2 ³/₄ in. (7 cm.) high

Of pear shape, delicately painted in shades of iron-red with a five-clawed dragon chasing a flaming pearl, three of the four feet with claws picked out in white enamel

1936-1009 (CB. 372)

310 | **Porcelain**

1840-1900, a coiled dragon in iron-red on the base
2 in. (5 cm.) high

Of globular shape, painted with a continuous scene of two five-clawed dragons amidst fire-scrolls and clouds, each grasping at a flaming pearl

1936-1008 (CB. 365)

For an identical bottle, with the same coiled dragon on the base, see Sotheby's, New York, The Gerry P. Mack Collection, 25 October 1997, lot 267. For a Guangxu-marked bottle decorated with an iron-red five-clawed dragon, see Robert Kleiner, *Treasures from the Sanctum of Enlightened Respect: Chinese Snuff Bottles from the Denis Low Collection*, No. 150.

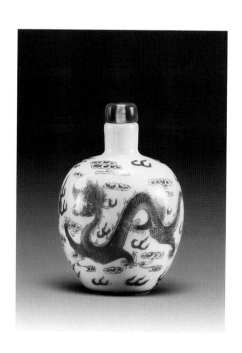

311 | Porcelain

1800-1900
2 ³/₄ in. (7 cm.) high

Of cylindrical shape, painted in blue and white with a tiger on a grassy bank looking up at a five-clawed dragon amidst stylized clouds, pendant beaded lappets at the neck, light crackle to the glaze

1936-534 (CB. 293)

For two other bottles of cylindrical shape depicting the same subject but painted in sepia enamels, see Robert Hall, *Chinese Snuff Bottles II*, No. 9; and another illustrated by Ka Bo Tsang in an article entitled 'The Tiger: King of All Animals', *JICSBS*, Winter 1998, p. 8, fig. 14, where the manifold meanings of the depiction are discussed at length.

Dragons and tigers are both emblematic of power, talent and leadership.

312 | Porcelain

1800-1900
2 ⁷/₈ in. (7.3 cm.) high

Of cylindrical shape, boldly painted in blue and white with a coiling five-clawed dragon chasing a flaming pearl, all under a lightly crackled glaze

1936-1015 (CB. 296)

For another example of this popular design and shape, see Robert W. L. Kleiner, *Chinese Snuff Bottles, The White Wings Collection*, No. 90, where the author discusses the term soft-paste at length and the use of the 'five-clawed' dragon.

See also another illustrated by the same author, *Chinese Snuff Bottles from the Collection of John Ault*, No. 185.

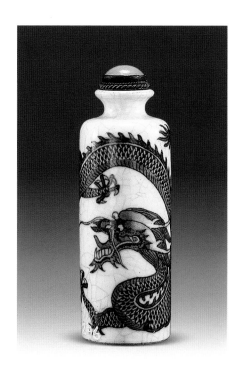

313 | **Porcelain**

1800-1900
2 ⁷⁄₈ in. (7.3 cm.) high

Of cylindrical shape, painted in blue and white with a coiling five-clawed dragon chasing a flaming pearl, all under a light crackled glaze

1936-1006 (CB. 299)

Provenance: The American Art Galleries, New York
The H. A. E. Jaehne Collection, 10-12 April 1923, lot 73, Sold at $17.50.
(See fig. 27 in the Introduction.)

See the preceding bottle in this collection, No. 312.

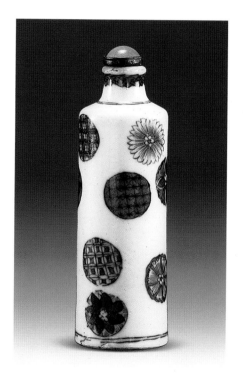

314 | **Porcelain**

1800-1900, Yongzheng four-character mark in underglaze blue
3 ³⁄₈ in. (8.5 cm.) high

Of cylindrical shape, painted with blue and white flower head roundels resembling Japanese *mon*, and roundels of cell pattern

1936-660 (CB. 314)

For an example of a similar subject on an earlier glass bottle in the collection, see No. 155.

315 | **Porcelain**

1820-1880
3 1/2 in. (9 cm.) high

Of cylindrical shape, a rare blue and white bottle painted on one side with a tall bearded male horseman standing with a lady, Mulan, dressed for riding in male attire

Mulan was a female who disguised herself as a male in order to go to battle, famed during the Han dynasty (206 B.C.-A.D. 220) and more recently popularized in an animated film by Disney.

For another rare depiction of Mulan on an enameled bottle, see Christie's, South Kensington, London, The Gerry P. Mack Collection, 4 October 1999, lot 10.

316 | **Porcelain**

1850-1900
3 1/8 in. (7.9 cm.) high

Of cylindrical shape, painted in blue and white with the Eight Horses of Mu Wang, variously recumbent, walking or at a gallop

1936-507 (CB. 310)

Mu Wang was the fifth sovereign of the Zhou dynasty (1100-256 B.C.). His eight horses are renowned in legend and became a popular motif in Chinese art.

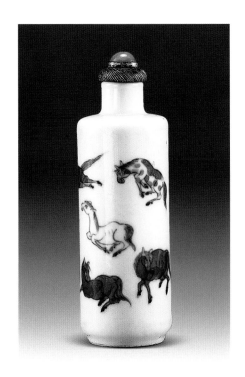

317 | **Porcelain**

1820-1900, Yongzheng mark in underglaze blue
2 1/4 in. (5.7 cm.) high

Of ovoid shape, painted in blue and white in a continuous scene with a five-clawed dragon amidst clouds above another rising from waves on one side, and descending and confronted dragons contesting a flaming pearl on the other, *ruyi* lappets at the neck

1936-630 (CB. 305)

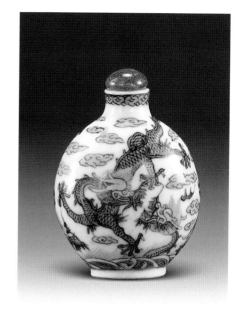

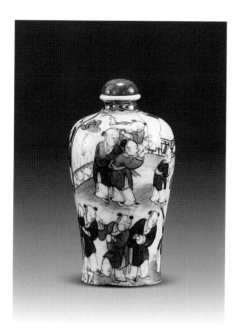

318 | **Porcelain**

1820-1900
2 3/8 in. (5.5 cm.) high

Of *meiping* shape, painted in a continuous scene with children playing musical instruments, lanterns, a hobbyhorse, kites and balls, carved concentric rings on the base

1936-1052 (CB. 287)

For a blue and white bottle with a Daoguang seal mark depicting boys at various pursuits, see an article by Ian Hardy entitled, 'Underglaze Blue Porcelain Snuff Bottles–Their Origins and Qualities', *JICSBS*, Autumn 1999, p. 18, fig. 9.

319 | **Porcelain**

1821-1850, Daoguang four-character mark in underglaze blue and of the period
2 9/16 cm. (6.5 cm.) high

Of tapering cylindrical shape painted in blue and white with boys at various playful activities including riding a hobbyhorse, lighting firecrackers, playing drums, flying kites, holding lanterns and playing ball, all in a courtyard setting

1936-519 (CB. 29 or 293)

For another blue and white bottle with scenes of boys at play, dated to the Daoguang period, see Clare Lawrence, *Miniature Masterpieces from the Middle Kingdom, The Monimar Collection of Chinese Snuff Bottles*, No. 99.

320 | **Porcelain**

1820-1900, Yongzheng four-character mark
2 ¹/₂ in. (6.4 cm.) high

Of globular shape, painted in blue and white with a bird in the branches of a fruiting tree, another flying above

1936-666 (CB. 311)

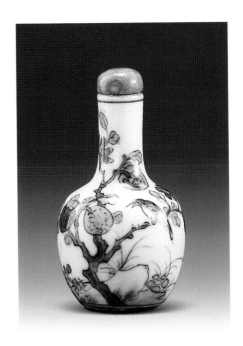

321 | **Porcelain**

1820-1900
2 ⁷/₈ in. (7.3 cm) high

Of oval shape, with cylindrical neck, painted in blue and white with two cranes in flight above a lotus pond

1936-547 (CB. 317)

Two cranes flying upward express the wish that the recipient of the picture may 'rise high'.

322 | **Porcelain**

1800-1900, Yongzheng underglaze blue six-character mark within two circles
2 ⁹/₁₆ in. (4 cm.) high

Of rounded ovoid shape, painted in *doucai* with two five-clawed dragons, one flying, the other rising from the waves, contesting a flaming pearl amidst clouds and fire scrolls, original flat and circular porcelain stopper painted with a flaming pearl

1936-858 (CB. 357)

Doucai ('contrasting color') enameling is quite unusual in snuff bottle production, and appears to be a response to the popularity of the larger *doucai* ceramic wares from Jingdezhen.

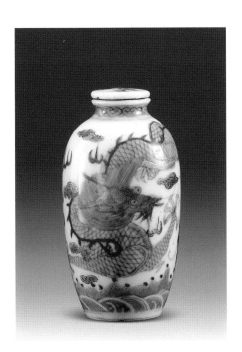

323 | **Porcelain**

1820-1900
2 ³/₁₆ in. (5.6 cm.) high

Of baluster shape, painted in a continuous scene in underglaze blue and iron-red with a seated lady and her boy assistant holding a silk thread between them, standing before a textile loom, an elderly figure standing nearby holding a fly whisk, all reserved on a black ground

1936-672 (CB. 388 or 517)

For a rectangular bottle of similar type painted with an equestrian figure on one side and scholars under pine on the other, see Sotheby's, New York, The Bob C. Stevens Collection, Part III, 25 June 1982, lot 70. See also a black ground bottle of baluster shape, depicting a scene from the *Romance of the Western Chamber* which, in subject matter, might well relate to this bottle, illustrated in an article by Larissa Kouzmenko, 'Snuff Bottles in the Museum of Oriental Art in Moscow', *JICSBS*, Winter 1998, p. 15, fig. 2.

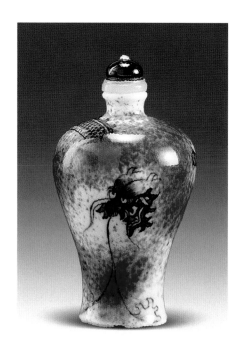

324 | **Porcelain**

1821-1850, *Shende Tang Zhi* four-character mark in underglaze blue, Daoguang
2 ³/₄ in. (7 cm.) high

Of *meiping* shape, extremely well painted with a four-clawed dragon
emerging from an unusual powder-blown underglaze copper-red cloud

1936-611 (CB. 370)

Very few bottles of this type appear to be published. Perhaps the most
comparable is an ovoid bottle sold at Christie's, London, 9 October 1972,
lot 5. It is described as 'gray and pale blue', the gray presumably referring
to an under-fired copper-red but similarly depicting a dragon emerging
from clouds emitting a cloud of vapors from its mouth.

Shende Tang Zhi can be read as: 'Made for Hall for the Cultivation of
Virtue'. This hall, built within the Old Summer Palace, is associated with the
Daoguang Emperor.

See another bottle in this collection, No. 192, for a discussion of this hall.

325 | **Porcelain**

1821-1850
2 ³/₄ in. (7cm.) high

Of *meiping* shape, painted with the eight auspicious Daoist emblems
including a gourd, fan, basket of flowers, flute, sword, bamboo tubes,
castanets, and lotus, all amidst clouds and fruit on an underglaze
copper-red ground

1936-1027 (CB. 371)

This bottle is an exceedingly fine example of kiln firing. The copper-red,
fired in a reduction kiln, is highly successful in its depth of color and its
evenness. The Daoist emblems are also remarkably detailed.

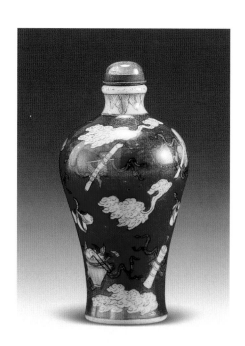

326 | **Porcelain**

1800-1900
2 ⁷/₈ in. (7.3 cm.) high

Of cylindrical shape, with rounded shoulders and tall slender neck, under an attractive mottled robin's egg blue glaze

1936-1039 (CB. 379)

Robin's egg blue glazed bottles are rare. For one other example, called 'clair-de-lune', with more slanted shoulders, see Bob C. Stevens, *The Collector's Book of Snuff Bottles*, p. 94, No. 268.

For three others of differing shape, see Christie's, New York, The Rachelle R. Holden Collection, 21 March 2000, lot 7; *Chinese Snuff Bottles, A Miniature Art from the Collection of Mary and George Bloch*, No. 178; and Christie's, London, The Edmund F. Dwyer Collection, 12 October 1987, lot 125.

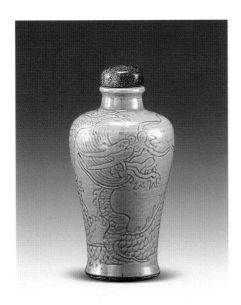

327 | **Porcelain**

1850-1900
2 ³/₈ in. (5.5 cm.) high

Of *meiping* shape, lightly incised with a five-clawed dragon chasing a flaming pearl under a mustard-yellow glaze

1936-1007 (CB. 381)

As with No. 322 in this collection, this bottle is an interpretation in miniature of a ceramic vase of Jingdezhen production.

328 | **Porcelain**

1800-1900
2 ⁷/₈ in. (7.3 cm.) high

Of cylindrical shape, painted in a continuous scene with Zhong Kui, the Demon Queller, with demons nearby and two bats above

1936-1005 (CB. 387)

See bottle No. 74 in this collection for a discussion of Zhong Kui, the Demon Queller. It is extremely unusual to find the combination of underglaze blue and turquoise on ceramic production in general and in snuff bottle production in particular.

329 | **Porcelain**

1850-1900
2 ¹/₄ in. (6.4 cm.) high

A double bottle, formed as two peapods painted in black with daisy or possibly stylized chyrsanthemum, on a swirling foliage ground, the rims gilt

1936-598 (CB. 390 or 519)

It is extremely unusual to find a porcelain snuff bottle enameled in these colors. It was a combination that was popular on ceramic vessels during the reign of the Yongzheng Emperor. For a vase of this very Imperial type, see Christie's, Hong Kong, 26-27 October 1989, lot 630.

However, the shape of this example is very similar to other snuff bottles which clearly date to the second half of the nineteenth century. See another example in this collection, No. 238.

For one other bottle using this unusual combination of colors, see Humphrey K. F. Hui, Margaret Polak and Christopher C. H. Sin, *Hidden Treasures of the Dragon*, No. 87. It has a two-character Qianlong mark on the base and is painted with a landscape. As on this bottle, the design is painted in black on the body and then overglazed in a transparent dark green enamel.

330 | **Porcelain**

1820-1880
1 3/4 in. (4.5 cm.) high

Of compressed baluster shape, painted in a continuous scene with the Eight Daoist Immortals amidst clouds

1936-1054 (CB. 338)

For two other rare examples of bottles decorated in underglaze brown on a yellow ground, one painted with figures on a terrace, the other with a Buddhistic lion, see Sotheby's, Hong Kong, 2 May 1996, lot 1233 and Sotheby's, New York, 17 September 1996, lot 151, respectively.

331 | **Porcelain**

1800-1900
2 13/16 in. (7.2 cm.) high

Of natural eggplant shape, molded with pendant leaves at the neck under a thick slightly over-fired smoky glaze

1936-986

See bottles No. 332 for a discussion of fruit and vegetable bottles.

332 | **Porcelain**

1850-1900
Between 1 ⁵/₈ in. (4.2 cm.) and 1 ⁷/₁₆ in. (3.7 cm.) long

Five miniature bottles, three molded as aubergines, one white crackle-glazed, one turquoise with green leaves and one of aubergine tone with green leaves; two molded as pea pods, both green-glazed.

1936-832 (CB. 464)

1936-867 (CB. 466)

1936-875 (CB. 469)

1936-1043-1 (CB. 470)-only one of pair illustrated.

1936-1043-2 (CB. 471)

These bottles belong to a fairly well known group of porcelain bottles molded primarily in the form of pea pods or eggplants (aubergine), and occasionally other fruit or vegetables. They are usually covered in an opaque lightly crackled monochrome glaze (sometimes using two colors) and appear to relate to a group of similar glazed larger vessels produced in the eighteenth and nineteenth centuries in Jingdezhen. The quality varies enormously. Some of the vegetables, particularly the pea-pods, exhibit a superb naturalistic quality, both in surface modulation and detailed edge finish.

For other examples, see Sotheby's, Hong Kong, Fine Chinese Snuff Bottles from the Collection of Arthur Gadsby, 2 May 1991, lot 211; Robert Hall, *Chinese Snuff Bottles II*, No. 7, from the Marian Mayer Collection; and Christie's, London, The Ko Family Collection, Part III, 18 June 1973, lot 46.

Inside-Painted and
Enamel Bottles

333 | Crystal, inside-painted

Signed Gugang Jushi on one side and Gan Xuan followed by the cyclical date, *Yihai qing he*, corresponding to the fourth month of 1815
3 5/16 in. (8.4 cm.) high

Of tapering cylindrical shape, painted on one side with a lone scholar in contemplation in a mountainous river landscape below a lengthy inscription, the date, a signature and seal, the other side with a gnarled pine, rockwork and orchids, and an inscription, an art name and a seal

1936-590 (CB. 16 or 91)

The poetic inscription to the side with the landscape reads:

(i)   *Chun yu yu qing shi*
(ii) *Shan Guan nong yan xia*
(iii) *lin jian you gao ren*
(iv) *Xiao yu luo tian wai*

This can be translated as:
(i)   The spring rains begin to clear;
(ii) The bright mountains are bathed in mists.
(iii) Lofty gentlemen are in the forest;
(iv) Their merry talk echoes through the heavens.

The inscription is followed by the date, fourth month of 1815 and a signature, which can be read as *Gan Xuan*. The seal is undecipherable.

The inscription to the side with the large gnarled pine tree reads:
(i) *Zhi lan bing yu shan chuan xiu*
(ii) *Song po chang liu tian di chun*

This can be translated as:
(i) Fungus (*lingzhi*) and orchids lend their elegance to the mountains and rivers
(ii) As the pine and cypress grow tall, spring fills heaven and earth.

The inscription is followed by the art name, *Gugang Jushi* ('retired scholar of Gugang') and an undecipherable seal.

This bottle is among the earliest of a small group of inside-painted bottles of the Lingnan School.

With the recent publication by Hugh Moss, Victor Graham and Ka Bo Tsang, *A Treasury of Chinese Snuff Bottles, The Mary and George Bloch Collection*, Vol. 4, Inside-Painted, pp. 9-19, a radical reassessment of the so-called 'Early School' has taken place. In summary, it shifts the beginnings of inside-painted production from Guangzhou in the south to Beijing in the north, and suggests that a group of inside-painted bottles with Manchu script are the earliest of the School.

Inside-painting of snuff bottles was then developed by Yiru Jushi (previously considered a mid-nineteenth century artist) and a school of followers. It then spread to the south with the Lingnan School in Guangdong province with painters Gan Xuanwen and Chen Quan as the most prominent artists and leading lights.

For further examples of Gan's work, see *ibid.*, Nos. 449-461.

This is the tallest of all Gan's bottles recorded. It would not normally be considered noteworthy in a snuff bottle; however, in this case it most certainly is, as it allows for a much larger surface on which to paint. The oval shape of the bottle, without interior corners for the artist to negotiate, also allows the surface to be used like a paper or silk canvas in the literati tradition. In this author's opinion, it is unquestionably the finest of the entire group.

334 | **Crystal, inside-painted**

The bottle circa 1850, the painting 1900-1930
2 ¹/₂ in. (6.4 cm.) high

Of rounded rectangular shape, painted with a continuous landscape scene of figures contemplating under pine and prunus, with two long-tailed birds amidst the branches on one side and small boats on a river near birds, rockwork and trees on the other; the crystal also carved on the exterior with a pine tree and rockwork

1936-583 (CB. 92)

It is most likely that the incised decoration on the exterior was carved prior to the painting on the inside of this bottle, which used the exterior decoration as a starting point.

335 | **Chalcedony, inside-painted**

1900-1920, indistinctly signed but probably Ye Zhongsan
2 ³/₁₆ in. (5.5 cm.) high

Of rounded rectangular shape, painted inside with a continuous scene of ten bug-eyed fan-tailed fish, the stone with brown swirling inclusions

1936-907 (CB. 38, 86 or 166)

Though indistinctly signed, we can be fairly confident that this is the work of Ye Zhongsan. For an example where the artist has profited from the use of a murky agate which provides a transparent watery backdrop for the depiction of fish, see Hugh Moss, Victor Graham and Ka Bo Tsang, *A Treasury of Chinese Snuff Bottles, The Mary and George Bloch Collection*, Vol. 4, Inside-Painted, No. 532.

Goldfish, *jinyu*, swimming in a pond, *tang*, represent wealth. The sounds of the words together evoke the auspicious phrase *jinyu mantang*, which literally means 'may your hall be filled with gold and jade'.

336 | Crystal, inside-painted

1900-1920, signed Ye Zhongsan
2 ⁷/₈ in. (7.3 cm.) high

Of elongated oval shape, painted in a continuous scene with a figure on a mule in a winter landscape below an inscription with the artist's name and seal to one side, and figures greeting one another at a gateway on the other

1936-724

The inscription reads:

(i) Yi tian feng xui shi qiao xie

(ii) Chi lao qi lu mi jiu jia

(iii) Shi wai bu zhi cheng zhan shi

(iv) Er long gang shang kan mei hua

This can be translated as:

(i) One day of wind and rain, (I come to) a stone bridge

(ii) An old man astride a donkey, searches for a tavern

(iii) Of the outside world I know not, of battles and fighting;

(iv) Atop Sleeping-dragon Hill, I survey the plum blossoms

The inscription is followed by the artist's name, *Ye Zhongsan*, and his seal.

The subject comes from the epic story, *Romance of the Three Kingdoms*.

For a full description of the scene on one side of this bottle, Liu Bei visiting Zhuge Liang's cottage, see an article by Gayle Gray Laverlochère entitled, 'Romance of the Three Kingdoms, Source of Snuff Bottle Subjects', *JICSBS*, Spring 1988, p. 11, fig. 6d, where she illustrates another Ye Zhongsan bottle with the same subject.

For a full description of the scene on the other side of the bottle, Huang Chengyan and his attendant, see an article by Ka Bo Tsang, entitled, 'Who is the Rider on the Donkey? Some New Observations', *JICSBS*, Summer 1994, p. 8, fig. 10, where she illustrates another Ye Zhongsan bottle, dated 1905, of the same subject.

337 | *Cloisonné* **Enamel**

1720-1800
2 in. (5.1 cm) high

Of moonflask shape, decorated with turquoise circular panels on each side, one decorated with magnolia and prunus, the other with a butterfly near peony and magnolia, all within a yellow *ruyi*-head surround set on a dark blue ground with stylized lotus on the narrow sides

1936-948 (CB. 519)

Literature: Edward Wenham, 'Antiques As Decoration', *Arts & Decoration*, New York, Winter, 1928, illustrated p. 59.

338 | *Cloisonné* **Enamel**

1720-1770
2 ¹/₈ in. (5.5 cm.) high

Of spade shape, with a cartouche on each side decorated with two fruit sprays and a bat on a pale turquoise-green ground, all set on a darker turquoise-blue ground with scrolling foliage in the Imperial style on the narrow sides

1936-949

Stylistically, this bottle compares well with late Ming dynasty *cloisonné* wares, though it probably dates to the early part of the eighteenth century. The extensive pitting to the enamel is common to *cloisonné* from the Ming dynasty up to the mid-eighteenth century.

This bottle can be compared to an example illustrated by Hugh Moss, Victor Graham and Ka Bo Tsang, *The Art of the Chinese Snuff Bottle,*

The J & J Collection, No. 265, which is dated between 1715 and 1760. The slightly less formalized design, the use of a less evenly cut wire '*cloisonné*', and the more muted color scheme of this bottle, suggest that it is the earlier of the two. The authors argue convincingly for an attribution to the Palace workshops, based mostly on comparison with Imperially-marked *cloisonné* wares.

339 | *Cloisonné* and *Champlevé* enamel

1770-1860
2 ³/₁₆ in. (5.5 cm.) high

Of rounded shape, decorated primarily in turquoise and dark blue enamels with stylized *chilong* surrounding a central *shou* medallion on each face within a lobed cartouche, the sides with scrolling flowers and foliage, the neck with a band of *leiwen* above a band of *ruyi* heads

1936-820

For a similar example, see Christie's, London, The Ko Family Collection, Part VI, 8 November 1976, lot 205. For others, with slight variations, see Hugh Moss, Victor Graham and Ka Bo Tsang, *The Art of the Chinese Snuff Bottles, The J & J Collection*, No. 267; Robert W. L. Kleiner, *Chinese Snuff Bottles from the Burghley House Collection*, No. 65, which has an identical stopper.

For an example with an identical design but totally executed with *cloisonné* enamel, see Hugh M. Moss, *Snuff Bottles of China*, No. 272. For another example, using both *cloisonné and champlevé* but with bats rather than the *chilong*

of this bottle, see Lilla S. Perry, *Chinese Snuff Bottles, The Adventures and Studies of a Collector*, No. 162.

For a discussion of *cloisonné and champlevé* enamels, see Hugh Moss, Victor Graham, and Ka Bo Tsang, *op. cit*, No. 266.

340 | *Cloisonné* Enamel

1840-1900
2 ¹/₂ in. (6.3 cm.) high

Of tall hexagonal shape, decorated on each of the six sides with single floral sprays of peony, daisy or lotus, and orchid on a mustard-yellow ground, with prunus blossoms on the shoulder and a band of pendant *lingzhi* heads around the neck

1936-825

In *cloisonné* production, the use of yellow as a ground color became popular in the nineteenth century. The hexagonal shape was a favorite of the ceramic kilns at Jingdezhen, particularly for *famille verte* wares.

341 | *Cloisonné* **Enamel**

1840-1900
2 ½ in. (6.5 cm.) high

Of ovoid shape, decorated in a continuous scene with stylized bamboo, prunus, orchid and daisy on a white ground, a black dragonfly on one side and a small blue butterfly on the other

1936-826

This unusual geometric style of decoration is extremely effective, set off, as it is, by the plain white ground. It is an infrequently used ground color in *cloisonné* production.

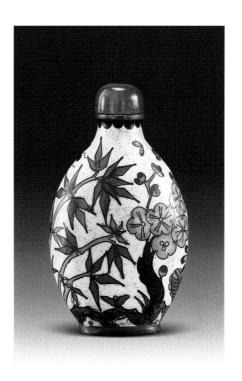

342 | *Cloisonné* **Enamel**

1850-1900
2 ½ in. (6.4 cm.) high

Of rounded shape, decorated with a single red lotus and meandering leafy scrolls on a white ground, the narrow sides with lion-mask handles

1936-528 (CB. 2)

343 | **Enamels on copper**

1723-1735, Yongzheng four-character black enamel mark in a line and of the period, Guangzhou
2 ⁵/₁₆ in. (5.9 cm.) high

Of ovoid shape, painted on both sides with large leaf-shaped cartouches, one side depicting a lady seated on a stool before a side table, contemplating her reflection in her hand-held circular bronze mirror, her consort standing thoughtfully behind her, the other side painted with the same couple in a similar interior setting, all on a lemon-yellow ground

1936-676

The scene of a lady admiring her reflection in a mirror was a popular one in Chinese art. Perhaps the most famous depiction of such a scene is on a handscroll in the British Museum, London, entitled *Admonitions of the Instructress to the Palace Ladies,* attributed to Gu Kaizhi, active ca. 344 – ca. 406. See Shane McCausland, *The Admonitions Scroll* (forthcoming). Another painting from the Museum of Fine Arts, Boston, by Su Hanchen, active between the 1120s and the 1160s, entitled, *Lady at Her Dressing Table in a Garden,* shows a scene similar to that on this bottle, with a profusion of details, including tables and vases; see Wu Tung in *Tales from the Land of Dragons: 1,000 Years of Chinese Painting,* No. 25.

Thereafter, the scene was a continual favorite, expressing the material well-being of the sitter, whilst the reflection alluded to the inner mood. It continued in the Ming and Qing dynasties primarily in the form of paintings on silk.

For another Guangzhou enamel bottle of more slender form, painted with a Chinese subject of scholars under trees, but also using the simple blue line border at the foot and neck, see Hugh M. Moss, *Snuff Bottles of China,* No. 267.

A leaf-shaped panel set against a monochrome ground was a standard feature to be found on ceramics coming from Jingdezhen in the Yongzheng period on wares for the Court, but particularly on pieces for export. For an export example, see Sotheby's, New York, The Mildred R. and Rafi Y. Mottahedeh Collection, 19 October 2000, lot 166.

The provincial quality of this enamel is self-evident and well represents the majority of enamels emanating from Guangzhou at that time. The method of painting, primarily using a wash effect of the enamel, is standard for this southern center and quite unlike the meticulous stippling techniques of Beijing production. It is possible that the enamel workshops in Guangzhou were set up before those in Beijing. It is well documented, for instance, that the Kangxi Emperor ordered trained artists from Guangzhou to move to Beijing as early as 1719, see *Tributes from Guangdong to the Qing Court,* pp. 54-55.

344 | **Enamels on copper**

1736-1795, Qianlong four-character black enamel mark painted on two peaches on the base and of the period, Guangzhou
2 ¹/₄ in. (5.7 cm.) high

Of double gourd shape, painted with a yellow cloth and iron-red dragon roundels wrapped around the central section of the waisted bottle holding in place peony sprigs, a bamboo-handled fan, and a fish-shaped musical stone, the wrap tied with a tasseled ring on one side, all on a pale turquoise-blue ground with further peony sprays and five bats

1936-712

The motif of a tied-cloth or brocade around a snuff bottle was a popular one during the reigns of the Yongzheng and Qianlong Emperors. It is primarily found in enamels, but also in porcelains.

A cloth tied around a vessel, be it a snuff bottle or otherwise, was a decorative device indicative of a gift. Gifts were often presented at court tied with precious brocade.

The subject on this bottle is superbly handled, with a mass of minute details on a beautifully balanced and controlled color scheme to form a homogenous whole. Rather unusually, for a gourd-shaped bottle of this design, the tied cloth to one side sits on the upper gourd above the waisted center, rather than on it, which is most often the case. It was almost certainly an intentional aesthetic judgment to allow the painter to accommodate the wealth of other details painted on the body. On other bottles, the tied cloth appears to fully squeeze the center of the bottle, in the manner that a bodice might accentuate the curves of a female body. The use of a pale turquoise-blue ground and soft pastel colors adds a light airy feeling to the design which counter-balances the plethora of details.

The use of two peaches on the base of this bottle, on which is painted the Qianlong mark, reinforces the auspicious nature of the gift, expressing long life to the recipient.

The example most similar to this one appears to be one illustrated by Hugh Moss, Victor Graham and Ka Bo Tsang, *The Art of the Chinese Snuff Bottle, The J & J Collection*, No. 179, which bears a black Yongzheng four-character mark set within a twin dragon surround and is painted with a pink tied cloth on a yellow ground. The authors note, *ibid.*, p. 298, that 'This type of mark, which also appears during the Qianlong period, was used at the Court apparently for Imperial birthdays, one of the several occasions each year which triggered massive tribute and production from the various Imperial workshops.'

Based on the many similarities of these two bottles, and the rarity of other Qianlong-marked bottles of double-gourd shape using this design, it is very likely that this bottle was produced in the early years of the Qianlong reign, perhaps between 1736-40.

For other Guangzhou enamel bottles with a Yongzheng mark on two peaches, see *Snuff Bottles of the Ch'ing Dynasty*, No. 6; and another from the Mary and George Bloch Collection (perhaps the same bottle) illustrated in *A Congregation of Snuff Bottle Connoisseurs*, No. 234, with a black ground, a yellow brocade wrap, an endless knot and a fat dragon fish; Robert Kleiner, *Chinese Snuff Bottles, The White Wings Collection*, No. 4; illustrated again in *Treasures from the Sanctum of Enlightened Respect: Chinese Snuff Bottles from the Denis Low Collection*, No. 6.

Yongzheng precursors with a brocade wrap but not of gourd shape, include a slender oviform bottle with a brown ground sold at Sotheby's, Hong Kong, 2 May 1991, lot 86, and a rounded Yongzheng-marked bottle with rows of stylized bats and a brocade wrap in *Chinese Snuff Bottles in the Collection of the National Palace Museum*, No. 22.

For an elongated oval bottle painted with a very similar color scheme depicting a brocade cloth, knotted on one side, and suspending an endless knot, tassels and a fan, see Robert Kleiner, *Chinese Snuff Bottles, The White Wings Collection*, No. 7. It has an unusual three-character mark, *Jingsi tang* ('Hall of Respectful Thoughts'), which the author believes was made for a private commission.

For other Qianlong-marked enamel bottles with a brocade wrap but not of double-gourd shape, see Robert W. L. Kleiner in *Chinese Snuff Bottles from the Collection of Mary and George Bloch*, No. 9, also painted on a pale blue ground; ten identical bottles of baluster shape forming part of a tribute of fifty bottles presented to the Qianlong Emperor in the 44th year of his reign (1780) illustrated in *Masterpieces of Snuff Bottles in the Palace Museum*, No. 206.

345 | Enamels on copper

1736-1795, *Qianlong yuzhi* four-character mark in blue enamel and of the period, Beijing

2 ¹/₂ in. (6.3 cm.) high

Of double gourd shape, painted in *famille rose* enamels with a continuous landscape scene of male and female golden pheasants beneath pine and branches near rockwork, begonia, daisy and peony, two further pairs of birds, one of each pair flying, the other perched in the pine branches dispersed around the body

1936-714

Yuzhi, ('Made by Imperial Command'), is an important Imperial designation. Five other bottles depicting the same subject are recorded, and the most comparable to Blair's, also of double gourd shape, bears a *Jiaqing yuzhi* mark. It is in the Seattle Art Museum and is illustrated in *Snuff Bottles of the Ch'ing Dynasty,* No. 15. Three of the four remaining examples are of baluster shape. One of these, from the Charles V. Swain Collection, also bearing a *Qianlong yuzhi* mark, is also illustrated in *Snuff Bottles of the Ch'ing Dynasty,* No. 14. The other two have the more usual Imperial designation, *Qianlong nianzhi.* Both are illustrated by Robert Kleiner, one in *Chinese Snuff Bottles in the Collection of Mary and George Bloch,* pp. 32-33, and the other in *Treasures from the Sanctum of Enlightened Respect: Chinese Snuff Bottles from the Denis Low Collection,* No. 5.

The fifth example, from a private Canadian collection, was exhibited at the Canadian Craft Museum, Vancouver, and is illustrated in a review of the exhibition, *Treasures to Hold; Chinese Snuff Bottles,* in the *JICSBS,* Winter 1992, p. 26, fig. 6. The bottle is of rounded flattened shape, but the type of mark is not noted.

The double gourd is an extremely difficult form to paint, but here the artist demonstrates complete control by the natural manner in which the decoration fills the space available.

As a shape, the double-gourd appears to have been more popular as a vehicle in glass snuff bottle production. For various examples, see *Masterpieces of Snuff Bottles in the Palace Museum,* Nos. 106-108.

For another Qianlong-marked Imperial enamel bottle painted with a pair of golden pheasant samidst rockwork, peony, morning glory and daisy, see *ibid.,* No. 16.

Bird painting had a long tradition from as early as the Song dynasty. The golden pheasant with its striking plumage was particularly popular. Interestingly, the Italian Jesuit painter Giuseppe Castiglione (1688-1766) adopted the subject after he was installed as the court painter, see *The Selected Paintings of Lang Shih-ning (Josephus Castiglione),* Vol. I, pl. 14, for his painting entitled *Glorious Spring* which is preserved in the National Palace Museum, Taiwan. It depicts a pair of golden pheasants on a rock between flowering shrubs. See also a Qianlong marked porcelain vase of pear shape with the same subject illustrated in *Tianjin Shi Yishu Bowuguan cang ci,* Tianjin Municipal Museum, Nos. 169-170.

346 | **Enamels on copper**

1736-1795. Qianlong four-character mark in blue enamel, and of the period, Beijing

2 in. (5.1 cm.) high

Of rounded shape, painted in *famille rose* enamels with a continuous scene of a butterfly above orchids on one side, and a grasshopper amidst pinks growing from convoluted rockwork below a dragonfly on the other, all between a purple *ruyi* band at the foot and multi-colored lappets and a blue whorl band at the neck

1936-713

This bottle can be linked to a small group of exceedingly fine Imperial Qianlong bottles made in the Beijing Palace workshops and painted with purely Chinese naturalistic subjects. It can also be compared to an even smaller group of enameled glass bottles made at the Palace workshops during the same period.

The bottle with the most similar subject matter is illustrated in *Chinese Snuff Bottles, A Miniature Art from the Collection of Mary and George Bloch*, No. 7. Another, from the same collection, is illustrated by Robert W. L. Kleiner in *Chinese Snuff Bottles from the Collection of Mary and George Bloch*, No. 7.

Another slightly more vigorous example, painted with birds and flowers, is illustrated by Hugh Moss, Victor Graham and Ka Bo Tsang in *The Art of the Chinese Snuff Bottle, The J & J Collection*, No. 177, which itself relates closely to two other enamel bottles in the same collection, Nos. 175 and 176.

A similar bottle, illustrated by Rachelle R. Holden in *Rivers and Mountains Far from the World*, No. 31, has birds on branches on one side and flowers on the other. The borders are similar.

See also two others illustrated in *Masterpieces of Snuff Bottles in the Palace Museum*, No. 12 and No. 16. The first is delicately painted with flowers and a bird in a continuous scene on a white ground, while the second depicts pheasants and flowers which almost completely fill the white ground.

347 | **Enamels on copper**

1736-1795, Qianlong four-character blue enamel marks and of the period, Guangzhou
1 27/33 in. (4.7 cm.) high

A pair of oval bottles, each painted in a continuous scene with an elegant female seated on a rocky outcrop below a knotty pine in a river landscape on one side and a boy walking a buffalo towards a gnarled willow on the other, all set between scrolling foliage bands at the foot and a whorl band at the neck, one bottle depicted in a slightly larger scale with subtle variations in the background

77a: 1936-709

77b: 1936-710

Scenes of pastoral idylls have long been popular in Chinese art; however, as a subject on enamel bottles, they are quite rare.

The example most comparable to this was offered at Sotheby's, London, 5 December 1983, lot 248. The reverse, not illustrated in the catalogue, is described as follows: 'the reverse with an elaborately dressed maiden, her hair piled into a double chignon, reclining on an outcrop of pierced rockwork, beneath a pine tree, a lake in the background, a petal collar round the neck.' This could easily be describing this pair of bottles. The other side, which is illustrated in the Sotheby's catalogue, depicts a hatted boy riding a water buffalo beside a winding river. The only difference is that the boy in this example is walking. The disposition of the bands at the neck and foot are also similar. All bear Qianlong four-character marks.

Another bottle, illustrated by Hugh Moss, Victor Graham and Ka Bo Tsang, in *The Art of the Chinese Snuff Bottle, The J & J Collection,*

No. 176, is similar in depicting a Chinese pastoral scene. The position of a male scholar under the branches of a twisting willow mirrors closely that of the lady in this example, bending to follow the curved outline of the bottle.

Another Chinese-subject bottle depicting a boy walking in a landscape, and a lady seated on rockwork to the other side, is illustrated in *Masterpieces of Snuff Bottles in the Palace Museum*, No. 13.

Another example, of baluster shape, presumably from the same workshop, with a very similar technique and style of painting, but depicting European-subject pastoral scenes including buffalo, see *Chinese Snuff Bottles*, No. 240.

For another European-subject bottle with goatherds and their flock, see Sotheby's, New York, The Mei Ling Collection, 15 March 1984, lot 77.

348 | Enamels on copper

1723-50, Yongzheng four-character purple enamel mark in a line and probably of the period, Guangzhou.
2 ⁵/₈ in. (6.6 cm.) high

Of oval shape, painted in pink or pale purple enamel in reserve with a dense scrolling foliage ground with small prunus flower heads, the stamens picked out in green

1936-722

Provenance: The American Art Galleries, New York, The Ton-Ying Collection, 5 February 1925, lot 70. (See fig. 31 in the Introduction.)

For another enamel bottle attributed to the Guangzhou (Canton) workshops, dated to between 1725-1750 and painted with a continuous formalized floral design, see Hugh Moss, Victor Graham and Ka Bo Tsang, *The Art of the Chinese Snuff Bottle, The J & J Collection*, No. 181. Though the shape differs slightly, and the design incorporates a wider range of colors and flora than this bottle, it is quite apparent that they were produced at the same center and are probably close in date. That example, however, unlike this one, bears no reign mark but has a stylized petal painted on the foot.

For another bottle of similar type with a petal mark on the base, see Bob C. Stevens, *The Collector's Book of Chinese Snuff Bottles*, No. 988. It too has a dense floral scroll on a pale ground and extensive use of black enamel and gilt.

For a more rare Yongzheng-marked example, see Viviane Jutheau, *Guide du Collectionneur de Tabatières Chinoises*, p. 55.

This example of prunus blossoms dispersed over a dense meandering foliage ground appears to be one of the earliest uses of this design in the snuff bottle oeuvre. It might derive from the popular decoration of 'prunus and cracked-ice' on blue and white porcelains of the Kangxi period. These were shipped in large numbers from the port of Guangzhou in the seventeenth and eighteenth centuries.

The use, though limited on this bottle, of a black enamel in bands on the neck and foot also indicates an early production date. It was a popular color during the reigns of the Kangxi and Yongzheng Emperors in both the enamel and porcelain workshops. Its use declined after this date. See also No. 353, for an early bottle using a black enamel ground.

349 | Enamels on copper

1730-1780, Guangzhou
2 ¹/₂ in. (6.3 cm.) high

Of oval shape, painted on each side with a flower head and scrolling foliage in the center dividing confronted one-clawed blue *chilong* below a descending bat at the shoulder, all on a dark aubergine ground, the mouth wide, a flower head on the base

1936-730

See the previous bottle, No. 354, for a discussion of Guangzhou (Canton) enamels of this type.

For other examples decorated with *chilong* and a floral ground, see *A Congregation of Snuff Bottle Connoisseurs*, No. 238; and Sotheby's, New York, the Bob C. Stevens Collection, Part III, 26 March 1982, lot 83, painted in a less stylized fashion, with one green and one red dragon amidst blue clouds on a pale yellow ground.

The significance of the single claw found on the Blair dragons has yet to be ascertained.

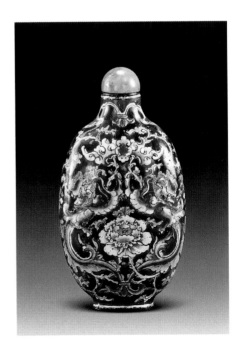

350 | Enamels on copper

1736-1795, Qianlong four-character black enamel mark and of the period, Guangzhou

2 in. (5 cm.) high

Of rounded shape, each side painted in a continuous scene with a pair of spotted deer on a grassy knoll amidst rockwork, *lingzhi* and flowers, all between an iron-red and yellow whorl band at the foot and a flower head and leaf band below another whorl band at the neck

1936-693

A similar bottle is illustrated by Hugh Moss, *Chinese Snuff Bottles: 6, Chinese Snuff Bottles from the Collection of the Rt. Hon. The Marquess of Exeter, K.C.M.G.*, pp. 106-107, No. E. 19. It too bears a Qianlong mark, though in brown enamel. The border decoration at the neck and foot appears identical to this one, as does the style and technique of the enameling itself. The design of birds and butterflies amidst prunus, peonies and rocks is remarkably close in overall conception and natural subject matter. There are also close parallels in the stippled effect of the sky.

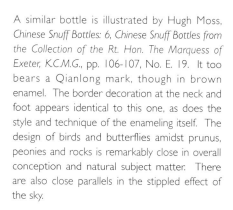

The design of deer in landscape settings appears on snuff bottles in the reign of the Yongzheng Emperor. An example bearing a four-character Yongzheng mark in black enamel, painted with a design of six deer in a landscape with pine, and of more elongated oviform shape, is illustrated by Robert Hall, in *Chinese Snuff Bottles*, No. 69; and also by Robert Kleiner in *Chinese Snuff Bottles, A Miniature Art from the Collection of Mary and George Bloch*, p. 63, No. 12.

Another bottle with a very similar border pattern, again depicting a natural subject matter of birds amidst flowers and rocks, but of cylindrical baluster shape, is illustrated in *Chinese Snuff Bottles*, p. 102, No. 243.

A Qianlong-marked bottle illustrated in *Snuff Bottles in the Collection of the National Palace Museum*, No. 15, though probably painted slightly later in the Qianlong reign, displays a similarity of technique, in particular the stippled ground which acts as a backdrop to the two naturalistically rendered cartouches of flowers and rockwork. The technique and style continued into the reign of the Jiaqing Emperor. For an example, see *Masterpieces of Snuff Bottles in the Palace Museum*, p. 67, No. 35, which illustrates the end product of this type of Guangzhou enamel.

This bottle is painted in extremely fine detail by a sure hand, comfortable with the use of space in the design.

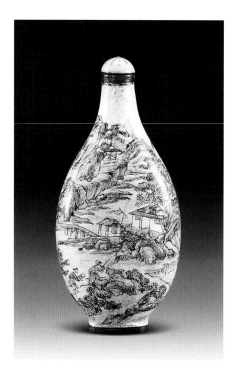

351 | **Enamels on copper**

1740-1790, Guangzhou
3 in. (7.6 cm.) high

Of elongated pear shape, painted in *famille rose* enamels with a continuous scene of numerous figures in a bucolic rocky river landscape, one side with fisherman on a boat, two boys each on a buffalo, figures carrying loads and another at a city entrance, the other side with a scholar and his assistant

1936-823

This is a very rare enamel bottle. Few are recorded that depict such a naturalistic mountainous landscape, following the classic Chinese tradition of verticality. It appears loosely based on the green-blue painting style of the Tang dynasty which was popularized in the Ming and Qing dynasties.

For one other rare example in the State Hermitage Museum, St. Petersburg, dated to between 1700-1725, see an article by Tatiana Arapova, 'Enamel Decorations of Snuff Bottles in Glass, Porcelain and Metals,' *JICSBS*, Spring 1996, pp. 8-9, fig. 14. From the side illustrated, it does not appear to have any figures set in the landscape.

352 | **Enamels on copper**

1796-1820, Jiaqing six-character iron-red seal mark and of the period, Guangzhou
2 ³/₈ in. (5.5 cm.) high

Of rounded shape, painted in a continuous scene with the 'hundred boys' standing in rows in building entrances and on the banks of a river, variously holding lanterns depicting an elephant, Buddhistic lion and fish, lighting firecrackers or playing musical instruments

1936-953

For two nearly identical examples, see Christie's, New York, 28 March 1996, lot 112; and Christie's, New York, 25 March 1998, lot 265, which is also illustrated by Robert Kleiner in *Treasures from the Sanctum of Enlightened Respect: Chinese Snuff Bottles from the Denis Low Collection*, No. 11. It is rare to find Jiaqing-marked enamel bottles. The National Palace Museum, Taipei, illustrates only one other example (which depicts European children at play in a Chinese landscape), whilst illustrating a large number of Yongzheng and Qianlong-marked examples and even a few Kangxi-marked bottles. See *Snuff Bottles in the Collection of the National Palace Museum*, pp. 80-87.

The subject of 'one hundred boys' was a popular one and can be found painted or carved in numerous other media. For a Qianlong bottle of very similar shape and neck design, which may well have been the inspiration for the shape of this type of bottle, see Robert Kleiner, *Chinese Snuff Bottles in the Collection of Mary and George Bloch*, No. 13. It is more finely painted and depicts a lady and children in a river landscape.

353 | Enamels on copper

1720-1750, Guangzhou
2 ³/₄ in. (6.9 cm.) high

Of elongated oval form, painted with a lady and a boy on each side, almost certainly representing the Virgin Mary and the Christ Child under a tree on a black ground, on one side she holds a staff and orb, and the child a *gu*-shaped beaker vase, on the other he holds an apple or an orb

1936-824

For two other European-subject Guangzhou enamel bottles on black grounds, see Hugh Moss, *Snuff Bottles of China*, Nos. 265-266.

The most compelling comparison can be made between this bottle and another of almost identical design but on a blue, rather than black, ground, see Jana Volf, The Chinese Porcelain Company, *Chinese Snuff Bottles and Jade Carvings from the Douglas, Gnam and Other Collections*, No. 75. The figures are described as a shepherdess and child, and the bottle, from the collection of Mrs. John Sheafe Douglas, is dated to the eighteenth century.

The bottle in this collection is extensively restored, and there is the possibility that the black ground is a later addition. The bottle may have begun life with the same color scheme as the Douglas bottle.

The religious subject is almost certainly taken from a baroque European print, probably dating to the late seventeenth or eighteenth century.

The use of black enamel, if we assume for the moment that it is original, was favored during the reigns of the Kangxi and Yongzheng Emperors. For a Yongzheng-marked gourd-shaped Guangzhou enamel bottle with a black ground, see Robert Kleiner, *Treasures from the Sanctum of Enlightened Respect: Chinese Snuff Bottles from the Denis Low Collection*, No. 6.

Another interesting comparison can be made with a Yongzheng-marked Guangzhou enamel bottle which is nearly identical in shape, and with similarly treated borders at the foot and neck, see Robert Kleiner, *Chinese Snuff Bottles in the Collection of Mary and George Bloch*, No. 20.

354 | **Enamels on copper**

1770-1840, Guangzhou
2 ¹/₈ in. (5.4 cm.) high

Of rounded shape, with Guangzhou *famille rose* cartouches on each side, each painted with a mirror image of a European gentleman and a lady, he holding a snuff bottle, she reading a book, set before a river landscape with the corner of a building just behind them, all within a *champlevé* raised gilt-copper scrolling floral and c-scroll surround, further engraved gilt-copper lotus and scrolling foliage to the narrow sides, all with turquoise, dark blue and green enamel, a begonia flower head on the base

1936-728 (CB. 499)

Literature: Edward Wenham, 'Antiques As Decoration', *Arts & Decoration*, New York, Winter, 1928, illustrated p. 58. (See fig. 18 in the Introduction.)

This bottle is exceedingly rare for its depiction of a snuff bottle held in the gentleman's hand. However, when compared with a large group of enamel *champlevé, cloisonné* and gold bottles, it is found to be of less fine quality. It is also one of the few such bottles without a Qianlong mark. It is, unquestionably, a product of the Guangzhou workshops and though possibly dating to late in the Qianlong period, it might also date to the nineteenth century.

The shape of the neck and foot, slightly flaring, is different from all the Qianlong-marked examples of this group, which generally have cylindrical or tapering necks. On the few examples with slightly flaring necks, the feet are short and vertical.

The best examples of this whole group have either *cloisonné* enamel surrounds with inset Beijing enamel plaques, see *Snuff Bottles in the Collection of the National Palace Museum*, No. 11, or gold-bodied *champlevé* bottles with inset Beijing enamel plaques, see Hugh Moss, Victor Graham and Ka Bo Tsang, *The Art of the Chinese Snuff Bottle, The J & J Collection*, No. 169.

See also, an enamel bottle with *cloisonné* enamels on the shoulder and neck illustrated in *Snuff Bottles in the Collection of the National Palace Museum*, No. 16.

In terms of quality, the next level down of this group appears to be *champlevé* enamel copper bottles inset with Guangzhou enamel panels, resembling the finest of the Beijing group, see *Masterpieces of Snuff Bottles in the Palace Museum*, Nos. 27-31, which all bear Qianlong marks and, with the exception of Nos. 30 and 31, are painted with European subjects of ladies and children.

To this group can be added two illustrated by Robert Kleiner, in *Chinese Snuff Bottles in the Collection of Mary and George Bloch*, No. 15, previously sold at Sotheby's, New York, The Mei Ling Collection, 15 March 1984, lot 76; and another, No. 16.

Two other bottles, which are variations of this type, are known. One is inset with European-subject panels depicting a lady, on a *repoussé* copper ground, see Parke-Bernet Galleries, New York, 11 October 1979, lot 175, and later sold at Sotheby's, New York, The Bob C. Stevens Collection, Part II, 26 March 1982, lot 82. The other bottle has two almost identical French enamel panels inset on a cast gilt-bronze body, with a scroll ground, see Robert Kleiner, *op. cit.*, No. 14, where he discusses the possible attribution of these panels to the Beijing Palace Workshops rather than to France.

For an example of a later bottle, probably produced to imitate this group, but at a low cost, see Sotheby's, London, 5 December 1983, lot 250. It is made of cast bronze and is inset with paper-cut scenes under glass on each side, one depicting figures, the other a cluster of fruit.

355 | Enamels on copper

1736-1795, Qianlong four-character blue enamel marks and of the period, Guangzhou
1 ⁷/₈ in. (4.9 cm.) high

A pair of ovoid shape, each painted with quatrefoil panels on both sides, one side of each depicting a slightly different scene of a seated European gentleman and a dog near a European-style building, the other side of each bottle with a European gentleman and a lady in a river landscape, he holding a bow in both depictions and an arrow in one, with variations in their placement and that of the buildings, both bottles with dark ground borders, one gilt with four of the eight Daoist emblems between flower heads, the other with flower heads

72a: 1936-715-2

72b: 1936-715-1 (This bottle only is illustrated.)

Stylistically, the figures can be likened to those on another Guangzhou bottle illustrated by Robert Kleiner, in *Chinese Snuff Bottles from the Collection of Mary and George Bloch*, No. 11. The somewhat quirky pose of each of the standing figures on the reverse of these bottles is similar to those on the Bloch example, as is the dotted treatment of the leaves, which form a canopy over the figures and the river landscape background.

It is also interesting to compare with a Qianlong-marked Guangzhou Imperial enamel wine ewer, sold at Christie's, Hong Kong, Masterworks of Chinese Art, 5-6 November 1997, lot 938A. It is painted with a European-subject panel on each side in an identically-shaped cartouche and depicts four European ladies and a boy holding a bow and wearing a quiver of arrows on his back.

See also another Guangzhou snuff bottle, similar in design to all of these, which depicts two hounds to one side and a lady in a river landscape setting on the other. It sold at Christie's, New York, 2 December 1993, lot 451.

The subject appears to be derived from a European print source, possibly French or Swiss. Interestingly, for a 'pair' there are a number of variations to the design on each of these bottles. The buildings behind the seated figure and his dog are interpreted quite differently. One has square towers and sloping rooflines with two lines of receding perspective, the other has circular towers with domed spires and one line of receding perspective. The figures on the reverse are also posed differently. In one the male figure strides away from his female companion and holds a bow and arrows, whilst on the other the figures are confronted and he holds the bow whilst the lady clutches the arrows. The themes of hunting and love are here inextricably entwined.

The treatment of the narrow sides with gilt decoration on a black ground appears to be based on early Beijing precursors. The use of black was uncommon in the Qianlong period.

356 | **Enamels on copper**

1736-1795, Qianlong four-character blue-enamel mark and of the period, Beijing
1 ⁷/₈ in. (4.9 cm.) high

Of rounded shape, painted in *famille rose* enamels with a European lady and boy under a tree on each side, one lady with a billowing orange scarf and a basket of flowers draped around her right shoulder, the boy tugging at the handle; the other lady holding a small sprig of flowers in her raised left hand, the boy squeezing her right arm and trying to peer around her, the narrow sides with leafy foliage, c-scrolls and a central flower head on a dark aubergine ground

1936-705

Provenance: American Art Galleries, New York,
          The A. W. Bahr Collection, 17-19 January 1916, lot 57.
          (See fig. 22 in the Introduction.)

This bottle can be closely compared to two others, both illustrated by Robert W. L. Kleiner, one in *Chinese Snuff Bottles from the Collection of Mary and George Bloch*, No. 2; and the other in *Treasures from the Sanctum of Enlightened Respect: Chinese Snuff Bottles from the Denis Low Collection*, No. 2. The *rocaille* borders and disposition of the figures are quite similar in both cases, though buildings replace the trees found on this example. The handling of the child on each side is also remarkably similar. It is tempting to see the same hand at work on all three examples.

As in bottles 357 and 358, in this collection, this bottle shows the sitters pushed to the foreground of the scene. The slightly claustrophobic effect is further enforced by the figure of the boy squeezing around the lady.

357 | **Enamels on copper**

1736-1795, Qianlong four-character blue enamel mark and of the period, Beijing
1 ¹⁵/₁₆ in. (5 cm.) high

Of rounded shape, painted with a European lady with flowers in her hair and a boy on each side, one lady carrying a basket of flowers over her right shoulder, the boy tugging at the strap to peer around her, set near a building and foliage, the other lady in an interior setting, placing her arms around the shoulders of a boy gazing out from just in front of her, a table supporting a vase and a trumpet glass behind her, all set within a circular rope-twist border below fanciful multi-colored c-scrolls and *ruyi* lappets, the narrow sides painted with small cartouches of European buildings in puce on a beige ground with mustard-yellow floral scrolling between flower heads

1936-703

This exquisite bottle can best be compared to two other examples, one in Robert Kleiner, *Chinese Snuff Bottles in the Collection of Mary and George Bloch*, No. 4; the other illustrated by Hugh Moss, Victor Graham and Ka Bo Tsang, *The Art of the Chinese Snuff Bottle, The J & J Collection*, No. 173. All three must be from the same workshop, if not the same hand, so similar are the techniques employed, the quality and the style. These include the careful shading, particularly to the clothing and the fine stippling to the sky, trees and the faces. The figures are similarly 'pushed' to the foreground.

The treatment of one lady's left hand, with first and little fingers extended, is an idiosyncratic one, and identical to the treatment of one hand on the J & J Collection bottle, which can also be closely compared to a bottle illustrated in *Snuff Bottles in the Collection of the National Palace Museum*, No. 14.

The Bloch bottle has the same rope-twist

cartouche as this one and delightful ruby vignettes with European buildings on the narrow sides.

Another bottle with different borders but similar puce landscape vignettes on the narrow sides was sold at Christie's, New York, 2 June 1994, lot 505.

Hugh Moss, Victor Graham and Ka Bo Tsang, *op. cit.*, p. 280, note that 'the ruby vignettes painted in the side panels are taken directly from imported enamel panels. A small group of European enamel panels converted into boxes and covers during the Qianlong period, apparently in the Palace workshops, is known, and one of these has ruby enameled panels on a white ground.'

These ruby and white vignettes are found on high Imperial ceramics, glassware and enamels.

For another similar bottle, see Parke-Bernet Galleries, New York, The Mrs. Elmer A. Claar Collection, 12 May 1970, lot 526.

358 | **Enamels on copper**

1736-1795, Qianlong four-character blue enamel mark and of the period, Beijing
1 ⁷/₈ in. (4.9 cm.) high

Of rounded shape, painted with a European lady with a billowing scarf and flowers in her hair set before a European-style building and foliage on each side, one holding a dish of fruit and flowers, the other holding a tall pear-shaped vessel with a spreading foot and cover, the narrow sides with leafy rocaille foliage, stylized flower heads, hibiscus and morning glory on a multi-colored ground

1936-706

This bottle relates very closely to the example illustrated by Robert W. L. Kleiner in *Chinese Snuff Bottles from the Collection of Mary and George Bloch*, No. 2. Again we see the use of European buildings acting as a backdrop to the European scene. The sky is treated with a similar mottled effect. The mid-ground is also painted with trees or hedgerows. The treatment to the neck, a single band of whorls, is also similar.

Both these bottles can be linked to one illustrated in *Snuff Bottles in the Collection of the National Palace Museum,* No. 14, which also has a simple band at the neck, morning glory dispersed around the sides amidst other flowers, and a rope border, which encircles the vignettes on the Palace Museum bottle and is used below the main scenes on this bottle.

See also another illustrated in *Masterpieces of Snuff Bottles in the Palace Museum*, No. 20.

359 | **Enamels on copper**

1736-1795, Qianlong four-character blue enamel mark and of the period, Beijing
1 ²⁹/₃₂ in. (4.8 cm.) high

Of rounded shape, painted with a European lady in front of a European building and foliage on each side, one lady dressed as a shepherdess holding a crook over her shoulder supporting a basket of flowers, the other lady with a billowing scarf watching a flying bat, the narrow sides with feathery foliage, c-scrolls and flower heads on an unusual sandy-tan ground, all between lotus petals above a band of green waves at the foot and *ruyi*-shaped lappets around the neck

1936-711

European-subject enamel bottles depicting a lady and child, very broadly speaking, appear to follow two formats in the positioning of the figures. This and the two following bottles, Nos. 360 and 361, illustrate one format, that of figures placed in the mid ground with space around them. Bottles, Nos. 356, 357 and No. 358, illustrate the other format, that of figures placed in the foreground, almost 'pushed' up against the surface plain.

This example and Nos. 360 and 361 bear close comparison with a group of bottles painted with Chinese subjects, see Hugh Moss, Victor Graham and Ka Bo Tsang. *The Art of the Chinese Snuff Bottle, The J & J Collection*, Nos. 175-177. There is less attention to detail on all these bottles and a freedom of brushstroke perhaps more indicative of a Chinese hand. This particular group seems to fall more naturally into the Chinese subject group. Even the facial treatment, light shading and more 'open' feel of the cartouche are similar.

See also a bottle illustrated by Bob C. Stevens, *The Collector's Book of Snuff Bottles*, No. 980.

360 | **Enamels on copper**

1736-1795, Qianlong four-character blue enamel mark and of the period, Beijing
1 15/16 in. (4.9 cm.) high

Of rounded shape, painted in *famille rose* enamels with shaped cartouches framing a European lady with flowers in her hair and a boy with curly hair looking on, all set before foliage or trees, one lady holding a *ruyi* scepter in her raised left hand, the other raising a small pear-shaped vase, the narrow sides with feathery scrolling foliage and a large flower head on a mauve ground, all between a *ruyi* band above waves at the foot and a rope border at the shoulder below a larger *ruyi* band at the neck

1936-704

See No. 359.

361 | **Enamels on copper**

1736-1795, Qianlong four-character blue enamel mark and of the period, Beijing
1 ⅞ in. (4.8 cm.) high

Of rounded shape, painted with a European lady in a landscape setting on each side, one lady holding a dish of grapes in her raised left hand before Western buildings, the other lady holding her apron full of flowers with her right hand raised holding a single flower, all within shaped panels with scrolls and foliage between wavy lines suggestive of water at the foot and star bursts and feathery classic scrolls around the neck, a palmette between c-scrolls and stylized foliage on a pale coffee ground on the narrow sides

1936-707

Provenance: American Art Galleries, New York,
The A. W. Bahr Collection, 17-19 January 1916, lot 80.
(See fig. 23 in the Introduction.)

See another bottle in this collection, No. 359.

362 | **Enamels on copper**

1736-1795, Qianlong four-character blue enamel mark and of the period, Beijing
1 $^{15}/_{16}$ in. (4.9 cm.) high

Of rounded shape, painted with a European lady in a landscape on each side, one lady as a shepherdess with flowers in her hair and a crook slung across her shoulder supporting a basket of flowers, the other lady wearing a hat, holding a single flower in her raised right hand, and reading a book or possibly looking at her reflection in a small traveling mirror held in her right hand, all within scrolling foliage surrounds on a pale coffee ground below leaf lappets and c-scrolls at the neck and colorful hibiscus flower heads on a dark coffee-colored ground between feathery c-scrolls and *ruyi* lappets on the narrow sides

1936-708

See also No. 359.

A nearly identical panel on a Beijing enamel ewer and cover depicting a European lady wearing a yellow scarf and holding a rose in her raised hand was illustrated in the *Great National Treasures of China*, No. 93.

See also a bottle illustrated by Bob C. Stevens, *The Collector's Book of Snuff Bottles*, No. 980.

Basemarks

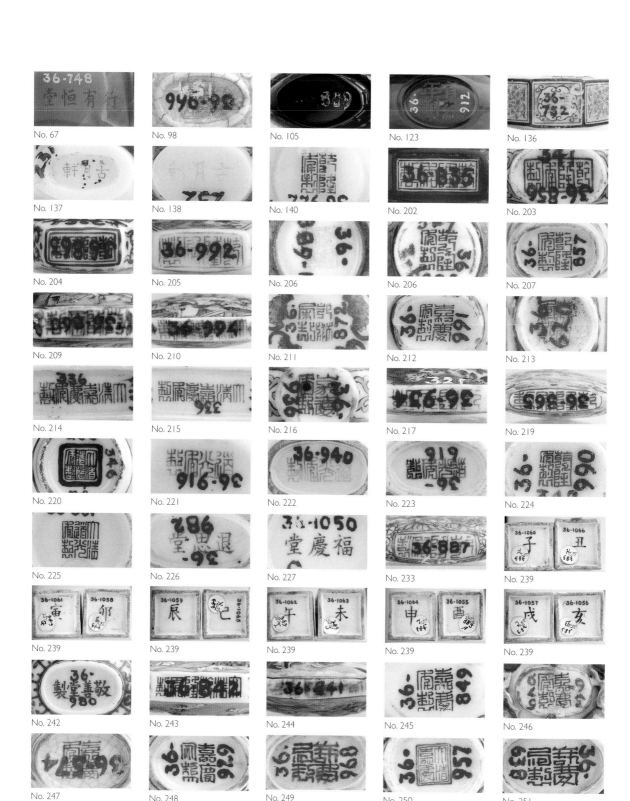

No. 67

No. 98

No. 105

No. 123

No. 136

No. 137

No. 138

No. 140

No. 202

No. 203

No. 204

No. 205

No. 206

No. 206

No. 207

No. 209

No. 210

No. 211

No. 212

No. 213

No. 214

No. 215

No. 216

No. 217

No. 219

No. 220

No. 221

No. 222

No. 223

No. 224

No. 225

No. 226

No. 227

No. 233

No. 239

No. 239

No. 239

No. 239

No. 239

No. 239

No. 242

No. 243

No. 244

No. 245

No. 246

No. 247

No. 248

No. 249

No. 250

No. 251

No. 252

No. 253

No. 254

No. 255

No. 260

No. 261

No. 262

No. 264

No. 265

No. 266

No. 268

No. 270

No. 271

No. 273

No. 275

No. 276

No. 277

No. 279

No. 281

No. 282

No. 288

No. 304

No. 306

No. 324

No. 343

No. 344

No. 345

No. 346

No. 347

No. 347

No. 348

No. 350

No. 352

No. 355

No. 355

No. 356

No. 357

No. 358

No. 359

No. 360

No. 361

No. 362

Bibliography

A Chinese-English Glossary and Illustrations of Antique. Edited by Gao Guopei and translated by Meng Jun. Hong Kong: The Woods Publishing Co., 1991.

Arapova, Tatiana. 'Enamel Decorations of Snuff Bottles in Glass, Porcelain, and Metals.' *Journal of the International Chinese Snuff Bottle Society (JICSBS)*, Spring 1996, pp. 4-12.

The Au Hang Collection of Chinese Snuff Bottles. Hong Kong: CA Design and Printing, 1993.

Avitabile, Gunhild. *Vom Schatz der Drachen: Chinesisches Porzellan des 19, und 20, Jahrunderts aus der Sammlung Weishaupt* (From the Dragon's Treasure: Chinese Porcelain from the 19th and 20th Centuries in the Weishaupt Collection). London: Bamboo Publishing Ltd., 1987.

Biyanhu shihua (History of Snuff Bottles). Compiled by Zhu Peichu and Xia Gengqi of the Palace Museum. Beijing: Forbidden City Press, 1988.

Brody, Alexander. *Old Wine into Old Bottles, A Collector's Commonplace Book.* Hong Kong: CA Design and Printing, 1993.

Bushell, Stephen W. *Oriental Ceramic Art.* New York: Crown Publishers, Inc., 1980 (reprinted).

Calicó, F, X. Calicó and J. Trigo. *Monedas Españolas desde Juana y Carlos a Isabel II, 1504 a 1868, 6 edicion.* Barcelona: Gabinete Numismatico Calicó, 1985.

Cammann, Schuyler V. R. *Substance and Symbol in Chinese Toggles.* Philadelphia: University of Pennsylvania, 1962.

Chang Lin-sheng. 'Ch'ing Dynasty Imperial Enameled Glassware.' *Arts of Asia*, May-June 1991, pp. 95-107.

Chinese Applied Art. Catalogue of an exhibition at the Manchester Art Gallery. Manchester: G. Faulkner, 1913.

Chinese Jewellery, Accessories and Glass. Catalogue of an exhibition at Spink & Son, Ltd., London, 6-20 December 1989. London: BAS Printers Ltd., 1991.

Chinese Snuff Bottles. A Miniature Art from the Collection of Mary and George Bloch. Hong Kong: Hong Kong Museum of Art, Urban Council, 1994.

Chinese Snuff Bottles (Hong Kong Museum of Art). Catalogue of an exhibition from 15 October to 26 November 1977. Hong Kong Museum of Art, 1977.

Chinese Snuff Bottles and Jade Carvings from the Douglas, Gnam and Other Collections. Catalogue of an exhibition at The Chinese Porcelain Company, New York, 1-23 December 1992. New York: The Chinese Porcelain Company, 1992.

Chinese Snuff Bottles from the Fernhill Park Collection. Catalogue of an exhibition at The Chinese Porcelain Company, New York, 9-13 October 1991. New York: The Chinese Porcelain Company: 1991.

A Congregation of Snuff Bottle Connoisseurs. An Exhibition of Chinese Snuff Bottles at the Tsui Museum of Art, Hong Kong. Hong Kong: CA Design and Printing, 1996.

Cort, Louise Allison and Jan Stuart. *Joined Colors: Decoration and Meaning in Chinese Porcelain.* Washington, D.C. & Hong Kong: Arthur M. Sackler Gallery, Smithsonian Institution & Tai Yip Co., 1993.

Fong Wen. *Images of the Mind: Selections from the Edward L. Elliot Family & J. B. Elliot Collections of Chinese Calligraphy and Painting.* Princeton, NJ: Princeton University, 1984.

Ford, John Gilmore. *Chinese Snuff Bottles. The Edward Choate O'Dell Collection.* Baltimore: The International Chinese Snuff Bottle Society, 1982.

Great National Treasures of China. Kaohsiung, Taiwan: National Palace Museum, 1995.

Hall, Robert. *Chinese Snuff Bottles.* London: Robert Hall, 1987.

___. *Chinese Snuff Bottles II.* London: Robert Hall, 1989.

___. *Chinese Snuff Bottles III.* London: Robert Hall, 1990.

___. *Chinese Snuff Bottles IV.* London: Robert Hall, 1991.

___. *Chinese Whispers.* London: Robert Hall, 1999.

___. 'The Japanese Connection.' *JICSBS*, Autumn 1996, pp. 4-15.

Hardy, Ian. 'Underglaze Blue Porcelain Snuff Bottles: Their Origins and Qualities.' *JICSBS*, Autumn 1999, pp. 12-21, 32.

Holden, Rachelle R. *Rivers and Mountains Far from the World. The Rachelle R. Holden Collection. A Personal Commentary.* New York: Rachelle R. Holden, 1994.

Howard, David S. and John Ayers. *China for the West.* London: Sotheby Parke-Bernet Publications, 1978.